Test Item File

MODERN SYSTEMS ANALYSIS & DESIGN

Test Item File

MODERN SYSTEMS ANALYSIS & DESIGN

Third Edition

Jeffrey A Hoffer
Joey F. George
Joseph S. Valacich

Lisa Miller

University of Central Oklahoma

Pearson Education

Upper Saddle River, New Jersey 07458

Acquisitions editor: Bob Horan
Associate editor: Lori Cerreto
Production editor: Carol Zaino
Manufacturer: Phoenix Color

ISBN 0-13-0605033-6

10 9 8 7 6 5 4 3 2 1

CONTENTS

Chapter 1
The Systems Development Environment

True-False Questions

1. The analysis and design of information systems is driven from a technical perspective.

   Answer: False   **Difficulty**: Med   **Reference**: p. 4

2. Information systems analysis and design is an organizational improvement process.

   Answer: True   **Difficulty**: Med   **Reference**: p. 4

3. The total information system includes hardware, system and application software, documentation and training materials, specific job roles associated with the overall system, controls, and the people who use the software along with their work methods.

   Answer: True   **Difficulty**: Med   **Reference**: p. 5

4. Techniques are comprehensive, multiple-step approaches to systems development that guide an analyst's work and influence the quality of the final product.

   Answer: False   **Difficulty**: Med   **Reference**: p. 6

5. A knowledge engineer is the organizational role most responsible for the analysis and design of information systems.

   Answer: False   **Difficulty**: Med   **Reference**: p. 6

6. The systems development environment in the late 1990s focused on systems integration.

   Answer: True   **Difficulty**: Med   **Reference**: p. 7

7. In many instances, organizations are not developing applications in-house, choosing instead to use an application on a per-use basis by accessing through an application service provider.

   Answer: True   **Difficulty**: Med   **Reference**: p. 7

8. Data, information, and data flow are the three key information system components.

   Answer: False   **Difficulty**: Med   **Reference**: p. 8

9. Information refers to raw facts about people, objects, and events in an organization.

   Answer: False   **Difficulty**: Med   **Reference**: p. 8

10. Processing logic describes the steps that transform the data and the events that trigger these steps.

    Answer: True   **Difficulty**: Med   **Reference**: p. 8

11.   The data logic approach concentrates on the flow, use, and transformation of data in an information system.

Answer: False   **Difficulty**: Med   **Reference**: p. 9

12.   The data-oriented approach views data as secondary to the application.

Answer: False   **Difficulty**: Med   **Reference**: p. 10

13.   The natural structure of the data is not specified within the traditional process-oriented approach.

Answer: True   **Difficulty**: Med   **Reference**: p. 9

14.   When you use the data-oriented approach to develop a system, databases are designed around processes.

Answer: False   **Difficulty**: Med   **Reference**: p. 10

15.   With a process-orientation, the state of the data is much uncontrolled duplication.

Answer: True   **Difficulty**: Med   **Reference**: p. 10

16.   With a process-orientation, data files are designed for the enterprise.

Answer: False   **Difficulty**: Med   **Reference**: p. 10

17.   The data-oriented approach depicts the ideal organization of data, independent of where and how data are used within a system.

Answer: True   **Difficulty**: Med   **Reference**: p. 10

18.   Using a data-oriented approach results in application dependence.

Answer: False   **Difficulty**: Med   **Reference**: p. 10

19.   Depending on the organization, an IS department may be an independent unit, part of another functional department, or exist in several major business units.

Answer: True   **Difficulty**: Easy   **Reference**: p. 11

20.   Diversity, tolerance, clear and complete communication, trust, mutual respect, and a reward structure are characteristics of successful teams.

Answer: True   **Difficulty**: Med   **Reference**: p. 12

21.   To help a team work well together, management needs to develop a reward structure that promotes shared responsibility and accountability.

Answer: True   **Difficulty**: Med   **Reference**: p. 12

22.   Team members must be rewarded by IS managers for their work as members of an effective work unit.

Answer: True   **Difficulty**: Med   **Reference**: p. 12

23. A stakeholder is a person who has an interest in an existing or new information system.

     Answer: True   **Difficulty**: Med   **Reference**: p. 12

24. Systems analysts are key to the systems development process.

     Answer: True   **Difficulty**: Easy   **Reference**: p. 13

25. Analytical skills help you understand the potential and the limitations of information technology.

     Answer: False   **Difficulty**: Med   **Reference**: p. 13

26. Management skills enable you to understand the organization and its functions, to identify opportunities and problems, and to analyze and solve problems.

     Answer: False   **Difficulty**: Med   **Reference**: p. 13

27. Sequence, repetition, and calculation are the three structured programming constructs.

     Answer: False   **Difficulty**: Med   **Reference**: p. 13

28. Systems analysts have the power to set the direction for systems development, propose and approve projects, and determine the relative importance of projects that have already been approved and assigned to other people in the organization.

     Answer: False   **Difficulty**: Med   **Reference**: p. 14

29. A transaction processing system is one of the four information systems classes.

     Answer: True   **Difficulty**: Easy   **Reference**: p. 15

30. The major focus of management information systems is capturing transaction data, which is then sent to a computerized database of all transactions.

     Answer: False   **Difficulty**: Med   **Reference**: p. 15

31. An expert system provides an interactive environment in which decision makers can quickly manipulate data and models of business operations.

     Answer: False   **Difficulty**: Med   **Reference**: p. 16

32. A decision support system uses knowledge gathered from experts to make recommendations to managers.

     Answer: False   **Difficulty**: Med   **Reference**: pp. 16-17

33. The systems development method associated with a decision support system is concerned with capturing, validating, and storing data and with moving data between each required step.

     Answer: False   **Difficulty**: Hard   **Reference**: p. 17

34. The systems development method associated with a management information system is concerned with understanding relationships between data so data can be accessed and summarized in a variety of ways.

Answer: True   **Difficulty**: Hard   **Reference**: p. 17

35. The systems development method associated with an expert system requires a specialized decision logic-orientation in which knowledge is elicited from experts and described by rules or other forms.

Answer: True   **Difficulty**: Hard   **Reference**: p. 17

36. A systems development methodology is a standard process followed in an organization to conduct all the steps necessary to analyze, design, implement, and maintain information systems.

Answer: True   **Difficulty**: Med   **Reference**: p. 18

37. The systems development life cycle is the traditional methodology used to develop, maintain, and replace information systems.

Answer: True   **Difficulty**: Med   **Reference**: p. 18

38. The systems development life cycle is a sequentially ordered set of phases.

Answer: False   **Difficulty**: Med   **Reference**: p. 18

39. In the systems development life cycle, it is possible to complete some activities in one phase in parallel with some activities of another phase.

Answer: True   **Difficulty**: Med   **Reference**: p. 18

40. Sometimes the systems development life cycle is iterative.

Answer: True   **Difficulty**: Easy   **Reference**: p. 18

41. Project initiation and planning is the first phase of the SDLC in which an organization's total information system needs are identified, analyzed, prioritized, and arranged.

Answer: False   **Difficulty**: Hard   **Reference**: p. 20

42. The second subphase in systems analysis is to investigate the system and determine the proposed system's scope.

Answer: False   **Difficulty**: Med   **Reference**: p. 21

43. Design is the fourth phase of the SDLC in which the current system is studied and alternative replacement systems are proposed.

Answer: False   **Difficulty**: Med   **Reference**: p. 21

44. Logical design is tied to a specific hardware and software platform.

Answer: False   **Difficulty**: Med   **Reference**: p. 21

45. During logical design, the analyst team decides which programming languages the computer instructions should be written in, which database systems and file structures will be used for the data, and which hardware platform, operating system, and network environment the system will run under.

    Answer: False   **Difficulty**: Hard   **Reference**: p. 21

46. During installation, the new system becomes part of the daily activities of the organization.

    Answer: True   **Difficulty**: Easy   **Reference**: p. 22

47. Maintenance is the final phase of the SDLC in which an information system is systematically repaired and improved.

    Answer: True   **Difficulty**: Med   **Reference**: p. 23

48. Involving the end user in analysis and design is a key advantage to the prototyping technique.

    Answer: True   **Difficulty**: Med   **Reference**: p. 26

49. RAD sacrifices human efficiency when rapidly building and rebuilding working systems.

    Answer: False   **Difficulty**: Med   **Reference**: p. 26

50. JAD is a structured process in which users, managers, and analysts work together for several days in a series of intensive meetings to specify or review system requirements.

    Answer: True   **Difficulty**: Med   **Reference**: p. 26

Multiple Choice Questions

51. The complex organizational process through which computer-based information systems are developed and maintained best defines:

    a. information systems analysis and design
    b. joint application design
    c. prototyping
    d. none of the above

    Answer: a   **Difficulty**: Med   **Reference**: p. 4

52. Software designed to support the payroll function would best be classified as:

    a. application software
    b. system software
    c. design software
    d. analysis software

    Answer: a   **Difficulty**: Med   **Reference**: p. 5

53. Computer software designed to support organizational functions or processes best defines:

    a. system software
    b. application software
    c. design software
    d. analysis software

    Answer: b   **Difficulty:** Med   **Reference:** p. 5

54. Comprehensive, multiple-step approaches to systems development that will guide your work and influence the quality of your final product defines:

    a. techniques
    b. tools
    c. methodologies
    d. data flows

    Answer: c   **Difficulty:** Med   **Reference:** p. 5

55. The particular processes that an analyst will follow to help ensure that his work is complete, well-done, and understood by project team members best defines:

    a. techniques
    b. tools
    c. methodologies
    d. data flows

    Answer: a   **Difficulty:** Med   **Reference:** p. 6

56. The person in an organization who has the primary responsibility for systems analysis and design is:

    a. the systems analyst
    b. the end user
    c. the internal auditor
    d. the business manager

    Answer: a   **Difficulty:** Med   **Reference:** p. 6

57. Which of the following is not one of the three key information system components that must be clearly understood by anyone who analyzes and designs systems?

    a. processing logic
    b. inheritance
    c. data flows
    d. data

    Answer: b   **Difficulty:** Med   **Reference:** p. 8

58. Raw facts that describe people, objects, and events in an organization best defines:

    a. data
    b. data flows
    c. information
    d. processes

    Answer: a   **Difficulty:** Med   **Reference:** p. 8

59. Data that have been processed and presented in a form suitable for human interpretation, often with the purpose of revealing trends or patterns best defines:

    a. data structure
    b. data
    c. information
    d. data flows

    Answer: c   **Difficulty:** Med   **Reference:** p. 8

60. The steps by which data are transformed or moved and a description of the events that trigger the occurrence of these steps best defines:

    a. processing logic
    b. data flow
    c. flow conversion
    d. data steps

    Answer: a   **Difficulty:** Med   **Reference:** p. 8

61. Indicating that the computation of a new credit balance will occur when a clerk presses a key on a credit card scanner to confirm a sales transaction is an example of:

    a. data flow
    b. processing logic
    c. information
    d. subordinate data

    Answer: b   **Difficulty:** Med   **Reference:** p. 8

62. An overall strategy to information systems development that focuses on the ideal organization of data, rather than where and how data are used best defines the:

    a. process-oriented approach
    b. data-organization approach
    c. data-oriented approach
    d. information-oriented approach

    Answer: c   **Difficulty:** Med   **Reference:** p. 10

73. Special-purpose computing tools used to generate code from specifications best defines:

   a. code generators
   b. design generators
   c. code designers
   d. codecs

   Answer: a   **Difficulty**: Med   **Reference**: p. 14

74. The group that has the power to set the direction for systems development, propose and approve projects, and determine the relative importance of the projects that have been approved to other people in the organization best describes:

   a. end users
   b. business managers
   c. information systems managers
   d. database administrator

   Answer: b   **Difficulty**: Med   **Reference**: p. 14

75. The department concerned with system interfaces and ease-of-use issues, training users, and writing user documentation and manuals is the:

   a. Human Factors Department
   b. Internal Auditing Department
   c. Database Department
   d. Network Department

   Answer: a   **Difficulty**: Med   **Reference**: p. 15

76. In many organizations, the person responsible for keeping track of changes in the system's design is the:

   a. database administrator
   b. systems administrator
   c. programmer
   d. internal auditor

   Answer: d   **Difficulty**: Med   **Reference**: p. 15

77. Which of the following is not one of the four classes of information systems?

   a. transaction processing systems
   b. decision support systems
   c. expert systems
   d. production systems

   Answer: d   **Difficulty**: Med   **Reference**: p. 15

78. Transaction processing systems:

a. automate the handling of data about business activities
b. are designed to help organizational decision makers make decisions
c. attempt to codify and manipulate knowledge rather than information
d. take relatively raw data that have been previously captured and convert them into a meaningful aggregated form that managers need to conduct their responsibilities

Answer: a   **Difficulty**: Med   **Reference**: p. 15

79. Which of the following can be considered a goal of TPS development?

a. improve transaction processing by speeding it up
b. use fewer people
c. improve efficiency and accuracy
d. all of the above

Answer: d   **Difficulty**: Med   **Reference**: p. 16

80. Management information systems:

a. automate the handling of data about business activities
b. are designed to help organizational decision makers make decisions
c. attempt to codify and manipulate knowledge rather than information
d. take relatively raw data that have been previously captured and convert them into a meaningful aggregated form that managers need to conduct their responsibilities

Answer: d   **Difficulty**: Med   **Reference**: p. 16

81. Decision support systems:

a. automate the handling of data about business activities
b. are designed to help organizational decision makers make decisions
c. attempt to codify and manipulate knowledge rather than information
d. take relatively raw data that have been previously captured and convert them into a meaningful aggregated form that managers need to conduct their responsibilities

Answer: b   **Difficulty**: Med   **Reference**: p. 16

82. Expert systems:

a. automate the handling of data about business activities
b. are designed to help organizational decision makers make decisions
c. attempt to codify and manipulate knowledge rather than information
d. take relatively raw data that have been previously captured and convert them into a meaningful aggregated form that managers need to conduct their responsibilities

Answer: c   **Difficulty**: Med   **Reference**: p. 17

83. Which of the following is an IS characteristic for a transaction processing system?

    a. often involves semi-structured problems and the need to access data at different levels of detail
    b. provides expert advice by asking users a sequence of questions dependent on prior answers
    c. has a high-volume, data capture focus
    d. draws on diverse yet predictable data resources to aggregate and summarize data

    Answer: c   **Difficulty**: Hard   **Reference**: p. 17

84. Which of the following is an IS characteristic for a management information system?

    a. often involves semi-structured problems and the need to access data at different levels of detail
    b. provides expert advice by asking users a sequence of questions dependent on prior answers
    c. has a high-volume, data capture focus
    d. draws on diverse yet predictable data resources to aggregate and summarize data

    Answer: d   **Difficulty**: Hard   **Reference**: p. 17

85. Which of the following is an IS characteristic for a decision support system?

    a. often involves semi-structured problems and the need to access data at different levels of detail
    b. provides expert advice by asking users a sequence of questions dependent on prior answers
    c. has a high-volume, data capture focus
    d. draws on diverse yet predictable data resources to aggregate and summarize data

    Answer: a   **Difficulty**: Hard   **Reference**: p. 17

86. Which of the following is an IS characteristic for an expert system?

    a. often involves semi-structured problems and the need to access data at different levels of detail
    b. provides expert advice by asking users a sequence of questions dependent on prior answers
    c. has a high-volume, data capture focus
    d. draws on diverse yet predictable data resources to aggregate and summarize data

    Answer: b   **Difficulty**: Hard   **Reference**: p. 17

87. Which of the following utilizes a process-orientation as its systems development method?

    a. management information system
    b. transaction processing system
    c. expert system
    d. decision support system

    Answer: b   **Difficulty**: Hard   **Reference**: p. 17

88. Which of the following utilizes data and decision logic orientations as its systems development methods?

    a. management information system
    b. transaction processing system
    c. expert system
    d. decision support system

    Answer: d   **Difficulty**: Hard   **Reference**: p. 17

89. Which of the following utilizes a specialized decision logic-orientation in which knowledge is elicited from experts and described by rules or other forms?

    a. management information system
    b. transaction processing system
    c. expert system
    d. decision support system

    Answer: c   **Difficulty**: Hard   **Reference**: p. 17

90. The traditional methodology used to develop, maintain, and replace information systems best defines:

    a. SDLC
    b. RAD
    c. OOAD
    d. prototyping

    Answer: a   **Difficulty**: Med   **Reference**: p. 18

91. Which of the following is a true statement regarding the SDLC phases?

    a. The life cycle is a sequentially ordered set of phases.
    b. It is not possible to complete some activities in one phase in parallel with those of another phase.
    c. The SDLC is not iterative.
    d. The life cycle can be thought of as a circular process in which the end of the useful life of one system leads to the beginning of another project to develop a new version of or replace an existing system.

    Answer: d   **Difficulty**: Hard   **Reference**: pp. 18-19

92. In which of the following SDLC phases does an organization determine whether or not resources should be devoted to the development or enhancement of each information system?

    a. project identification and selection
    b. project initiation and planning
    c. analysis
    d. system selection

    Answer: a   **Difficulty**: Hard   **Reference**: pp. 20-21

93. During the project initiation and planning phase, which of the following activities is undertaken?

    a. new system requirements are identified
    b. a formal, preliminary investigation is undertaken
    c. a presentation of why the system should or should not be developed by the organization is given
    d. both b and c

    Answer: d   **Difficulty**: Med   **Reference**: p. 21

94. Studying the current system and proposing alternative replacement systems best defines:

 a. project initiation and planning
 b. analysis
 c. logical design
 d. physical design

Answer: b   **Difficulty**: Med   **Reference**: p. 21

95. The output for the analysis phase is the:

 a. description of the alternative solution
 b. physical system specifications
 c. work plan for the project
 d. priorities for systems and projects proposal

Answer: a   **Difficulty**: Med   **Reference**: p. 21

96. Which of the following is a true statement regarding logical design?

 a. Logical design is tied to a specific hardware and software platform.
 b. Logical design does not concentrate on the business aspects of the system.
 c. Technical specifications are developed.
 d. The logical design phase produces functional, detailed specifications of all system elements.

Answer: d   **Difficulty**: Med   **Reference**: p. 21

97. Turning system specifications into a working system which is tested and then put into use describes which of the following?

 a. implementation
 b. physical design
 c. maintenance
 d. analysis

Answer: a   **Difficulty**: Med   **Reference**: p. 22

98. The phase of the SDLC in which an information system is systematically repaired and improved is referred to as:

 a. analysis
 b. implementation
 c. maintenance
 d. physical repair

Answer: c   **Difficulty**: Med   **Reference**: p. 23

99. Systems development methodologies and techniques based on objects rather than data or processes best defines:

    a. objects
    b. participatory design
    c. object-oriented analysis and design
    d. entity analysis and design

    Answer: c   **Difficulty**: Med   **Reference**: p. 25

100. An iterative process of systems development in which requirements are converted to a working system that is continually revised through close work between an analyst and users best defines:

    a. Joint Application Design
    b. Participatory Design
    c. prototyping
    d. Systems Development Life Cycle

    Answer: c   **Difficulty**: Med   **Reference**: p. 25

Fill In the Blanks

101. *__Information systems analysis and design__* is the complex organizational process whereby computer-based information systems are developed and maintained.

                                Difficulty: Med   **Reference**: p. 5

102. *__Application software__* is computer software designed to support organizational functions or processes.

                                Difficulty: Med   **Reference**: p. 5

103. *__Systems analyst__* is the organizational role most responsible for the analysis and design of information systems.

                                Difficulty: Med   **Reference**: p. 6

104. *__Data__* are raw facts about people, objects, and events in an organization.

                                Difficulty: Easy   **Reference**: p. 8

105. *__Information__* is data that have been processed and presented in a form suitable for human interpretation, often with the purpose of revealing trends or patterns.

                                Difficulty: Easy   **Reference**: p. 8

106. *__Data flow__* is data in motion, moving from one place in a system to another.

                                Difficulty: Med   **Reference**: p. 8

107. ***Processing logic*** refers to the steps by which data are transformed or moved and a description of the events that trigger these steps.

                  Difficulty: Med   **Reference**: p. 8

108. The ***process-oriented approach*** is an overall strategy to information systems development that focuses on how and when data are moved through and changed by an information system.

                  Difficulty: Med   **Reference**: p. 9

109. The ***data-oriented approach*** is an overall strategy of information systems development that focuses on the ideal organization of data rather than where and how data are used.

                  Difficulty: Med   **Reference**: p. 10

110. A ***database*** is a shared collection of logically related data designed to meet the information needs of multiple users in an organization.

                  Difficulty: Med   **Reference**: p. 10

111. ***Application independence*** is the separation of data and the definition of data from the applications that use these data.

                  Difficulty: Med   **Reference**: p. 10

112. A ***stakeholder*** is a person who has an interest in an existing or new information system.

                  Difficulty: Med   **Reference**: p. 12

113. A ***systems development methodology*** is a standard process followed in an organization to conduct all the steps necessary to analyze, design, implement, and maintain information systems.

                  Difficulty: Med   **Reference**: p. 18

114. The ***systems development life cycle*** is the traditional methodology used to develop, maintain, and replace information systems.

                  Difficulty: Med   **Reference**: p. 18

115. ***Project identification and selection*** is the first phase of the SDLC in which an organization's total information system needs are identified, analyzed, prioritized, and arranged.

                  Difficulty: Hard   **Reference**: p. 20

116. ***Project initiation and planning*** is the second phase of the SDLC in which a potential information systems project is explained and an argument for continuing or not continuing with the project is presented; a detailed plan is also developed for conducting the remaining phases of the SDLC for the proposed system.

                  Difficulty: Hard   **Reference**: p. 21

117. ***Analysis*** is the third phase of the SDLC in which the current system is studied and alternative replacement systems are proposed.

                  Difficulty: Med   **Reference**: p. 21

118. _**Design**_ is the fourth phase of the SDLC in which the description of the recommended solution is converted into logical and then physical system specifications.

                    Difficulty: Med   **Reference**: p. 21

119. _**Logical design**_ is the part of the design phase of the SDLC in which all functional features of the system chosen for development in analysis are described independently of any computer platform.

                    Difficulty: Med   **Reference**: p. 21

120. _**Physical design**_ is the part of the design phase of the SDLC in which the logical specifications of the system from logical design are transformed into technology-specific details from which all programming and system construction can be accomplished.

                    Difficulty: Med   **Reference**: p. 21

121. _**Implementation**_ is the fifth phase of the SDLC in which the information system is coded, tested, installed, and supported in the organization.

                    Difficulty: Easy   **Reference**: p. 22

122. _**Maintenance**_ is the final phase of the SDLC in which an information system is systematically repaired and improved.

                    Difficulty: Easy   **Reference**: p. 23

123. _**Object-oriented analysis and design**_ refers to systems development methodologies and techniques based on objects rather than data or processes.

                    Difficulty: Med   **Reference**: p. 25

124. _**Prototyping**_ is an iterative process of systems development in which requirements are converted to a working system that is continually revised through close work between an analyst and users.

                    Difficulty: Med   **Reference**: p. 25

125. _**Joint application design**_ is a structured process in which users, managers, and analysts work together for several days in a series of intensive meetings to specify or review system requirements.

                    Difficulty: Hard   **Reference**: p. 26

Matching Questions

Match each of the following terms with its corresponding definition.

   a. data
   b. information
   c. data flow
   d. processing logic
   e. database

126. A group of data that move through an information system and a description of the sources and destinations for each.

    Answer: c   **Reference:** p. 8

127. Raw facts about people, objects, and events in an organization.

    Answer: a   **Reference:** p. 8

128. Data that have been processed and presented in a form suitable for human interpretation, often with the purpose of revealing trends or patterns.

    Answer: b   **Reference:** p. 8

129. The steps by which data are transformed or moved and a description of the events that trigger the occurrence of these steps.

    Answer: d   **Reference:** p. 8

130. A shared collection of logically related data designed to meet the information needs of multiple users in an organization.

    Answer: e   **Reference:** p. 10

For the following questions, answer "a" if the approach is process oriented, and "b" if the approach is data oriented.

131. The system focus is on what the system is supposed to do and when.

    Answer: a   **Reference:** p. 10

132. The system focus is on the data the system needs to operate.

    Answer: b   **Reference:** p. 10

133. The state of the data is limited, controlled duplication.

    Answer: b   **Reference:** p. 10

134. The state of the data is much uncontrolled duplication.

    Answer: a   **Reference:** p. 10

135. The design stability is limited because business processes and the applications that support them change constantly.

> **Answer:** a   **Reference:** p. 10

136. The design stability is more enduring because the data needs of an organization do not change rapidly.

> **Answer:** b   **Reference:** p. 10

137. The data organization results in data files designed for each individual application.

> **Answer:** a   **Reference:** p. 10

138. The data organization results in data files designed for the enterprise.

> **Answer:** b   **Reference:** p. 10

Match each of the following IS characteristics with its corresponding IS type. (Answers may occur more than once.).

   a. transaction processing system
   b. management information system
   c. decision support system
   d. expert system

139. May involve forecasting future data from historical trends and business knowledge.

> **Answer:** b   **Reference:** p. 17

140. Provides guidance in identifying problems, finding and evaluating alternative solutions, and selecting or comparing alternatives.

> **Answer:** c   **Reference:** p. 17

141. High-volume, data capture focus.

> **Answer:** a   **Reference:** p. 17

142. Draws on diverse yet predictable data resources to aggregate and summarize data.

> **Answer:** b   **Reference:** p. 17

143. Provides expert advice by asking users a sequence of questions that are dependent on prior answers and lead to a conclusion or recommendation.

> **Answer:** d   **Reference:** p. 17

144. Potentially involves groups of decision makers.

> **Answer:** c   **Reference:** p. 17

145. Often involves semi-structured problems and the need to access data at different levels of detail.

> **Answer:** c   **Reference:** p. 17

Match each of the following SDLC phases with its corresponding definition.

      a. maintenance
      b. design
      c. analysis
      d. implementation
      e. project initiation and planning
      f. project identification and selection

146. The first phase of the SDLC in which an organization's total information system needs are identified, analyzed, prioritized, and arranged.

            Answer: f   **Reference:** p. 20

147. The second phase of the SDLC in which a potential information systems project is explained and an argument for continuing or not continuing with the project is presented; a detailed plan is also developed for conducting the remaining phases of the SDLC for the proposed system.

            Answer: e   **Reference:** p. 21

148. The third phase of the SDLC in which the current system is studied and alternative replacement systems are proposed.

            Answer: c   **Reference:** p. 21

149. The fourth phase of the SDLC in which the description of the recommended solution is converted into logical and then physical system specifications.

            Answer: b   **Reference:** p. 21

150. The fifth phase of the SDLC, in which the information system is coded, tested, installed, and supported in the organization.

            Answer: d   **Reference:** p. 22

151. The final phase of the SDLC in which an information system is systematically repaired and improved.

            Answer: a   **Reference:** p. 23

Match each of the following phases and subphases with its corresponding products, outputs, or deliverables.

      a. maintenance
      b. physical design
      c. analysis
      d. logical design
      e. implementation
      f. project initiation and planning
      g. project identification and selection

152. Code, documentation, training procedures, and support capabilities.

            Answer: e   **Reference:** p. 23

153. New versions or releases of software with associated updates to documentation, training, and support.

   Answer: a   **Reference**: p. 23

154. Priorities for systems and projects; an architecture for data, networks, hardware, and IS management ais the result of associated systems planning activities.

   Answer: g   **Reference**: p. 23

155. Detailed steps, or work plan, for a project; specification of system scope and high-level system requirements or features; assignment of team members and other resources; system justification or business case.

   Answer: f   **Reference**: p. 23

156. Description of current system and where problems or opportunities are with a general recommendation on how to fix, enhance, or replace the current system; explanation of alternative systems and justification for the chosen alternative.

   Answer: c   **Reference**: p. 23

157. Technical, detailed specifications of all system elements; acquisition plan for new technology.

   Answer: b   **Reference**: p. 23

158. Functional, detailed specifications of all system elements.

   Answer: d   **Reference**: p. 23

Essay Questions

159. *List and define the six major SDLC phases.*

Project identification and selection is the first phase of the SDLC in which an organization's total information system needs are identified, analyzed, prioritized, and arranged. Project initiation and planning is the second phase of the SDLC in which a potential information systems project is explained, and an argument for continuing or not continuing with the project is presented; a detailed plan is also developed for conducting the remaining phases of the SDLC for the proposed system. Analysis is the third phase of the SDLC in which the current system is studied and alternative replacement systems are proposed. During the design phase, a description of the recommended solution is converted into logical and then physical system specifications. Implementation is the fifth phase of the SDLC in which the information system is coded, tested, installed, and supported in the organization. Maintenance is the final phase of the SDLC in which an information system is systematically repaired and improved.

160. *Discuss two different approaches to improving development.*

Prototyping is defined as an iterative process of systems development by which requirements are converted to a working system that is continually revised through close work between an analyst and users. The analyst builds the prototype from requirements supplied by the end users. Once the prototype is completed, it is evaluated by the end users. Based on the feedback provided by the end users, the analyst will modify the prototype. This results in an iterative process that continues until users are satisfied. Prototyping has two advantages: (1) the large extent to which prototyping involves the user in analysis and design; and (2) its ability to capture requirements in concrete form. Joint Application Design (JAD) is defined as a structured process in which users, managers, and analysts work together for several days in a series of intensive meetings to specify or review system requirements. By promoting group participation, time and organizational resources are better managed. Also, the group is more likely to develop a shared understanding of the IS purpose.

161. *List and define the four classes of information systems.*

Transaction processing systems automate the handling of data about business activities. Management information systems take relatively raw data available through a TPS and converts them into a meaningful aggregated form that managers need to conduct their responsibilities. Decision support systems are designed to help organizational decision makers make decisions. Expert systems attempt to codify and manipulate knowledge rather than information.

162. *What are methodologies, techniques, and tools?*

Methodologies are comprehensive, multiple-step approaches to systems development. Techniques are particular processes that you follow to help ensure that your work is complete, well done, and understood by others. Tools are typically computer programs that make it easier to use and benefit from techniques and to follow faithfully the guidelines of the overall development methodology. The techniques and tools should support the chosen methodology. Methodologies, techniques, and tools work together to form an organizational approach to systems analysis and design.

163. *Define process-oriented approach and data-oriented approach.*

A process-oriented approach is defined as an overall strategy to information systems development that focuses on how and when data are moved through and changed by an information system. In contrast, the data-oriented approach is defined as an overall strategy to information systems development that focuses on the ideal organization of data, rather than where and how data are used.

164. *Identify the products of the SDLC phases.*

The products for project identification and selection include priorities for systems and projects; an architecture for data, networks, hardware, and IS management is the result of associated systems planning activities. Products for the project initiation and planning phase include detailed steps, or work plan, for the project; specification of system scope and high-level system requirements or features; assignment of team members and other resources; and the system justification or business case. The products for the analysis phase include a description of the current system and where problems or opportunities are with a general recommendation on how to fix, enhance, or replace the current system; and an explanation of alternative systems and justification. Logical design results in functional detailed specifications of all system elements. Physical design results in technical, detailed specifications of all systems elements; and an acquisition plan for new technology. Implementation provides code, documentation, training procedures, and support capabilities. Maintenance products include new versions or releases of software with associated updates to documentation, training and support.

165. *Briefly describe the three key information system components.*

Data, information, and processing logic are the three key information system components. Data are raw facts about people, objects, and events in an organization. Information is data that have been processed and presented in a form suitable for human interpretation. Processing logic are the steps by which data are transformed or moved and a description of the events that trigger these steps.

166. *Where might the IS department be located in an organization?*

The IS department might be an independent unit, part of another functional department, or there may be IS departments within several major business units.

167. *Identify six characteristics of successful teams.*

The six characteristics are (1) diversity in backgrounds, skills, and goals; (2) tolerance of diversity, uncertainty, and ambiguity; (3) clear and complete communication; (4) trust; (5) mutual respect and putting one's own views second to the team; and (6) reward structure that promotes shared responsibility and accountability.

168. *What is the IS manager's role in systems development?*

The IS manager allocates resources, oversees approved systems development projects, may attend project review meetings, reviews written status reports on project progress, and may prescribe what methodologies, techniques, and tools are to be used, and reporting procedures. Also, IS managers may provide career advice to systems analysts.

Chapter 2
Succeeding as a Systems Analyst

True-False Questions

1. Systems thinking is a key analytical skill.

   Answer: True   **Difficulty**: Easy   **Reference**: p. 31

2. Resource, project, risk, and organizational knowledge are the four sets of analytical skills required by a systems analyst.

   Answer: False   **Difficulty**: Med   **Reference**: p. 32

3. A system is an interrelated set of components, with an identifiable boundary, working together for some purpose.

   Answer: True   **Difficulty**: Med   **Reference**: p. 32

4. Accounts payable, accounts receivable, and payroll are components of an accounting system.

   Answer: True   **Difficulty**: Med   **Reference**: p. 33

5. A dependent component is a subsystem that relies on another subsystem for its input.

   Answer: False   **Difficulty**: Med   **Reference**: p. 33

6. Customers, suppliers, and mechanics are part of an automobile repair shop's environment.

   Answer: True   **Difficulty**: Med   **Reference**: p. 33

7. Components within a boundary can be changed whereas components outside a boundary cannot be changed.

   Answer: True   **Difficulty**: Med   **Reference**: p. 33

8. Security, filtering, coding and decoding, and buffering are interface functions.

   Answer: True   **Difficulty**: Med   **Reference**: p. 34

9. An open system interacts freely with its environment, taking in input and returning output.

   Answer: True   **Difficulty**: Med   **Reference**: p. 35

10. All business information systems are open systems.

    Answer: True   **Difficulty**: Med   **Reference**: p. 35

11. Modularity is the process of breaking a system into its components.

    Answer: False   **Difficulty**: Med   **Reference**: p. 36

12. Cohesion is the extent to which subsystems depend on each other.

   Answer: False   **Difficulty**: Med   **Reference**: p. 36

13. Subsystems should be loosely coupled with each other.

   Answer: True   **Difficulty**: Med   **Reference**: p. 36

14. A logical system description focuses on the system's function and purpose without regard to how the system will be physically implemented.

   Answer: True   **Difficulty**: Med   **Reference**: p. 37

15. A logical system description would specify that a system should accept orders, route orders to the warehouse, and generate invoices, but would not specify a particular hardware/software platform.

   Answer: True   **Difficulty**: Med   **Reference**: p. 37

16. A physical system description would specify that a system should check inventory levels and place orders for items low in stock, but this description would not specify a particular hardware/software platform.

   Answer: False   **Difficulty**: Med   **Reference**: p. 37

17. A physical system description is developed before a logical system description.

   Answer: False   **Difficulty**: Med   **Reference**: p. 37

18. For every physical system description, there are several logical system descriptions.

   Answer: False   **Difficulty**: Med   **Reference**: p. 39

19. A systems analyst should be aware of an organization's policies, standards of practice, informal organization structure, and values and mission.

   Answer: True   **Difficulty**: Easy   **Reference**: p. 40

20. Identification, selection, implementation, and maintenance are the four phases of Simon's problem-solving model.

   Answer: False   **Difficulty**: Med   **Reference**: p. 41

21. During Simon's intelligence phase, alternatives are formulated.

   Answer: False   **Difficulty**: Med   **Reference**: p. 41

22. The recognition that the company's current inventory tracking system is outdated corresponds to Simon's design phase.

   Answer: False   **Difficulty**: Med   **Reference**: p. 41

23. Simon's design phase corresponds to that part of analysis where alternative solutions are formulated.

   Answer: True   **Difficulty**: Hard   **Reference**: p. 41

24. Familiarity with data flow diagramming, UML, and object-oriented technology are required analytical skills.

    Answer: False   **Difficulty**: Med   **Reference**: p. 42

25. Resource, project, risk, and change management are required management skills for a systems analyst.

    Answer: True   **Difficulty**: Med   **Reference**: p. 43

26. Budgeting, tracking and accounting for resource consumption, and evaluating the quality of resources used are resource management capabilities.

    Answer: True   **Difficulty**: Med   **Reference**: p. 44

27. The goal of project management is to prevent projects from coming in late and going over budget.

    Answer: True   **Difficulty**: Med   **Reference**: p. 44

28. As a project manager, your first task is to determine how tasks are related to each other and who will be responsible for each task.

    Answer: False   **Difficulty**: Hard   **Reference**: p. 44

29. As a project manager, the most important element is securing resources from abusive use.

    Answer: False   **Difficulty**: Med   **Reference**: p. 44

30. More skills and less expense are two advantages of using an independent contractor.

    Answer: True   **Difficulty**: Med   **Reference**: p. 44

31. Contracts and relationship managers are two mechanisms for managing independent contractors.

    Answer: True   **Difficulty**: Med   **Reference**: p. 44

32. Risk management is the ability to anticipate what might go wrong in a project.

    Answer: True   **Difficulty**: Easy   **Reference**: p. 44

33. Risk management includes knowing where to place resources so they can do the most good and prioritizing activities to achieve the greatest gain.

    Answer: True   **Difficulty**: Med   **Reference**: p. 44

34. Change management includes the ability to deal with technical issues related to change, such as obsolescence and reusability.

    Answer: True   **Difficulty**: Med   **Reference**: p. 45

35. Communication skills, working alone and with a team, facilitating groups, and managing expectations of users and managers are important management skills for a systems analyst.

    Answer: False   **Difficulty**: Med   **Reference**: p. 45

36. Oral communication and listening skills are considered by many information system professionals as the most important communication skills analysts need to succeed.

    Answer: True   **Difficulty**: Med   **Reference**: p. 45

37. Conducting interviews can be very expensive and time-consuming.

    Answer: True   **Difficulty**: Easy   **Reference**: p. 45

38. Since questionnaires provide no direct means by which to ask follow-up questions, questionnaire results are often viewed as having more bias than interview results.

    Answer: False   **Difficulty**: Med   **Reference**: p. 46

39. A project's progress is often documented through meeting agendas, meeting minutes, interview summaries, and project schedules.

    Answer: True   **Difficulty**: Med   **Reference**: p. 46

40. Practice is one way to improve communication skills.

    Answer: True   **Difficulty**: Easy   **Reference**: p. 46

41. A shared vision, sense of team identity, and good debating skills are characteristics of a high-performance team.

    Answer: False   **Difficulty**: Med   **Reference**: p. 47

42. Competent team members, effective communication, and a sense of autonomy are characteristics of a high-performance team.

    Answer: True   **Difficulty**: Med   **Reference**: p. 47

43. During a JAD, the most important resource a systems analyst has access to is a CASE tool.

    Answer: False   **Difficulty**: Med   **Reference**: p. 48

44. Successfully managing user expectations is related to successful systems implementation.

    Answer: True   **Difficulty**: Med   **Reference**: p. 48

45. Waiting patiently for group members to answer the questions you ask them is one of several guidelines for running an effective meeting.

    Answer: True   **Difficulty**: Med   **Reference**: p. 49

46. An endorsed development methodology, approved development platforms, well-defined roles for people in the development process, and a common language are four standards of practice.

    Answer: True   **Difficulty**: Hard   **Reference**: p. 49

47. Structured development lays out specific procedures and techniques to be used during the development process.

    Answer: False   **Difficulty**: Med   **Reference**: p. 49

48. SQL, COBOL, and UML are common development languages.

    Answer: True   **Difficulty**: Med   **Reference**: p. 50

49. The stakeholder approach specifies that any potential actions that could reduce the welfare of the members of society must be eliminated.

    Answer: False   **Difficulty**: Hard   **Reference**: p. 52

50. The stockholder approach holds that any action taken by a business is ethically acceptable as long as it is legal, not deceptive, and maximizes profits for stockholders.

    Answer: True   **Difficulty**: Hard   **Reference**: p. 52

Multiple Choice Questions

51. Which of the following skills is the most important for the systems analyst to possess?

    a.   interpersonal skills
    b.   analytical skills
    c.   technical skills
    d.   all of the above

    Answer: d   **Difficulty**: Med   **Reference**: pp. 31-32

52. An interrelated set of components, with an identifiable boundary, working together for some purpose, best defines:

    a.   environment
    b.   system component
    c.   system
    d.   constraint

    Answer: c   **Difficulty**: Med   **Reference**: p. 32

53. Which of the following is not a system characteristic?

    a.   interface
    b.   boundary
    c.   input
    d.   scope

    Answer: d   **Difficulty**: Med   **Reference**: pp. 32-33

54. Dependence of one subsystem on one or more subsystems defines:

     a. interrelated components
     b. boundary
     c. component
     d. dependency

     Answer: a   **Difficulty**: Med   **Reference**: p. 33

55. The line that marks the inside and outside of a system, and that sets off the system from its environment, best defines:

     a. delineation mark
     b. boundary
     c. scope
     d. interface

     Answer: b   **Difficulty**: Med   **Reference**: p. 33

56. The overall goal or function of a system best defines:

     a. purpose
     b. goal
     c. objective
     d. scope

     Answer: a   **Difficulty**: Med   **Reference**: p. 33

57. The environment of a state university would not include:

     a. students
     b. the legislature
     c. the president's office
     d. news media

     Answer: c   **Difficulty**: Hard   **Reference**: pp. 33-34

58. The points at which the system meets its environment best defines:

     a. boundary points
     b. interfaces
     c. contact points
     d. merge points

     Answer: b   **Difficulty**: Med   **Reference**: pp. 33-34

59. Which of the following functions does an interface not provide?

    a.   coding and decoding
    b.   filtering
    c.   summarizing
    d.   boundary establishment

    Answer: d   **Difficulty**: Hard   **Reference**: p. 34

60. If designed well, which of the following will permit different systems to work together without being too dependent on each other?

    a.   inputs and outputs
    b.   interfaces
    c.   programs
    d.   subsystems

    Answer: b   **Difficulty**: Med   **Reference**: p. 34

61. Everything external to a system that interacts with the system best defines:

    a.   external interface
    b.   process
    c.   environment
    d.   constraint

    Answer: c   **Difficulty**: Med   **Reference**: p. 33

62. A limit to what a system can accomplish best defines:

    a.   constraint
    b.   boundary
    c.   control procedure
    d.   limitation

    Answer: a   **Difficulty**: Med   **Reference**: p. 34

63. Whatever a system takes from its environment to fulfill its purpose best defines:

    a.   interface
    b.   output
    c.   information
    d.   input

    Answer: d   **Difficulty**: Med   **Reference**: p. 34

64. A system that interacts freely with its environment, taking input and returning output, best defines:

    a.   free system
    b.   open system
    c.   closed system
    d.   receptive system

    Answer: b   **Difficulty**: Med   **Reference**: p. 35

65. A system that is cut off from its environment and does not interact with its environment is a(n):

    a. closed system
    b. entropic system
    c. unresponsive system
    d. open system

    Answer: a   **Difficulty**: Med   **Reference**: p. 35

66. Being able to break down a system into its components defines:

    a. coupling
    b. cohesion
    c. decomposition
    d. modularity

    Answer: c   **Difficulty**: Med   **Reference**: p. 36

67. Which of the following is not a function of decomposition?

    a. permits different parts of the system to be built at the same time by the same person
    b. allows attention to be concentrated on the part of the system pertinent to a particular audience, without confusing people with details irrelevant to their interests
    c. facilitates the focusing of attention on one area (subsystem) at a time without interference from other parts
    d. breaks a system into smaller, more manageable and understandable subsystems

    Answer: a   **Difficulty**: Hard   **Reference**: p. 36

68. Which of the following is a direct result of decomposition?

    a. coupling
    b. open systems
    c. cohesion
    d. modularity

    Answer: d   **Difficulty**: Med   **Reference**: p. 36

69. The extent to which subsystems depend on each other refers to:

    a. modularity
    b. coupling
    c. decomposition
    d. dependence

    Answer: b   **Difficulty**: Med   **Reference**: p. 36

70. Dividing a system up into chunks of a relatively uniform size defines:

    a. decomposition
    b. modularity
    c. sizing
    d. structure

    Answer: b   **Difficulty**: Med   **Reference**: p. 36

71. The extent to which a system or a subsystem performs a single function defines:

    a. decomposition
    b. cohesion
    c. sizing
    d. decoupling

    Answer: b   **Difficulty**: Med   **Reference**: p. 37

72. Portraying the purpose and function of the system without tying the description to any specific physical implementation defines:

    a. logical system description
    b. physical system description
    c. logical reference
    d. unrestricted view

    Answer: a   **Difficulty**: Med   **Reference**: p. 37

73. A description of a system that focuses on how the system will be materially constructed refers to:

    a. logical system description
    b. physical reference
    c. restricted view
    d. physical system description

    Answer: d   **Difficulty**: Med   **Reference**: p. 37

74. The first step in systems thinking is:

    a. thinking about the essential characteristics of a specific situation
    b. questioning assumptions
    c. being able to identify something as a system
    d. identifying the environment

    Answer: c   **Difficulty**: Med   **Reference**: p. 37

75. Which of the following is a true statement?

    a. Information systems can be seen as subsystems in larger organizational systems, taking input from, and returning output to, their organizational environments.
    b. Information systems can be seen as supersystems in an organizational environment.
    c. A business system is a subsystem of an information system.
    d. Generally, information systems are closed systems.

    Answer: a   **Difficulty**: Med   **Reference**: p. 38

76. Which of the following is a true statement?

    a. For a logical information system description, it is irrelevant whether a customer's order shows up in the kitchen as a piece of paper or as lines of text on a monitor screen.
    b. For every logical information system description, there can be only one physical implementation of it.
    c. For every physical implementation, there must be at least two logical information system descriptions.
    d. For a physical representation, it is irrelevant how the input activity occurs.

    Answer: a   **Difficulty**: Hard   **Reference**: p. 39

77. Which of the following is not an area of organizational knowledge for a systems analyst?

    a. standards and procedures
    b. influence and inclinations of key personnel
    c. products, services, and markets
    d. modularity and cohesion

    Answer: d   **Difficulty**: Hard   **Reference**: p. 40

78. Which of the following is the correct sequencing of Simon's problem-solving model?

    a. implementation, design, choice, intelligence
    b. design, choice, intelligence, implementation
    c. choice, design, implementation, intelligence
    d. intelligence, design, choice, implementation

    Answer: d   **Difficulty**: Med   **Reference**: p. 41

79. Collecting all information relevant to the problem is performed during Simon's:

    a. design phase
    b. intelligence phase
    c. choice phase
    d. implementation phase

    Answer: b   **Difficulty**: Med   **Reference**: p. 41

80. Formulating alternatives is done during Simon's:

    a. design phase
    b. intelligence phase
    c. choice phase
    d. implementation phase

    Answer: a   **Difficulty**: Med   **Reference**: p. 41

81. Placing the solution into practice is done during Simon's:

    a. design phase
    b. intelligence phase
    c. choice phase
    d. implementation phase

    Answer: d   **Difficulty**: Med   **Reference**: p. 41

82. Which of the following is not a true statement regarding technical skills?

    a. A systems analyst should develop a single set of technical skills to use throughout his career.
    b. The level of technical skill required will vary by job assignment and point in your career.
    c. Information technology, techniques, and methodologies change quickly.
    d. As an analyst, you must understand alternative technologies.

    Answer: a   **Difficulty**: Med   **Reference**: p. 42

83. Having a familiarity with hardware, operating system software, data communication standards and software, decision support system generators, and systems development tools is characteristic of which skill?

    a. management
    b. organization
    c. analytical
    d. technology

    Answer: d   **Difficulty**: Med   **Reference**: pp. 42-43

84. Which of the following is not a management skills category?

    a. interpersonal
    b. resource
    c. project
    d. risk

    Answer: a   **Difficulty**: Med   **Reference**: pp. 43-44

85. The most important resource is:

    a. time
    b. money
    c. people
    d. equipment

    Answer: c   **Difficulty**: Easy   **Reference**: p. 43

86. Preventing projects from being late and going over budget is the goal of:

    a. resource management
    b. project management
    c. risk management
    d. time management

    Answer: b   **Difficulty**: Med   **Reference**: p. 44

87. Knowing where to place resources (such as people) where they can do the most good, and prioritizing activities to achieve the greatest gain is characteristic of:

    a. resource management
    b. project management
    c. risk management
    d. time management

    Answer: c   **Difficulty**: Med   **Reference**: p. 44

88. Knowing how to get people to make a smooth transition from one information system to another, giving up their old ways of doing things and accepting new ways is characteristic of:

    a. resource management
    b. change management
    c. risk management
    d. project management

    Answer: b   **Difficulty**: Med   **Reference**: p. 45

89. The single, most important interpersonal skill for an analyst is:

    a. time management
    b. communication
    c. resource management
    d. managing user and manager expectations

    Answer: b   **Difficulty**: Med   **Reference**: p. 45

90. Which of the following is a true statement?

    a. Interviews are popular because they do not take up a lot of time.
    b. Questionnaires are more effective than interviews.
    c. Interviews can be time-consuming and expensive.
    d. Questionnaires have the disadvantage of being more biased in how the results are interpreted, because the questions and the answers are not standardized.

    Answer: c   **Difficulty**: Med   **Reference**: p. 45

91. Which of the following is a true statement regarding writing and presenting?

    a. The larger the organization and the more complicated the systems development project, the more writing you will have to do.
    b. Part of oral presentations involves preparing slides, overhead transparencies, or multimedia presentations, including system demonstrations.
    c. To be effective, you need to write both clearly and persuasively.
    d. All of the above are correct.

    Answer: d   **Difficulty**: Med   **Reference**: p. 46

92. High-performance team characteristics include a:

    a. sense of team identity
    b. result-driven structure
    c. sense of autonomy
    d. all of the above

    Answer: d   **Difficulty**: Med   **Reference**: p. 47

93. Ginzberg found that successfully managing user expectations is related to successful systems:

    a. design
    b. implementation
    c. project planning and initiation
    d. project identification and selection

    Answer: b   **Difficulty**: Med   **Reference**: p. 48

94. Which of the following is not a guideline for running an effective meeting?

    a. Use physical movement to focus on yourself or on the group, depending on which is called for at the time.
    b. Reward group member participation with thanks and respect.
    c. Make statements instead of asking questions.
    d. Be a good listener.

    Answer: c   **Difficulty**: Med   **Reference**: p. 49

95. Indicating specific procedures and techniques to be used during the development process best defines:

    a. endorsed development methodology
    b. approved development platforms
    c. role definition
    d. technique identification

    Answer: a   **Difficulty**: Med   **Reference**: p. 49

96. The ACM Code of Ethics and Professional Conduct places an emphasis on:

    a. personal responsibility, honesty, and respect for relevant laws
    b. quality systems analysis, development, and implementation
    c. improving public understanding of computing and its consequences, acquiring and maintaining professional competence, and the systems development life cycle
    d. fairness, ethics, and teamwork

    Answer: a   **Difficulty**: Med   **Reference**: p. 50

97. When considered as one of the standards of practice, a common language refers to:

    a. laying out specific procedures and techniques to be used during the development process
    b. using a special language such as data flow diagramming as a means of communication
    c. using a special language such as computer jargon as a means of communication
    d. using a particular development platform

    Answer: b   **Difficulty**: Med   **Reference**: p. 50

98. According to Smith and Hasnas, which of the following approaches suggests eliminating potential actions that could reduce the welfare of the members of society?

    a. stockholder approach
    b. golden rule approach
    c. social contract approach
    d. stakeholder approach

    Answer: c   **Difficulty**: Med   **Reference**: p. 52

99. Which of the following suggests that an action is ethical as long as it is legal, not deceptive, and maximizes profits?

    a. stockholder approach
    b. golden rule approach
    c. social contract approach
    d. stakeholder approach

    Answer: a   **Difficulty**: Med   **Reference**: p. 52

100. If you are designing database queries and data analysis routines to support business analysis and decision making, often for one department, you are called a(n):

    a. trainer
    b. decision support analyst
    c. end-user support specialist
    d. project manager

    Answer: b   **Difficulty**: Med   **Reference**: p. 54

Fill In the Blanks

101. A *system* is an interrelated set of components, with an identifiable boundary, working together for some purpose.

                    Difficulty: Easy   **Reference**: p. 32

102. A *component* is an irreducible part or aggregation of parts that make up a system.

                    Difficulty: Med   **Reference**: p. 33

103. *Interrelated components* refers to the dependence of one subsystem on one or more subsystems.

                    Difficulty: Med   **Reference**: p. 33

104. A *boundary* is the line that marks the inside and outside of a system and that sets off the system from its environment.

                    Difficulty: Med   **Reference**: p. 33

105. A *purpose* is the overall goal or function of a system.

        Difficulty: Easy   **Reference**: p. 33

106. *Environment* refers to everything external to a system that interacts with the system.

        Difficulty: Med   **Reference**: p. 33

107. An *interface* is the point of contact where a system meets its environment or where subsystems meet each other.

        Difficulty: Med   **Reference**: p. 34

108. A *constraint* is a limit to what a system can accomplish.

        Difficulty: Med   **Reference**: p. 34

109. *Input* is whatever a system takes from its environment in order to fulfill its purpose.

        Difficulty: Easy   **Reference**: p. 34

110. *Output* is whatever a system returns to its environment in order to fulfill its purpose.

        Difficulty: Easy   **Reference**: p. 34

111. An *open system* is a system that interacts freely with its environment, taking input and returning output.

        Difficulty: Med   **Reference**: p. 35

112. A *closed system* is a system that is cut off from its environment and does not interact with it.

        Difficulty: Med   **Reference**: p. 35

113. *Modularity* refers to dividing a system up into chunks or modules of a relatively uniform size.

        Difficulty: Med   **Reference**: p. 36

114. *Coupling* is the extent to which subsystems depend on each other.

        Difficulty: Hard   **Reference**: p. 36

115. *Cohesion* is the extent to which a system or a subsystem performs a single function.

        Difficulty: Hard   **Reference**: p. 37

116. *Logical system description* describes a system, focusing on the system's function and purpose without regard to how the system will be physically implemented.

        Difficulty: Med   **Reference**: p. 37

117. *Physical system description* describes a system, focusing on how the system will be materially constructed.

        Difficulty: Med   **Reference**: p. 37

118.   *Intelligence*, *design*, *choice*, and *implementation* are the four phases of Simon's problem-solving approach.

Difficulty: Med   **Reference**: p. 41

119.   *Risk management* is the ability to anticipate what might go wrong in a project.

Difficulty: Med   **Reference**: p. 44

120.   *Communication skills*, *working alone and with a team*, *facilitating groups*, and *managing expectations of users and managers* are four important interpersonal skills.

Difficulty: Hard   **Reference**: p. 45

121.   An *endorsed methodology*, *approved development platforms*, *well-defined roles for people in the development process*, and a *common language* are four standards of practice.

Difficulty: Hard   **Reference**: p. 49

122.   Smith and Hasnas suggest that the *stockholder*, *stakeholder*, and *social contract* approaches are three different ways to view business problems with ethical considerations.

Difficulty: Hard   **Reference**: p. 52

123.   The *stockholder approach* holds that any action taken by a business is ethically acceptable as long as it is legal, not deceptive, and maximizes profits for stockholders.

Difficulty: Med   **Reference**: p. 52

124.   The *stakeholder approach* suggests that any action that violates the rights of any one stakeholder must be rejected.

Difficulty: Med   **Reference**: p. 52

125.   The *social contract approach* rejects actions that are fraudulent/deceptive, dehumanize employees, or involve discrimination.

Difficulty: Hard   **Reference**: p. 52

Matching Questions

Match each of the following terms with its definition.

 a. open system
 b. modularity
 c. coupling
 d. decomposition
 e. closed system

126. The extent to which subsystems depend on each other

 Answer: c   **Reference:** p. 36

127. Dividing a system up into chunks of a relatively uniform size

 Answer: b   **Reference:** p. 36

128. Breaking down a system into its components

 Answer: d   **Reference:** p. 36

129. A system that interacts freely with its environment, taking input and returning output

 Answer: a   **Reference:** p. 35

130. A system that is cut off from its environment and does not interact with it

 Answer: e   **Reference:** p. 35

Match each of the following phases of Simon's problem-solving model to its description.

 a. choice
 b. intelligence
 c. design
 d. implementation

131. Placing the solution into practice

 Answer: d   **Reference:** p. 41

132. Collecting all information relevant to the problem

 Answer: b   **Reference:** p. 41

133. Formulating alternatives

 Answer: c   **Reference:** p. 41

134. Selecting the best alternative

 Answer: a   **Reference:** p. 41

Match each of the following skill types with appropriate examples. (Answers may occur more than once.)

    a.   technical
    b.   analytical
    c.   management
    d.   interpersonal

135.   Systems thinking

          Answer: b   **Reference**: p. 32

136.   Communication skills

          Answer: d   **Reference**: p. 45

137.   Predicting resource usage

          Answer: c   **Reference**: p. 44

138.   Working knowledge of database management and operating systems

          Answer: a   **Reference**: p. 43

139.   Organizational knowledge

          Answer: b   **Reference**: p. 32

140.   Ability to anticipate what might go wrong in a project

          Answer: c   **Reference**: p. 44

141.   Understanding of computers

          Answer: a   **Reference**: p. 43

142.   Understanding of data communication standards and software for local and wide area networks

          Answer: a   **Reference**: p. 43

143.   Problem identification

          Answer: b   **Reference**: p. 40

Match each of the following skills with its appropriate area of involvement.

  a. technical
  b. analytical
  c. management
  d. interpersonal

144. Involves systems thinking, organizational knowledge, problem identification, and problem analyzing and solving

        Answer: b   **Reference:** p. 32

145. Involves understanding how computers, data networks, database management and operating systems, and a host of other technologies work, their potential, and their limitations

        Answer: a   **Reference:** p. 42

146. Involves resource, project, risk, and change management

        Answer: c   **Reference:** p. 43

147. Involves communication skills, working alone and with a team; facilitating groups, and managing expectations of users and managers

        Answer: d   **Reference:** p. 45

Match each of the following terms with its definition.

    a.   component
    b.   interrelated components
    c.   boundary
    d.   purpose
    e.   interface
    f.   environment
    g.   input
    h.   output
    i.   constraint

148.   An irreducible part or aggregation of parts that make up a system

                   Answer: a   **Reference:** p. 33

149.   Dependence of one subsystem on one or more subsystems

                   Answer: b   **Reference:** p. 33

150.   The overall goal or function of a system

                   Answer: d   **Reference:** p. 33

151.   Point of contact where a system meets its environment or where subsystems meet each other

                   Answer: e   **Reference:** p. 34

152.   A limit to what a system can accomplish

                   Answer: i   **Reference:** p. 34

153.   Everything external to a system that interacts with the system

                   Answer: f   **Reference:** p. 33

154.   The line that marks the inside and outside of a system

                   Answer: c   **Reference:** p. 33

155.   Whatever a system takes from its environment in order to fulfill its purpose

                   Answer: g   **Reference:** p. 34

156.   Whatever a system returns to its environment in order to fulfill its purpose

                   Answer: h   **Reference:** p. 34

Essay Questions

157.   *Identify and briefly describe the four major categories of skills that an analyst needs to succeed.*

Analytical, technical, management, and interpersonal skills are needed by the analyst to succeed. Analytical skills include systems thinking, organizational knowledge, problem identification, and problem analyzing and solving. Systems thinking involves an understanding of basic system concepts, especially how it relates to information systems. Organizational knowledge refers to obtaining a basic understanding of how organizations work. While problem identification is the ability to define differences, problem solving involves the process of finding a way to reduce the differences which exist between a current situation and a desired situation. Technical skills require an understanding of how computers, data networks, database management and operating systems, and other various technologies work, their potential, and their limitations. Management skills include resource, project, risk, and change management. Resource management skills involve an understanding of how to obtain and work effectively with organizational resources. Examples of resource management are predicting resource usage, tracking and accounting for resource consumption, and learning how to use resources effectively. Project management skills refer to the ability to effectively manage projects crucial to a systems analyst's job, and prevent projects from being late and going over budget. Risk management is the ability to anticipate what might go wrong in a project. Helping people to make a smooth transition from one information system to another requires change management. Interpersonal skills involve relating to and working with other people. Various interpersonal skills needed to work with others include communication skills, working alone or in a team, facilitating groups, and managing expectations of users and managers. While communication skills can take a variety of forms, the goal is to communicate clearly and effectively with others. Working alone or with a team requires the ability to organize and manage schedules, commitments, and deadlines. While participating in group sessions, such as JAD, an analyst will be working with several people. The ability to facilitate group interaction is an important skill to master. Successful system implementation is related to successfully managing user expectations.

158.   *List and define the nine characteristics of a system.*

The first characteristic, component, is defined as an irreducible part or aggregation of parts that make up a system. The second system characteristic, interrelated components, refers to the dependence of one subsystem on one or more subsystems. A boundary, the third characteristic, is the line that marks the inside and outside of a system. Purpose, the fourth characteristic, is the overall goal or function of a system. Everything external to a system that interacts with the system defines the fifth characteristic, environment. Interfaces are points of contact where a system meets its environment or where subsystems meet each other. Whatever a system takes from its environment in order to fulfill its purpose defines input. Output, the eighth characteristic, is whatever a system returns to its environment in order to fulfill its purpose. The ninth characteristic, constraints, refers to limits to what a system can accomplish.

159.   *Identify four ways that you can improve your communication skills.*

Four suggestions for improving communication skills were supplied in the chapter. Individuals should take every opportunity to practice their communication skills. Speaking to civic organizations, conducting training classes, or participating in clubs can be of benefit. Videotaping presentations and critically evaluating skills can provide feedback. Using writing centers to critique writing abilities can be of benefit. Finally, enrolling in business and technical writing classes offered by colleges and organizations can provide opportunities for improvement.

160. *Briefly discuss the "ACM Code of Ethics and Professional Conduct."*

The Association for Computing Machinery, ACM, is a professional society consisting of information system professionals and academicians. The association has developed a code of ethics for its members. This code of ethics is referred to as "ACM Code of Ethics and Professional Conduct." The Code emphasizes personal responsibility, honesty, and respect for relevant laws. The Code consists of four major sections: (1.0) General Moral Imperatives; (2.0) More Specific Professional Responsibilities; (3.0) Organizational Leadership Imperatives; and (4.0) Compliance with the Code.

161. *Briefly describe Smith and Hasnas's three different ways to view business problems.*

Smith and Hasnas identified the stockholder, stakeholder, and social contract approaches. The stockholder approach suggests that an action is ethical as long as it is legal, not deceptive, and maximizes profits for stockholders. The stakeholder approach examines the rights of each stakeholder and rejects any action that violates the rights of a stakeholder. This approach also balances the rights of the different stakeholder groups. The social contract approach focuses on society, eliminating actions that are fraudulent, dehumanizing, and discriminatory. This approach also rejects actions that reduce the welfare of society's members, and chooses a remaining option that maximizes probability of financial success.

162. *What is resource management? Identify six resource management capabilities.*

Resource management involves obtaining and working effectively with such organizational resources as people, documentation, information technology, and money. Resource capabilities include budgeting, tracking and accounting for resource consumption, learning how to use resources effectively, evaluating the quality of resources used, securing resources from abusive use, and relinquishing and obsoleting resources.

163. *Identify six ways that you can stay up-to-date with technology.*

Many resources are available; these include trade publications, professional societies, college courses, seminars, electronic bulletin boards, and web sites.

164. *Identify nine guidelines for running an effective meeting.*

The nine guidelines are: (1) become comfortable with your role as facilitator by gaining confidence in your ability, being clear about your purpose, and finding a style that is right for you; (2) at the beginning of the meeting make sure the group understands what is expected of them and of you; (3) use physical movement to focus on yourself or on the group, depending on which is called for at the time; (4) reward group member participation with thanks and respect; (5) ask questions instead of making statements; (6) be willing to wait patiently for group members to answer the questions you ask them; (7) be a good listener; (8) keep the group focused; (9) encourage group members to feel ownership of the group's goals and of their attempts to reach those goals.

165. *Using a pizza parlor as a guide, provide an example of each system characteristic.*

A pizza parlor consists of many components, including inventory, delivery, food preparation, and sales. Each of these components is interrelated, since a pizza delivery sale causes the pizza to be prepared, delivered, and an inventory adjustment. The boundary encompasses the pizza delivery system, food preparation, delivery, and inventory processes. The environment includes customers, suppliers, and inspectors. The system's purpose is to produce a high-quality, low-cost pizza. The counter and telephone serve as interfaces. A constraint is the limited delivery area. While invoices and orders serve as input, receipts and supply replenishment orders serve as output.

166.   *Other than the nine system characteristics, identify four important system concepts.*

Decomposition, modularity, coupling, and cohesion are four important system concepts. Decomposition breaks a system into smaller components. Modularity divides a system into uniform chunks, and coupling refers to the extent of a subsystem's dependency on another subsystem. Cohesion addresses the extent to which a system performs a single function.

167.   *Identify six interface functions.*

The six interface functions are security, filtering, coding and decoding, detecting and correcting errors, buffering, and summarizing and transforming raw data into a desired level of detail.

Chapter 3
Managing the Information Systems Project

True-False Questions

1. The focus of project management is to assure that systems development projects meet customer expectations and are delivered within budget and time constraints.

    Answer: True   **Difficulty**: Med   **Reference**: p. 62

2. The project manager is responsible for initiating, planning, executing, and closing down the project.

    Answer: True   **Difficulty**: Easy   **Reference**: p. 62

3. A deliverable is an end product in a phase of the SDLC.

    Answer: True   **Difficulty**: Easy   **Reference**: p. 62

4. A resource analysis plan determines if the proposed information system makes sense for the organization from an economic and operational standpoint.

    Answer: False   **Difficulty**: Med   **Reference**: p. 62

5. A systems development project may be undertaken to take advantage of business opportunities or to solve business problems.

    Answer: True   **Difficulty**: Med   **Reference**: p. 63

6. In order to determine the resources required for project completion, an organization should analyze the project's scope and determine the project's probability of successful completion.

    Answer: True   **Difficulty**: Med   **Reference**: p. 64

7. The most instrumental person to the successful completion of a project is the database analyst.

    Answer: False   **Difficulty**: Med   **Reference**: p. 64

8. When a project manager is getting projects completed through the effective utilization of resources, she is performing a risk and change management activity.

    Answer: False   **Difficulty**: Hard   **Reference**: p. 65

9. When a project manager works closely with customers to assure project deliverables meet expectations, she is performing a customer relations activity.

    Answer: True   **Difficulty**: Med   **Reference**: p. 65

10. Project planning is the first phase of the project management process in which activities are performed to assess the size, scope, and complexity of the project and to establish procedures to support later project activities.

    Answer: False   **Difficulty**: Med   **Reference**: p. 66

11. Establishing a relationship with the customer is a project initiation activity.

     Answer: True   **Difficulty**: Med   **Reference**: p. 66

12. Establishing the project initiation plan involves organizing an initial core of project team members to assist in accomplishing the project initiation activities.

     Answer: False   **Difficulty**: Hard   **Reference**: p. 66

13. The focus of the developing a communications plan activity is to collect and organize the tools that will be used while managing the project.

     Answer: False   **Difficulty**: Med   **Reference**: p. 67

14. The project workbook serves as a repository for all project correspondence, inputs, outputs, deliverables, procedures, and standards established by the project team.

     Answer: True   **Difficulty**: Easy   **Reference**: p. 67

15. Project initiation is the second phase of the project management process, which focuses on defining clear, discrete activities and the work needed to complete each activity within a single project.

     Answer: False   **Difficulty**: Med   **Reference**: p. 68

16. Project planning involves defining clear, discrete activities and the work needed to complete each activity within a single project.

     Answer: True   **Difficulty**: Med   **Reference**: p. 68

17. Task identification structure refers to the process of dividing a project into manageable tasks and logically ordering them to ensure a smooth evolution between tasks.

     Answer: False   **Difficulty**: Med   **Reference**: p. 69

18. Task sequence depends on which tasks produce deliverables needed in other tasks, when critical resources are available, the constraints placed on the project by the client, and the process outlined in the SDLC.

     Answer: True   **Difficulty**: Med   **Reference**: pp. 69-70

19. A logic model is a graphical representation of a project that shows each task as a horizontal bar whose length is proportional to its time for completion.

     Answer: False   **Difficulty**: Med   **Reference**: p. 70

20. Gantt charts show how tasks must be ordered and when an activity should begin and end.

     Answer: False   **Difficulty**: Med   **Reference**: p. 70

21. Creating a work breakdown structure requires that you decompose phases into activities and activities into specific tasks.

     Answer: True   **Difficulty**: Med   **Reference**: p. 70

22. Having a known method or technique is characteristic of a task.

Answer: True   **Difficulty**: Med   **Reference**: p. 70

23. Project time estimates for task completion and overall system quality are significantly influenced by the assignment of people to tasks.

Answer: True   **Difficulty**: Med   **Reference**: p. 71

24. During the development of a preliminary schedule activity, you specify how various deliverables are produced and tested by you and your project team.

Answer: False   **Difficulty**: Med   **Reference**: p. 71

25. A PERT diagram depicts project tasks and their interrelationships.

Answer: True   **Difficulty**: Easy   **Reference**: p. 72

26. A Statement of Work is developed during the project execution phase.

Answer: False   **Difficulty**: Hard   **Reference**: p. 73

27. The Statement of Work provides a detailed estimate of the project's tasks and resource requirements.

Answer: False   **Difficulty**: Med   **Reference**: p. 73

28. During project execution, plans created in prior phases are put into action.

Answer: True   **Difficulty**: Easy   **Reference**: p. 74

29. When executing the Baseline Project Plan, the project manager will initiate the execution of project activities, acquire and assign resources, orient and train new team members, keep the project on schedule, and assure the quality of project deliverables.

Answer: True   **Difficulty**: Med   **Reference**: p. 74

30. A slipped completion date for an activity may initiate a change to the Baseline Project Plan.

Answer: True   **Difficulty**: Med   **Reference**: p. 75

31. The meeting minutes project team communication method has a low formality rating.

Answer: False   **Difficulty**: Med   **Reference**: p. 76

32. The hallway discussion project team communication method has a medium to high formality rating.

Answer: False   **Difficulty**: Med   **Reference**: p. 76

33. The status report project team communication method is used to inform project team members.

Answer: True   **Difficulty**: Med   **Reference**: p. 76

34. A project can terminate naturally or unnaturally.

Answer: True   **Difficulty**: Easy   **Reference**: p. 76

35. Within the context of the SDLC, project closedown occurs when the design phase is completed.

    Answer: False　　　　　　**Difficulty**: Med　　　　　　**Reference**: p. 77

36. Team members are assessed as part of the conducting postproject reviews activity.

    Answer: False　　　　　　**Difficulty**: Med　　　　　　**Reference**: p. 77

37. The focus of closing the customer contract activity is to ensure that all contractual terms of the project have been met.

    Answer: True　　　　　　**Difficulty**: Med　　　　　　**Reference**: p. 77

38. Projects are deemed a success or failure at project closedown.

    Answer: True　　　　　　**Difficulty**: Easy　　　　　　**Reference**: p. 77

39. Gantt charts do not show how tasks must be ordered.

    Answer: True　　　　　　**Difficulty**: Med　　　　　　**Reference**: p. 78

40. When compared to PERT charts, Gantt charts are more useful for depicting the activities associated with large projects.

    Answer: False　　　　　　**Difficulty**: Med　　　　　　**Reference**: p. 78

41. Gantt charts visually show the time overlap of tasks whereas PERT does not show time overlap but does show which tasks could be done in parallel.

    Answer: True　　　　　　**Difficulty**: Med　　　　　　**Reference**: p. 79

42. The ability to easily make changes to a project is a very powerful feature of most project management environments.

    Answer: True　　　　　　**Difficulty**: Med　　　　　　**Reference**: p. 79

43. A work method is any person, group of people, piece of equipment, or material used in accomplishing an activity.

    Answer: False　　　　　　**Difficulty**: Med　　　　　　**Reference**: p. 80

44. Critical path scheduling is a scheduling technique whose order and duration of a sequence of task activities directly affect the completion date of a project.

    Answer: True　　　　　　**Difficulty**: Med　　　　　　**Reference**: p. 80

45. A major disadvantage of the PERT technique is its inability to represent completion times and show interrelationships between activities.

    Answer: False　　　　　　**Difficulty**: Med　　　　　　**Reference**: p. 80

46. If an activity's optimistic time is 4 weeks, its realistic time is 6 weeks, and its pessimistic time is 8 weeks, then its estimated time would be 6 weeks.

    Answer: True　　　　　　**Difficulty**: Med　　　　　　**Reference**: p. 81

47. If an activity's optimistic time is 3 months, its realistic time is 5 months, and its pessimistic time is 10 months, then its estimated time would be 5.5 months.

  Answer: True   **Difficulty**: Med   **Reference**: p. 81

48. If an activity's optimistic time is 4 days, its realistic time is 10 days, and its pessimistic time is 25 days, then its estimated time would be 11.5 days.

  Answer: True   **Difficulty**: Med   **Reference**: p. 81

49. An activity on the critical path will have a slack time of 1.

  Answer: False   **Difficulty**: Med   **Reference**: pp. 83-84

50. Microsoft Outlook is an example of project management software.

  Answer: False   **Difficulty**: Easy   **Reference**: p. 85

Multiple Choice Questions

51. A planned undertaking of related activities to reach an objective that has a beginning and an end best defines:

  a. task development
  b. activity plan
  c. project
  d. task schedule

  Answer: c   **Difficulty**: Med   **Reference**: p. 62

52. An individual with a diverse set of skills--management, leadership, technical, conflict management, and customer relationship--who is responsible for initiating, planning, executing, and closing down a project best defines:

  a. systems analyst
  b. consultant
  c. project scheduler
  d. project manager

  Answer: d   **Difficulty**: Med   **Reference**: p. 62

53. Which of the following are primary reasons for undertaking systems development projects?

  a. to take advantage of business opportunities
  b. to solve business problems
  c. to use state-of-the-art technology
  d. both a and b

  Answer: d   **Difficulty**: Med   **Reference**: p. 63

54. Arguably, the most instrumental person to the successful completion of any project is the:

    a. project manager
    b. chief information officer
    c. department manager
    d. staff consultant

    Answer: a   **Difficulty**: Med   **Reference**: p. 64

55. Which of the following are activities involved in managing a project?

    a. closing down the project
    b. planning the project
    c. executing the project
    d. all of the above

    Answer: d   **Difficulty**: Med   **Reference**: p. 64

56. A controlled process of initiating, planning, executing, and closing down a project best defines:

    a. systems development
    b. project management
    c. project development
    d. systems management

    Answer: b   **Difficulty**: Med   **Reference**: p. 64

57. Influencing the activities of others toward the attainment of a common goal through the use of intelligence, personality, and abilities refers to which of the following project manager activities?

    a. conflict management
    b. management
    c. leadership
    d. team management

    Answer: c   **Difficulty**: Med   **Reference**: p. 65

58. Managing conflict within a project team to assure that conflict is not too high or too low best defines which of the following project manager activities:

    a. conflict management
    b. leadership
    c. team management
    d. problem solving

    Answer: a   **Difficulty**: Med   **Reference**: p. 65

59. Identifying, assessing, and managing the risks and day-to-day changes that occur during a project best
     defines which of the following project manager activities:

     a.   conflict management
     b.   risk and change management
     c.   team management
     d.   problem solving

     Answer: b   **Difficulty**: Med   **Reference**: p. 65

60. Skills that include interpreting system requests and specifications, site preparation and user training,
     and contact point for customers best represent:

     a.   customer relations
     b.   conflict management
     c.   leadership
     d.   team management

     Answer: a   **Difficulty**: Med   **Reference**: p. 65

61. Skills that include defining and sequencing activities, communicating expectations, assigning
     resources to activities, and monitoring outcomes best represent:

     a.   technical problem solving
     b.   management
     c.   leadership
     d.   team management

     Answer: b   **Difficulty**: Med   **Reference**: p. 65

62. The phase of the project management process in which activities are performed to assess the size,
     scope, and complexity of the project and to establish procedures to support later project activities best
     defines:

     a.   project initiation
     b.   scope development
     c.   project planning
     d.   project assessment

     Answer: a   **Difficulty**: Med   **Reference**: p. 66

63. Which of the following project management activities is associated with project initiation?

     a.   establishing a relationship with the customer
     b.   describing project scope, alternatives, and feasibility
     c.   estimating resources and creating a detailed resource plan
     d.   identifying and assessing risks

     Answer: a   **Difficulty**: Med   **Reference**: p. 66

64. Defining the necessary activities required to organize the initiation team while they are working to define the scope of the project is the focus of which of the following activities?

    a. establishing the project initiation team
    b. establishing management procedures
    c. establishing the project initiation plan
    d. establishing the project management environment and project workbook

    Answer: c   **Difficulty**: Med   **Reference**: p. 66

65. An on-line or hard copy repository for all project correspondence, inputs, outputs, deliverables, procedures, and standards that is used for performing project audits, orientation of new team members, communication with management and customers, scoping future projects, and performing post-project reviews is called:

    a. a project workbook
    b. a schedule book
    c. a project planner
    d. project management software

    Answer: a   **Difficulty**: Med   **Reference**: p. 67

66. Which of the following is not an element of project planning?

    a. setting a Baseline Project Plan
    b. identifying and assessing risk
    c. determining project standards and procedures
    d. establishing management procedures

    Answer: d   **Difficulty**: Med   **Reference**: p. 69

67. Developing an understanding of the content and complexity of the project is the purpose of:

    a. describing the project scope, alternatives, and feasibility
    b. determining project standards and procedures
    c. developing a Statement Of Work
    d. setting a Baseline Project Plan

    Answer: a   **Difficulty**: Med   **Reference**: p. 69

68. The process of dividing the project into manageable tasks and logically ordering them to ensure a smooth evolution between tasks defines:

    a. task division
    b. work breakdown structure
    c. work structuring
    d. project division

    Answer: b   **Difficulty**: Med   **Reference**: p. 69

69. Which of the following is not a guideline for defining a task?

    a. A task should have well accepted predecessor and successor steps.
    b. A task should have a single and identifiable deliverable.
    c. A task should have a known method or technique.
    d. A task should always be completed by one person.

    Answer: d   **Difficulty**: Med   **Reference**: p. 70

70. A graphical representation of a project that shows each task activity as a horizontal bar whose length is proportional to its time for completion defines:

    a. PERT chart
    b. data diagram
    c. project chart
    d. Gantt chart

    Answer: d   **Difficulty**: Med   **Reference**: p. 70

71. Which of the following is a true statement regarding project time estimates?

    a. Project time estimates for task completion and overall system quality are significantly influenced by the assignment of people to tasks.
    b. Resource estimates should not be revised based upon the skills of the actual person assigned to a particular activity.
    c. Staff learning can be enhanced by assigning individuals to tasks which are "over their heads."
    d. Project time estimates are always on target.

    Answer: a   **Difficulty**: Med   **Reference**: p. 71

72. During which of the following activities do you use the information regarding tasks and resource availability to assign time estimates to each activity in the work breakdown structure?

    a. dividing the project into manageable tasks
    b. develop a preliminary schedule
    c. describing project scope, alternatives, and feasibility
    d. developing a Statement Of Work

    Answer: b   **Difficulty**: Med   **Reference**: p. 71

73. Indicating when and how written and oral reports will be provided by the team, how team members will coordinate work, what messages will be sent to announce the project to interested parties, and what kinds of information will be shared with vendors and external contractors involved with the project describes:

    a. determining project standards and procedures
    b. developing a Statement Of Work
    c. developing a communication plan
    d. setting a Baseline Project Plan

    Answer: c   **Difficulty**: Med   **Reference**: p. 72

74. Risks can arise from:

    a. the use of new technology
    b. resistance to change
    c. availability of critical resources
    d. all of the above

    Answer: d   **Difficulty**: Med   **Reference**: p. 73

75. The third phase of the project management process in which the plans created in the prior phases are put into action is:

    a. project planning
    b. project execution
    c. project planning
    d. project close down

    Answer: b   **Difficulty**: Med   **Reference**: p. 74

76. Which of the following occurs during project execution?

    a. monitoring project progress against the baseline plan
    b. conducting post-project reviews
    c. establishing the project initiation plan
    d. establishing the project workbook

    Answer: a   **Difficulty**: Med   **Reference**: p. 74

77. Changes to the Baseline Project Plan might be motivated by:

    a. a slipped completion date of an activity
    b. a bungled activity that must be redone
    c. the identification of a new activity that becomes evident later in the project
    d. all of the above

    Answer: d   **Difficulty**: Easy   **Reference**: p. 75

78. The responsibility for keeping all team members informed of the project status best describes the:

    a. monitoring project progress against the Baseline Project Plan activity
    b. communicating the project status activity
    c. executing the baseline project plan activity
    d. project update activity

    Answer: b   **Difficulty**: Med   **Reference**: p. 76

79. Which of the following states correctly the formality and use of a project workbook?

    a. In terms of formality, the project workbook would be rated low to medium. In terms of use, the project workbook would be used to inform and serve as a permanent record.
    b. In terms of formality, the project workbook would be rated high. In terms of use, the project workbook would be used to resolve issues.
    c. In terms of formality, the project workbook would be rated high. In terms of use, the project workbook would be used to inform and serve as a permanent record.
    d. In terms of formality, the project workbook would be rated low. In terms of use, the project workbook would be used to resolve issues.

    Answer: c   **Difficulty**: Hard   **Reference**: p. 76

80. Which of the following states correctly the formality and use of hallway discussions?

    a. In terms of formality, hallway discussions would be rated medium. In terms of use, hallway discussions would be used to inform.
    b. In terms of formality, hallway discussions would be rated high. In terms of use, hallway discussions would be used to inform.
    c. In terms of formality, hallway discussions would be rated low. In terms of use, hallway discussions would be used to inform and resolve issues.
    d. In terms of formality, hallway discussions would be rated high. In terms of use, hallway discussions would serve as a permanent record.

    Answer: c   **Difficulty**: Hard   **Reference**: p. 76

81. The final phase of the project management process that focuses on bringing a project to an end is called:

    a. project evaluation
    b. project closedown
    c. project initiation and planning
    d. project review

    Answer: b   **Difficulty**: Med   **Reference**: p. 76

82. Which of the following is not an element of project close down?

    a. conducting post project reviews
    b. closing the customer contract
    c. closing down the project
    d. communicating the project status

    Answer: d   **Difficulty**: Med   **Reference**: p. 77

83. Ensuring that all contractual terms of the project have been met is done during:

    a. conducting postproject reviews
    b. closing the customer contract
    c. closing down the project
    d. communicating the project status

    Answer: b   **Difficulty**: Med   **Reference**: p. 77

84. Determining the strengths and weaknesses of project deliverables, the processes used to create them, and the project management process is done during:

    a. conducting postproject reviews
    b. closing the customer contract
    c. closing down the project
    d. communicating the project status

    Answer: a   **Difficulty:** Med   **Reference:** p. 77

85. When comparing a Gantt chart to a PERT chart, which of the following is a true statement?

    a. Gantt shows the sequence dependencies between activities, whereas PERT shows the duration of activities.
    b. PERT shows the time overlap of activities, whereas Gantt does not show time overlap.
    c. Some forms of Gantt charts can show slack time available within an earliest start and latest finish duration, whereas PERT shows this by data within activity rectangles.
    d. both a and b

    Answer: c   **Difficulty:** Med   **Reference:** p. 79

86. A diagram that depicts project activities and their interrelationships is called a:

    a. PERT chart
    b. data diagram
    c. project chart
    d. Gantt chart

    Answer: a   **Difficulty:** Easy   **Reference:** p. 72

87. Any person, group of people, piece of equipment, or material used in accomplishing an activity is referred to as a(n):

    a. entity
    b. resource
    c. identifier
    d. agent

    Answer: b   **Difficulty:** Easy   **Reference:** p. 80

88. A scheduling technique where the order and duration of the sequence of activities directly affect the completion date of a project refers to:

    a. sequencing strategy
    b. Gantt scheduling
    c. critical path scheduling
    d. activity scheduling

    Answer: c   **Difficulty:** Med   **Reference:** p. 80

89. Optimistic time is:

    a. the maximum period of time for an activity to be completed
    b. the minimum period of time for an activity to be completed
    c. the planner's "best guess" of the amount of time the activity actually will require for completion
    d. the maximum period of time for an entire project to be completed

    Answer: b   **Difficulty:** Med   **Reference:** p. 81

90. Pessimistic time is:

    a. the maximum period of time for an activity to be completed
    b. the minimum period of time for an activity to be completed
    c. the planner's "best guess" of the amount of time the activity actually will require for completion
    d. the maximum period of time for an entire project to be completed

    Answer: a   **Difficulty:** Med   **Reference:** p. 81

91. Realistic time is:

    a. the maximum period of time for an activity to be completed
    b. the minimum period of time for an activity to be completed
    c. the planner's "best guess" of the amount of time the activity actually will require for completion
    d. the maximum period of time for an entire project to be completed

    Answer: c   **Difficulty:** Med   **Reference:** p. 81

92. What would be the estimated time for completion if the time estimates for report design are as follows: optimistic = 3 weeks; pessimistic = 9 weeks; realistic = 6 weeks?

    a. 3 weeks
    b. 6 weeks
    c. 18 weeks
    d. 5 weeks

    Answer: b   **Difficulty:** Med   **Reference:** p. 81

93. What would be the estimated time for completion if time estimates for programming are as follows: optimistic = 4 weeks; pessimistic = 6 weeks; realistic = 5 weeks?

    a. 5 weeks
    b. 6 weeks
    c. 15 weeks
    d. 3 weeks

    Answer: a   **Difficulty:** Med   **Reference:** p. 81

94. What would be the estimated time for completion if time estimates for installation are as follows: optimistic = 1 week; pessimistic = 1 week; realistic = 1 week?

    a. 5 weeks
    b. 6 weeks
    c. 3 weeks
    d. 1 week

    Answer: d   **Difficulty**: Med   **Reference**: p. 81

95. A critical path is:

    a. a sequence of activities whose order and durations indirectly affect the completion date of a project
    b. a sequence of activities whose order and durations directly affect the completion date of a project
    c. a sequence of activities whose order must be performed in parallel
    d. a sequence of activities whose duration cannot last more than 40 percent of the time allotted to the project

    Answer: b   **Difficulty**: Med   **Reference**: p. 83

96. Which of the following is true regarding Gantt chart construction?

    a. To construct the Gantt chart, a horizontal bar is drawn for each activity that reflects its sequence and duration.
    b. To show precedence relationships, arrows are used to connect actions.
    c. Arrows are used to reflect the sequence of activities.
    d. Squares are used to represent activities.

    Answer: a   **Difficulty**: Med   **Reference**: p. 83

97. Which of the following is a true statement regarding PERT charts?

    a. The critical path of a PERT network is represented by the sequence of connected activities that produce the longest overall time period.
    b. All activities with a slack time equal to zero are on the critical path.
    c. Nodes not on the critical path can be delayed (for some amount of time) without delaying the final completion of the project.
    d. all of the above

    Answer: d   **Difficulty**: Med   **Reference**: p. 83

98. The amount of time that an activity can be delayed without delaying the project refers to:

    a. noncritical time
    b. slack time
    c. down time
    d. delay time

    Answer: b   **Difficulty**: Med   **Reference**: p. 83

99. Slack time is equal to:

    a. the difference between an activity's latest and earliest expected completion time
    b. the latest expected completion time
    c. the difference between the start time and realistic time for each activity
    d. the sum of an activity's latest and earliest expected completion time

    Answer: a   **Difficulty**: Med   **Reference**: p. 84

100. Automated tools available to help you manage a development project are referred to as:

    a. diagram generators
    b. project management software
    c. systems development software
    d. none of the above

    Answer: b   **Difficulty**: Med   **Reference**: p. 84

Fill In the Blanks

101. A *project manager* is a systems analyst with a diverse set of skills—management, leadership, technical, conflict management, and customer relationship—who is responsible for initiating, planning, executing, and closing down a project.

    Difficulty: Easy   **Reference**: p. 62

102. A *project* is a planned undertaking of related activities to reach an objective that has a beginning and an end.

    Difficulty: Easy   **Reference**: p. 62

103. A *deliverable* is an end product in a phase of the SDLC.

    Difficulty: Med   **Reference**: p. 62

104. A *feasibility study* determines if the proposed information system makes sense for the organization from an economic and operational standpoint.

    Difficulty: Med   **Reference**: p. 62

105. *Project management* is a controlled process of initiating, planning, executing, and closing down a project.

    Difficulty: Easy   **Reference**: p. 64

106. *Project initiation*, *project planning*, *project execution*, and *project closedown* are the four phases of project management.

    Difficulty: Med   **Reference**: p. 64

107. Influencing the activities of others toward the attainment of a common goal through the use of intelligence, personality, and abilities describes the ***leadership*** project manager activity.

   Difficulty: Med   **Reference**: p. 65

108. Getting projects completed through the effective utilization of resources describes the ***management*** project manager activity.

   Difficulty: Med   **Reference**: p. 65

109. Working closely with customers to assure project deliverables meet expectations describes the ***customer relations*** project manager activity.

   Difficulty: Med   **Reference**: p. 65

110. Designing and sequencing activities to attain project goals describes the ***technical problem solving*** project manager activity.

   Difficulty: Med   **Reference**: p. 65

111. Managing conflict within a project team to assure that conflict is not too high or too low describes the ***conflict management*** project manager activity.

   Difficulty: Med   **Reference**: p. 65

112. Managing the project team for effective team performance describes the ***team management*** project manager activity.

   Difficulty: Med   **Reference**: p. 65

113. ***Project initiation*** is the first phase of the project management process in which activities are performed to assess the size, scope, and complexity of the project and to establish procedures to support later project activities.

   Difficulty: Med   **Reference**: p. 66

114. A ***project workbook*** is an on-line or hard-copy repository for all project correspondence, inputs, outputs, deliverables, procedures, and standards that is used for performing project audits, orientating new team members, communicating with management and customers, identifying future projects, and performing post project reviews.

   Difficulty: Med   **Reference**: p. 67

115. ***Project planning*** is the second phase of the project management process, which focuses on defining clear, discrete activities and the work needed to complete each activity within a single project.

   Difficulty: Med   **Reference**: p. 68

116. ***Work breakdown structure*** is the process of dividing the project into manageable tasks and logically ordering them to ensure a smooth evolution between tasks.

   Difficulty: Med   **Reference**: p. 69

117. A *__Gantt chart__* is a graphical representation of a project that shows each task as a horizontal bar whose length is proportional to its time for completion.

Difficulty: Med   **Reference**: p. 70

118. A *__PERT chart__* is a diagram that depicts project tasks and their interrelationships.

Difficulty: Med   **Reference**: p. 72

119. *__Project execution__* is the third phase of the project management process in which the plans created in the prior phases are put into action.

Difficulty: Med   **Reference**: p. 74

120. *__Project closedown__* is the final phase of the project management process that focuses on ending the project.

Difficulty: Med   **Reference**: p. 76

121. *__Resources__* are any person, group of people, piece of equipment, or material used in accomplishing an activity.

Difficulty: Easy   **Reference**: p. 80

122. *__Critical path scheduling__* is a scheduling technique whose order and duration of a sequence of task activities directly affect the completion date of a project.

Difficulty: Med   **Reference**: p. 80

123. A *__critical path__* is the shortest time in which a project can be completed.

Difficulty: Med   **Reference**: p. 83

124. *__Slack time__* is the amount of time that an activity can be delayed without delaying the project.

Difficulty: Med   **Reference**: p. 83

125. *__Project management software__* is a tool that is available to help you manage a development project.

Difficulty: Easy   **Reference**: p. 84

Matching Questions

Match each of the following project planning activities with its corresponding definition.

    a.   developing a communication plan
    b.   developing a preliminary schedule
    c.   estimating resources and creating a resource plan
    d.   dividing the project into manageable tasks
    e.   describing project scope, alternatives, and feasibility

126.   Separate the entire project into manageable tasks and then logically order them to ensure a smooth evolution between tasks.

               Answer: d   **Reference**: p. 69

127.   During this activity, a plan is created and used to help assemble and deploy resources in the most effective manner.

               Answer: c   **Reference**: p. 71

128.   During this activity, you use the information regarding tasks and resource availability to assign time estimates to each activity in the work breakdown structure.

               Answer: b   **Reference**: p. 71

129.   The focus of this activity is to outline the communication procedures between management, project team members, and the customer.

               Answer: a   **Reference**: p. 72

130.   The purpose of this activity is to develop an understanding of the content and complexity of the project.

               Answer: e   **Reference**: p. 69

Based on the optimistic, realistic, and pessimistic time estimates provided, determine the expected time. (Estimates are based on weeks.)

     a. 1 week
     b. 6 weeks
     c. 5 weeks
     d. 5.5 weeks
     e. 3 weeks

131.   Optimistic = 1; realistic = 5; pessimistic = 9

                         Answer: c   **Reference:** p. 81

132.   Optimistic = 5; realistic = 6; pessimistic = 7

                         Answer: b   **Reference:** p. 81

133.   Optimistic = 2; realistic = 6; pessimistic = 7

                         Answer: d   **Reference:** p. 81

134.   Optimistic = 1; realistic = 1; pessimistic = 1

                         Answer: a   **Reference:** p. 81

135.   Optimistic = 1; realistic = 3; pessimistic = 5

                         Answer: e   **Reference:** p. 81

Match each of the following project management phases with the activities associated with it. (Answers may occur more than once.)

    a.   project initiation
    b.   project planning
    c.   project execution
    d.   project close down

136.   Identify and assess risk

          Answer: b   **Reference:** p. 69

137.   Conduct post-project reviews

          Answer: d   **Reference:** p. 77

138.   Monitor project progress against the baseline plan

          Answer: c   **Reference:** p. 74

139.   Establish a relationship with the customer

          Answer: a   **Reference:** p. 66

140.   Close the customer contract

          Answer: d   **Reference:** p. 77

141.   Establish the project management environment and project workbook

          Answer: a   **Reference:** p. 66

142.   Communicate the project status

          Answer: c   **Reference:** p. 74

143.   Develop a Statement Of Work

          Answer: b   **Reference:** p. 69

144.   Create a preliminary budget

          Answer: b   **Reference:** p. 69

145.   Establish the project initiation plan

          Answer: a   **Reference:** p. 66

For each of the following statements, answer "a" if the statement is representative of a Gantt chart, and answer "b" if the statement is representative of a PERT chart.

146. Shows slack time available for each activity within activity rectangles.

       Answer: b   **Reference**: p. 79

147. Shows the time overlap of activities.

       Answer: a   **Reference**: p. 79

148. Shows the sequence dependencies between activities.

       Answer: b   **Reference**: p. 79

149. Visually shows the duration of activities.

       Answer: a   **Reference**: p. 79

150. Does not show time overlap, but shows what activities could be done in parallel.

       Answer: b   **Reference**: p. 79

Match each of the following activities with its corresponding skills.

    a. technical problem solving
    b. management
    c. customer relations
    d. team management
    e. risk and change management
    f. leadership
    g. conflict management

151. Environmental scanning, risk and opportunity identification and assessment, forecasting, resource redeployment

           Answer: e   **Reference:** p. 65

152. Communication, liaison between management, users, and developers, assigning activities, monitoring progress

           Answer: f   **Reference:** p. 65

153. Communication within and between teams, peer evaluations, conflict resolution, team building, self-management

           Answer: d   **Reference:** p. 65

154. Interpreting system requests and specifications, defining activities and their sequence, making tradeoffs between alternative solutions, designing solutions to problems

           Answer: a   **Reference:** p. 65

155. Interpreting system requests and specifications, site preparation and user training, contact point for customers

           Answer: c   **Reference:** p. 65

156. Defining and sequencing activities, communicating expectations, assigning resources to activities, monitoring outcomes

           Answer: b   **Reference:** p. 65

157. Problem solving, smoothing out personality differences, compromising, goal setting

           Answer: g   **Reference:** p. 65

Essay Questions

158. *Briefly define and compare Gantt charts and PERT charts.*

A PERT chart is a graphical depiction of project task activities and their interrelationships. The distinguishing feature of PERT is that the ordering of activities is shown by connecting an activity with its predecessor and successor activities. A Gantt chart is a graphical representation of a project that shows each task activity as a horizontal bar whose length is proportional to its time for completion. The two charts have features which enable them to more easily demonstrate certain aspects of a project more so than the other chart. Gantt shows the duration of activities; PERT shows the sequence dependencies between activities. Gantt shows the time overlap of activities; PERT does not show time overlap but does show what activities could be done in parallel. Some forms of Gantt charts can show slack time available within an earliest start and latest finish duration; PERT shows this by data within activity rectangles.

159. *Identify and briefly discuss the four phases involved in managing a project.*

The project management process occurs in four phases. Each phase requires that several activities be performed. The four phases include: initiating the project, planning the project, executing the project, and closing down the project. Each of the four phases is briefly highlighted below. The first phase, project initiation, includes activities which are performed to assess the size, scope, and complexity of the project and to establish procedures to support later project activities. The associated elements of project initiation are establishing the project initiation team, establishing a relationship with the customer, establishing the project initiation plan, establishing management procedures, and establishing the project management environment and project workbook. Project planning, the second phase, focuses on defining clear, discrete activities and the work needed to complete each activity within a single project. Varied and numerous types of tasks are performed during this phase. The elements of project planning include describing project scope, alternatives, and feasibility; dividing the project into manageable tasks; estimating resources and creating a resource plan; developing a preliminary schedule; developing a communication plan; determining project standards and procedures; identifying and assessing risk; creating a preliminary budget; developing a Statement Of Work; and setting a Baseline Project Plan. Project execution, the third phase of the project management process, is the phase in which the plans created in the prior phases are put into action. The elements of project execution include executing the Baseline Project Plan, monitoring project progress against the baseline plan, managing changes to the Baseline Project Plan, maintaining the project workbook, and communicating the project status. The final phase of the project management process, project close down, focuses on bringing a project to an end. Project close down includes closing down the project, conducting postproject reviews, and closing the customer contract.

160. *Identify the common activities and skills of a project manager.*

The project manager must be equipped with a diverse set of skills. These skills include leadership, management, customer relations, technical problem solving, conflict management, team management, and risk change management. Leadership skills involve influencing the activities of others toward the attainment of a common goal through the use of intelligence, personality, and abilities. Sample leadership skills include monitoring progress, serving as a liaison between management, users, and developers, and assigning activities. Management skills involve getting projects completed through the effective utilization of resources. Sample management skills include communicating expectations, assigning resources to activities, and monitoring outcomes. Customer relations skills involve working closely with customers to ensure project deliverables meet expectations. Examples of skills required are interpreting system requests and specifications, defining activities and their sequence, and making tradeoffs between alternative solutions. Technical problem solving involves designing and sequencing activities to attain project goals. Examples include interpreting system requests and specifications, defining activities and their sequence, and making tradeoffs between alternative solutions. Conflict management manages conflict within a project team to assure that conflict is not too high or too low. Sample skills required are problem solving, smoothing out personality differences, and compromising. Team management requires managing the project team for effective team performance. Sample skills required are peer evaluations, self management, and team building. Risk and change management requires identifying, assessing, and managing the risks and day-to-day changes that occur during a project. Sample skills required are environmental scanning, risk and opportunity identification and assessment, and forecasting.

161. *Briefly explain the process of managing an information systems project.*

A project is a planned undertaking of a series of related activities to reach an objective that has a beginning and an end. Project management is a controlled process of initiating, planning, executing, and closing down a project. The individual responsible for the project and project management is the project manager. The project manager is an individual with a diverse set of skills. Management, leadership, technical, conflict management, and customer relationship are necessary skills that the project manager should have. Also, the project manager is responsible for initiating, planning, executing, and closing down a project.

162. *Briefly discuss project management software.*

When developing a project, automated project management tools are available for use by the project manager. While a wide variety of project management tools are available, most include features such as the ability to define and order tasks, assign resources to tasks, and easily modify tasks and resources. The tools run on a range of platforms; the tools vary in the number of task activities supported, the complexity of relationships, system processing and storage requirements, and cost.

163. *Define project initiation. Identify five project initiation activities.*

During project initiation, activities are performed to assess the size, scope, and complexity of the project and to establish procedures to support later project activities. The five project initiation activities are to establish a project team, a relationship with a customer, the project initiation plan, management procedures, and the project management environment and project workbook.

164. *Define project planning. Identify ten project planning activities.*

During project planning, the project manager focuses on defining clear, discrete activities and the work needed to complete each activity within a single project. Project planning activities include describing the project scope, alternatives, and feasibility; dividing the project into manageable tasks; estimating resources and creating a resource plan; developing a preliminary schedule; developing a communication plan; determining project standards and procedures; identifying and assessing risk; creating a preliminary budget; developing a Statement of Work; and setting a Baseline Project Plan.

165. *Construct a PERT chart using the following data. For each activity, identify its early start time, late start time, early finish time, late finish time, and slack. Identify the critical path.*

Activity	Optimistic Time	Pessimistic Time	Realistic Time	Expected Time	Preceding Task
A	4	8	6		--
B	7	11	9		A
C	3	7	5		A
D	9	13	11		A
E	6	10	8		B
F	3	9	6		C,D,E

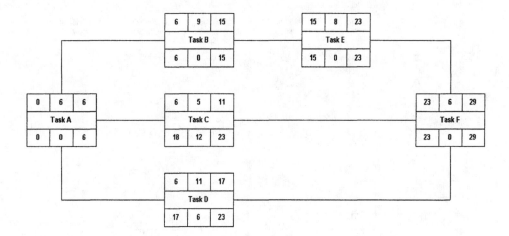

166. *Construct a Gantt chart using the following data.*

Activity	Optimistic Time	Pessimistic Time	Realistic Time	Expected Time	Preceding Task
A	4	8	6		--
B	7	11	9		A
C	3	7	5		A
D	9	13	11		A
E	6	10	8		B
F	3	9	6		C,D,E

ID	Task Name	Start	End	Duration
1	Task A	04/16/2001	04/23/2001	6d
2	Task B	04/24/2001	05/04/2001	9d
3	Task C	04/24/2001	04/30/2001	5d
4	Task D	05/01/2001	05/08/2001	6d
5	Task E	05/07/2001	05/16/2001	8d
6	Task F	05/09/2001	05/16/2001	6d

167. Construct a PERT chart using the following data. For each activity, identify its early start time, late start time, early finish time, late finish time, and slack. Identify the critical path. (You may round your answers for the expected times.)

Activity	Optimistic Time	Pessimistic Time	Realistic Time	Expected Time	Preceding Task
A	15	20	17		--
B	17	22	19		--
C	10	15	12		A
D	9	14	11		B
E	14	19	16		C,D
F	4	9	6		E
G	2	7	5		D
H	11	16	13		F,G
I	4	9	7		H

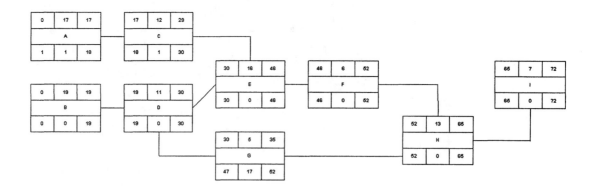

Chapter 4
Automated Tools for Systems Development

True-False Questions

1. CASE provides automated support for all or some portion of the systems development process.

    Answer: True   **Difficulty**: Easy   **Reference**: p. 94

2. CASE assists systems builders in managing the complexities of information systems projects and helps assure that high-quality systems are constructed on time and within budget.

    Answer: True   **Difficulty**: Med   **Reference**: p. 95

3. Organizations primarily adopt CASE to lower systems development costs.

    Answer: False   **Difficulty**: Med   **Reference**: p. 95

4. One of the main drawbacks of using CASE is that applications developed using CASE are not as portable as traditionally developed systems.

    Answer: False   **Difficulty**: Med   **Reference**: p. 95

5. Organizations use CASE to ease and improve the testing process through the use of automated checking.

    Answer: True   **Difficulty**: Med   **Reference**: p. 95

6. Organizations use CASE to increase the speed with which systems are designed and developed.

    Answer: True   **Difficulty**: Med   **Reference**: p. 95

7. The low cost of CASE has encouraged its widespread deployment within organizations.

    Answer: False   **Difficulty**: Med   **Reference**: p. 96

8. In most instances, people do not need extensive training in order to fully use CASE products.

    Answer: False   **Difficulty**: Med   **Reference**: p. 96

9. Generally speaking, it costs between $500 and $1,500 per year to provide CASE to one systems analyst.

    Answer: False   **Difficulty**: Med   **Reference**: p. 96

10. The big benefits of CASE come early in the SDLC.

    Answer: False   **Difficulty**: Med   **Reference**: p. 96

11. Factors influencing CASE adoption include the inability of some CASE tools to share information and the extent to which CASE can support all SDLC activities.

Answer: True   **Difficulty**: Med   **Reference**: p. 96

12. Many CASE products allow the systems analyst to choose among several methodologies or systems development philosophies.

Answer: False   **Difficulty**: Hard   **Reference**: p. 96

13. In many instances, reverse engineering and reengineering tools enable organizations to extend the life of existing systems.

Answer: True   **Difficulty**: Med   **Reference**: p. 96

14. IS personnel tend to welcome CASE because they believe it helps reduce the risk and uncertainty in managing the SDLC.

Answer: False   **Difficulty**: Hard   **Reference**: p. 97

15. Organizations reject CASE because of a lack of methodology standards within the organization.

Answer: True   **Difficulty**: Med   **Reference**: p. 98

16. Organizations reject CASE because of low organizational confidence in the IS department to deliver high-quality systems on time and within budget.

Answer: True   **Difficulty**: Med   **Reference**: p. 98

17. Organizations adopt CASE to improve worker skills.

Answer: True   **Difficulty**: Med   **Reference**: p. 98

18. Top management support, business contribution, and managing expectations are CASE implementation issues and strategies.

Answer: True   **Difficulty**: Med   **Reference**: p. 99

19. Cross life-cycle CASE tools primarily support the implementation and maintenance phases of the systems development life cycle.

Answer: False   **Difficulty**: Med   **Reference**: p. 99

20. A code wizard is a general type of CASE tool.

Answer: False   **Difficulty**: Med   **Reference**: pp. 99-100

21. Diagramming tools help prototype how systems "look and feel" to users.

Answer: False   **Difficulty**: Med   **Reference**: pp. 99-100

22. Analysis tools enable system process, data, and control structures to be represented graphically.

Answer: False   **Difficulty**: Med   **Reference**: p. 100

23. Documentation generators help produce both technical and user documentation in standard formats.

    Answer: True   **Difficulty**: Easy   **Reference**: p. 100

24. Most CASE products do not support ad hoc inquiry into and extraction from a repository.

    Answer: False   **Difficulty**: Easy   **Reference**: p. 100

25. More advanced CASE products support version control, user account management, and import and export facilities.

    Answer: True   **Difficulty**: Med   **Reference**: p. 100

26. During project initiation and planning, repository and documentation generators are used to develop project plans.

    Answer: True   **Difficulty**: Med   **Reference**: p. 101

27. During logical and physical design, diagramming tools are used to create process, logic, and data models.

    Answer: False   **Difficulty**: Hard   **Reference**: p. 101

28. During implementation, form and report generators are used to prototype designs.

    Answer: False   **Difficulty**: Med   **Reference**: p. 101

29. A primary drawback to the traditional development approach is the lack of integration among specification documents, program code, and supporting documentation.

    Answer: True   **Difficulty**: Med   **Reference**: p. 101

30. When comparing traditional systems development to CASE-based systems development, traditional systems development emphasizes analysis and design.

    Answer: False   **Difficulty**: Hard   **Reference**: p. 101

31. When comparing traditional systems development to CASE-based development, CASE-based systems development emphasizes intensive software testing.

    Answer: False   **Difficulty**: Hard   **Reference**: p. 101

32. Most CASE tools can generate a database schema directly from an ERD.

    Answer: True   **Difficulty**: Med   **Reference**: p. 104

33. One common purpose of form and report generators is to identify which data items to display or collect for each form or report.

    Answer: True   **Difficulty**: Med   **Reference**: p. 104

34. A benefit of using automated tools for developing forms and reports is that involved users may require less training than uninvolved users.

    Answer: True   **Difficulty**: Med   **Reference**: p. 104

35. Integrated CASE tools rely on common terminology, notations, and methods for systems development across all tools.

   Answer: True   **Difficulty**: Med   **Reference**: p. 106

36. An inference engine is one of the common components of a comprehensive CASE repository.

   Answer: False   **Difficulty**: Med   **Reference**: p. 107

37. Within a comprehensive CASE repository, the data dictionary combines information about an organization's business information and its application portfolio and provides automated tools to manage and control access to the repository.

   Answer: False   **Difficulty**: Hard   **Reference**: p. 107

38. A data dictionary is the repository of all data definitions for all organizational applications.

   Answer: True   **Difficulty**: Med   **Reference**: p. 107

39. Specific tool integration, project management, and reusability are three advantages of using a comprehensive CASE repository.

   Answer: True   **Difficulty**: Med   **Reference**: p. 109

40. Object reengineering is the ability to design software modules in a manner so that they can be used again and again in different systems without significant modification.

   Answer: False   **Difficulty**: Med   **Reference**: p. 109

41. Allowing one CASE tool to directly read the repository of another CASE tool is one way you can share data between CASE tools.

   Answer: True   **Difficulty**: Easy   **Reference**: p. 110

42. Converting repository contents into some neutral format, such as an ASCII file, and then importing these into another repository is one way you can share data between CASE tools.

   Answer: True   **Difficulty**: Med   **Reference**: p. 110

43. Documentation is the most important aspect to building maintainable systems.

   Answer: True   **Difficulty**: Med   **Reference**: p. 110

44. Code generators enable the automatic generation of program and database definition code directly from the design documents, diagrams, forms, and reports stored in the repository.

   Answer: True   **Difficulty**: Med   **Reference**: p. 111

45. Object-oriented, visual, and embedded artificial intelligence are three rapidly emerging development tools.

   Answer: True   **Difficulty**: Easy   **Reference**: p. 111

46. A CASE module is a chunk of program and data that is built to perform common functions within a system.

     Answer: False   **Difficulty**: Med   **Reference**: pp. 111-112

47. A major advantage of object-oriented development is that each object contains reusable code.

     Answer: True   **Difficulty**: Med   **Reference**: p. 112

48. Placing instructions and data together into a single object is called entity grouping.

     Answer: False   **Difficulty**: Med   **Reference**: p. 112

49. The goal of object-oriented development is to make software easier to create, simpler and more consistent to use, and more reliable.

     Answer: True   **Difficulty**: Med   **Reference**: p. 113

50. Visual tools enable systems developers to "draw" a design by using predefined objects.

     Answer: True   **Difficulty**: Easy   **Reference**: p. 114

Multiple Choice Questions

51. Software tools that provide automated support for some portion of the systems development process defines:

     a. project management
     b. CASE
     c. Gantt
     d. NOS

     Answer: b   **Difficulty**: Med   **Reference**: pp. 93-94

52. The purpose of CASE is to:

     a. make it much easier to enact a single design philosophy within an organization with many projects, systems, and people
     b. make it much easier to enact several design philosophies within an organization
     c. enable fast completion of the systems development activities
     d. enable multiple people to work on the same project

     Answer: a   **Difficulty**: Med   **Reference**: p. 94

53. CASE could be used to construct normalized relations during which of the following phases?

     a. implementation
     b. project identification and selection
     c. design
     d. implementation

     Answer: c   **Difficulty**: Med   **Reference**: p. 94

54. Data flow diagrams and state-transition diagrams could be drawn using a CASE tool during which of the following phases?

    a.   logical design
    b.   physical design
    c.   maintenance
    d.   analysis

    Answer: d   **Difficulty**: Med   **Reference**: p. 94

55. Organizations primarily adopt CASE to:

    a.   improve the quality and speed of the systems development process
    b.   reduce program testing time
    c.   increase the level of documentation
    d.   decrease program maintenance

    Answer: a   **Difficulty**: Med   **Reference**: p. 95

56. Which of the following is not an objective of CASE?

    a.   improve the integration of development activities via common methodologies
    b.   promote project uniqueness
    c.   improve software portability across environments
    d.   promote reusability of modules and documentation

    Answer: b   **Difficulty**: Med   **Reference**: p. 95

57. Which of the following is a CASE objective?

    a.   improve the integration of development activities via common methodologies
    b.   help standardize the development process
    c.   promote reusability of modules
    d.   all of the above

    Answer: d   **Difficulty**: Med   **Reference**: p. 95

58. Which of the following is a factor influencing the adoption of CASE within organizations?

    a.   The start-up cost of using CASE is a significant factor.
    b.   CASE tools cannot easily share information between tools.
    c.   CASE often lengthens the duration of early stages of the project.
    d.   all of the above

    Answer: d   **Difficulty**: Med   **Reference**: p. 96

59. Automated tools that read program source code as input and create graphical and textual representations of program design-level information such as program control structures, data structures, logical flow, and data flow defines:

   a. CASE
   b. reverse engineering
   c. reengineering
   d. conversion tools

   Answer: b   **Difficulty**: Hard   **Reference**: p. 97

60. Automated tools that read program source code as input, perform an analysis of the program's data and logic, and then automatically, or interactively with a systems analyst, alter an existing system in an effort to improve its quality or performance best defines:

   a. CASE
   b. reverse engineering
   c. reengineering
   d. conversion tools

   Answer: c   **Difficulty**: Hard   **Reference**: p. 97

61. Which of the following is not a true statement?

   a. Most CASE environments do not yet have reverse or reengineering capabilities.
   b. IS personnel with a managerial orientation tend to resist CASE.
   c. The culture of an organization can significantly influence the success of CASE adoption.
   d. Effective CASE adoption requires using a common development methodology.

   Answer: b   **Difficulty**: Hard   **Reference**: p. 97

62. As an impact of CASE, which of the following individuals will play a greater role in leading development projects by using CASE to reengineer their business processes?

   a. systems analysts
   b. users
   c. IS project managers
   d. functional managers

   Answer: d   **Difficulty**: Med   **Reference**: p. 98

63. Becoming much more active in the systems development process through the use of upper CASE tools is a possible CASE impact for:

   a. functional managers
   b. programmers
   c. systems analysts
   d. users

   Answer: d   **Difficulty**: Med   **Reference**: p. 98

64. As an impact of CASE, which of these individuals will have greater control over development projects and resources?

    a. IS project managers
    b. functional managers
    c. programmers
    d. systems analysts

    Answer: a   **Difficulty**: Med   **Reference**: p. 98

65. As a result of CASE, many routine tasks of this individual will be automated, making the communication skills of the individual most critical. This individual is the:

    a. functional manager
    b. systems analyst
    c. programmer
    d. user

    Answer: b   **Difficulty**: Med   **Reference**: p. 98

66. Which of the following is a driving organizational force for the adoption of CASE?

    a. permits multiple methodologies to be used within the organization
    b. high confidence in CASE products
    c. improve worker skills
    d. low cost of training personnel

    Answer: c   **Difficulty**: Med   **Reference**: p. 98

67. Which of the following is a resisting organizational force for the adoption of CASE?

    a. low cost of purchasing CASE
    b. a lack of confidence in CASE products
    c. low cost of training personnel
    d. improving the portability of new systems

    Answer: b   **Difficulty**: Med   **Reference**: p. 98

68. Which of the following is a common impact of CASE on individuals within an organization?

    a. Users will be much more active in the systems development process through the use of upper CASE tools.
    b. Top managers will play a more active role in setting priorities and strategic directions for IS by using CASE-based planning and through user-oriented system development methods.
    c. Functional managers will play a greater role in leading development projects by using CASE to reengineer their business processes.
    d. all of the above

    Answer: d   **Difficulty**: Med   **Reference**: p. 98

69. Organizations reject CASE because of:

    a.   a lack of confidence in CASE products
    b.   the high cost of training personnel
    c.   the high cost of purchasing CASE
    d.   all of the above

    Answer: d   **Difficulty**: Med   **Reference**: p. 98

70. Which of the following are CASE implementation issues and strategies?

    a.   CASE requires a substantial long-term investment.
    b.   The effects of CASE on the organization should be continuously monitored so that timely
         adjustments in strategy can be made.
    c.   Initial projects and personnel should be selected carefully.
    d.   all of the above

    Answer: d   **Difficulty**: Med   **Reference**: p. 99

71. CASE tools designed to support the information planning and the project identification and selection,
    project initiation and planning, analysis, and design phases of the systems development life cycle are
    called:

    a.   cross life cycle CASE
    b.   upper CASE
    c.   lower CASE
    d.   integrated CASE

    Answer: b   **Difficulty**: Med   **Reference**: p. 99

72. As a result of vendors "opening up" their systems, what has occurred?

    a.   Diagramming tools can now be used.
    b.   Through the use of standard databases and data conversion utilities, information can more easily
         be shared across products and tools.
    c.   Lower CASE products have been introduced to the market.
    d.   Documentation generators can be used during the project identification and selection phase.

    Answer: b   **Difficulty**: Med   **Reference**: p. 99

73. CASE tools designed to support the implementation and maintenance phases of the systems
    development life cycle are:

    a.   cross life-cycle CASE
    b.   upper CASE
    c.   lower CASE
    d.   integrated CASE

    Answer: c   **Difficulty**: Med   **Reference**: p. 99

74. CASE tools designed to support activities that occur across multiple phases of the systems development life cycle are:

    a. cross life cycle CASE
    b. upper CASE
    c. lower CASE
    d. integrated CASE

    Answer: a   **Difficulty**: Med   **Reference**: p. 99

75. The types of CASE tools that enable system process, data, and control structures to be represented graphically are called:

    a. analysis tools
    b. repository tools
    c. report generator tools
    d. diagramming tools

    Answer: d   **Difficulty**: Med   **Reference**: p. 99

76. CASE tools that can be used to support project identification and selection include:

    a. form and report generators to prototype designs; analysis and documentation generators to define specifications
    b. code generators and analysis, form, and report generators to develop the system; documentation generators to develop the system and user documentation
    c. diagramming and matrix tools to create and structure information
    d. repository and documentation generators to develop project plans

    Answer: c   **Difficulty**: Hard   **Reference**: p. 101

77. CASE tools that can be used to support implementation include:

    a. form and report generators to prototype designs; analysis and documentation generators to define specifications
    b. code generators and analysis, form, and report generators to develop the system; documentation generators to develop the system and user documentation
    c. diagramming and matrix tools to create and structure information
    d. repository and documentation generators to develop project plans

    Answer: b   **Difficulty**: Hard   **Reference**: p. 101

78. CASE tools that can be used to support project initiation and planning include:

    a. form and report generators to prototype designs; analysis and documentation generators to define specifications
    b. code generators and analysis, form, and report generators to develop the system; documentation generators to develop the system and user documentation
    c. diagramming and matrix tools to create and structure information
    d. repository and documentation generators to develop project plans

    Answer: d   **Difficulty**: Hard   **Reference**: p. 101

79. CASE tools that can be used to support logical and physical design include:

    a. form and report generators to prototype designs; analysis and documentation generators to define specifications
    b. code generators and analysis, form, and report generators to develop the system; documentation generators to develop the system and user documentation
    c. diagramming and matrix tools to create and structure information
    d. repository and documentation generators to develop project plans

    Answer: a   **Difficulty**: Hard   **Reference**: p. 101

80. CASE tools that can be used to support maintenance include:

    a. form and report generators to prototype designs; analysis and documentation generators to define specifications
    b. code generators and analysis, form, and report generators to develop the system; documentation generators to develop the system and user documentation
    c. diagramming and matrix tools to create and structure information
    d. using all CASE tools

    Answer: d   **Difficulty**: Med   **Reference**: p. 101

81. Entity relationship diagrams and data flow diagrams are constructed using:

    a. analysis tools
    b. diagramming tools
    c. report generator tools
    d. repository tools

    Answer: b   **Difficulty**: Med   **Reference**: pp. 102-103

82. Which of the following is a key difference between using traditional systems development and CASE-based development?

    a. Traditional systems development emphasizes coding and testing; while, CASE-based systems development emphasizes analysis and design.
    b. Traditional systems development emphasizes rapid interactive prototyping; while, CASE-based systems development emphasizes manual coding of programs.
    c. Traditional systems development emphasizes automated design checking; while, CASE-based systems development emphasizes maintaining code and documentation.
    d. Traditional systems development emphasizes manual documenting; while, CASE-based development emphasizes coding and testing.

    Answer: a   **Difficulty**: Hard   **Reference**: p. 101

83. The primary drawback to the traditional development approach is:

    a. the maintenance of program code
    b. the lack of integration between specification documents, program code, and supporting documentation
    c. the maintenance of documentation
    d. a reliance on rapid prototyping

    Answer: b   **Difficulty**: Med   **Reference**: p. 101

84.   Form and report generators are used to:

    a.   create, modify, and test prototypes of computer display forms and reports
    b.   create, modify, and test data flow diagrams for the user
    c.   create, modify, and test entity relationship diagrams for the user
    d.   link entities with data stores

Answer: a   **Difficulty**: Med   **Reference**: p. 104

85.   CASE tools that support the creation of system forms and reports in order to prototype how systems will "look and feel" to users are:

    a.   diagramming tools
    b.   analysis tools
    c.   form and report generators
    d.   documentation generators

Answer: c   **Difficulty**: Med   **Reference**: p. 104

86.   CASE tools that enable automatic checking for incomplete or incorrect specifications in diagrams, forms, and reports are called:

    a.   diagramming tools
    b.   analysis tools
    c.   form and report generators
    d.   documentation generators

Answer: b   **Difficulty**: Med   **Reference**: p. 105

87.   Central to I-CASE is:

    a.   the idea of using a common repository for all tools so that the information can be easily shared between tools and SDLC activities
    b.   the idea of integrating several organizational methodologies into one common methodology
    c.   the idea of associating specific terminology with selected phases of the SDLC
    d.   the idea of using common tools during upper life cycle development

Answer: a   **Difficulty**: Med   **Reference**: p. 106

88.   An automated systems development environment that provides numerous tools to create diagrams, forms, and reports; provides analysis, reporting, and code generation facilities; and seamlessly shares and integrates data across and between tools is referred to as:

    a.   upper CASE
    b.   lower CASE
    c.   cross life cycle CASE
    d.   integrated CASE

Answer: d   **Difficulty**: Med   **Reference**: p. 106

89. A centralized database that contains all diagrams, forms and report definitions, data structure, data definitions, process flows and logic, and definitions of other organizational and system components, and that provides a set of mechanisms and structures to achieve seamless data-to-tool and data-to-data integration best defines:

   a. repository
   b. dictionary
   c   document base
   d. Upper CASE

   Answer: a   **Difficulty**: Med   **Reference**: p. 106

90. An automated tool used to manage and control access to an organization's business information and application portfolio as components within a comprehensive repository defines:

   a. data dictionary
   b. DBMS
   c. information repository
   d. data manager

   Answer: c   **Difficulty**: Med   **Reference**: p. 107

91. The repository of all data definitions for all organizational applications is the:

   a. data dictionary
   b. organization's database
   c. information repository
   d. data storage location

   Answer: a   **Difficulty**: Med   **Reference**: p. 107

92. A feature of a data dictionary that enables one description of a data item to be stored and accessed by all individuals so that a single definition for a data item is established and used is called:

   a. integration
   b. cross referencing
   c. centralization
   d. standardization

   Answer: b   **Difficulty**: Med   **Reference**: p. 107

93. The ability to design software modules in a manner so that they can be "reused" in other systems without significant modification best defines:

   a. reengineering
   b. reverse engineering
   c. software conversion
   d. reusability

   Answer: d   **Difficulty**: Med   **Reference**: p. 109

94. Besides using a single CASE repository, you can share data between CASE tools by:

    a. allowing one CASE tool to directly read the repository of another CASE tool
    b. converting repository contents into some neutral format, like an ASCII file, and then importing these into another repository
    c. manually entering specifications contained in one repository into another repository
    d. all of the above

    Answer: d   **Difficulty**: Med   **Reference**: p. 110

95. CASE tools that enable the easy production of both technical and user documentation in standard formats are:

    a. diagramming tools
    b. documentation generators
    c. analysis tools
    d. form and report generators

    Answer: b   **Difficulty**: Easy   **Reference**: p. 110

96. CASE tools that enable the automatic generation of program and database definition code directly from the design documents, diagrams, forms, and reports stored in the repository are:

    a. code generators
    b. documentation generators
    c. compilers
    d. interpreters

    Answer: a   **Difficulty**: Med   **Reference**: p. 111

97. Which of the following can be thought of as a chunk of program and data that is built to perform common functions within a system?

    a. object
    b. capsule
    c. container
    d. block

    Answer: a   **Difficulty**: Med   **Reference**: pp. 111-112

98. The process of grouping data and instructions together into a single object is called:

    a. grouping
    b. inheritance
    c. encapsulation
    d. normalizing

    Answer: c   **Difficulty**: Med   **Reference**: p. 112

99.   One of the major advantages of object-oriented development is:

    a.   that it makes extensive use of intelligent agents
    b.   that each object contains easily reusable code
    c.   that object-oriented development is less expensive
    d.   that it emphasizes coding and testing

Answer: b   **Difficulty**: Med   **Reference**: p. 112

100.   Types of development tools include each of the following except:

    a.   object-oriented tools
    b.   visual development tools
    c.   intelligent agents
    d.   development engines

Answer: d   **Difficulty**: Med   **Reference**: p. 117

Fill In the Blanks

101.   *CASE* refers to software tools that provide automated support for some portion of the systems development process.

                            Difficulty: Easy   **Reference**: p. 94

102.   *Reverse engineering* refers to automated tools that read program source code as input and create graphical and textual representations of program design-level information such as program control structures, data structures, logical flow, and data flow.

                            Difficulty: Med   **Reference**: p. 97

103.   *Reengineering* refers to automated tools that read program source code as input, perform an analysis of the program's data and logic, and then automatically, or interactively with a systems analyst, alter an existing system in an effort to improve its quality or performance.

                            Difficulty: Med   **Reference**: p. 97

104.   *Upper CASE* are CASE tools designed to support the information planning and the project identification and selection, project initiation and planning, analysis, and design phases of the systems development life cycle.

                            Difficulty: Med   **Reference**: p. 99

105.   *Lower CASE* are CASE tools designed to support the implementation and maintenance phases of the systems development life cycle.

                            Difficulty: Med   **Reference**: p. 99

106.   *Cross life-cycle CASE* refers to CASE tools designed to support activities that occur across multiple phases of the systems development life cycle.

                            Difficulty: Hard   **Reference**: p. 99

107. During the ***project identification and selection*** phase, an analyst might use a CASE tool's diagramming and matrix tools to create and structure information.

                      Difficulty: Hard   **Reference**: p. 101

108. During the ***project initiation and planning*** phase, an analyst might use a CASE tool's repository and documentation generators to develop project plans.

                      Difficulty: Hard   **Reference**: p. 101

109. During the ***analysis*** phase, an analyst might use a CASE tool's diagramming capabilities to create process, logic, and data models.

                      Difficulty: Hard   **Reference**: p. 101

110. During the ***logical and physical design*** phase, an analyst might use a CASE tool's form and report generators to prototype designs, and use analysis and documentation generators to define specifications.

                      Difficulty: Hard   **Reference**: p. 101

111. During the ***implementation*** phase, an analyst might use a CASE tool's code generators and analysis, form, and report generators to develop the system, and use documentation generators to develop system and user documentation.

                      Difficulty: Med   **Reference**: p. 101

112. During the ***maintenance*** phase, an analyst might use all of the CASE tools.

                      Difficulty: Med   **Reference**: p. 101

113. ***Diagramming tools*** are CASE tools that support the creation of graphical representations of various system elements such as process flow, data relationships, and program structures.

                      Difficulty: Med   **Reference**: p. 102

114. ***Form and report generators*** are CASE tools that support the creation of system forms and reports in order to prototype how systems will "look and feel" to users.

                      Difficulty: Easy   **Reference**: p. 104

115. ***Analysis tools*** are CASE tools that enable automatic checking for incomplete, inconsistent, or incorrect specifications in diagrams, forms, and reports.

                      Difficulty: Med   **Reference**: p. 105

116. ***I-CASE*** refers to an automated systems development environment that provides numerous tools to create diagrams, forms, and reports; provides analysis, reporting, and code generation facilities; and seamlessly shares and integrates data across and between tools.

                      Difficulty: Med   **Reference**: p. 106

117. A ***repository*** is a centralized database that contains all diagrams, form and report definitions, data structure, data definitions, process flows and logic, and definitions of other organizational and system components; it provides a set of mechanisms and structures to achieve seamless data-to-tool and data-to-data integration.

Difficulty: Med   **Reference**: p. 106

118. ***Information repository*** refers to automated tools used to manage and control access to organizational business information and application portfolio as components within a comprehensive repository.

Difficulty: Med   **Reference**: p. 107

119. A ***data dictionary*** is the repository of all data definitions for all organizational applications.

Difficulty: Med   **Reference**: p. 107

120. ***Cross referencing*** is a feature performed by a data dictionary that enables one description of a data item to be stored and accessed by all individuals so that a single definition for a data item is established and used.

Difficulty: Med   **Reference**: p. 107

121. ***Reusability*** is the ability to design software modules in a manner so that they can be used again and again in different systems without significant modification.

Difficulty: Med   **Reference**: p. 109

122. ***Documentation generators*** are CASE tools that enable the easy production of both technical and user documentation in standard formats.

Difficulty: Med   **Reference**: p. 110

123. ***Code generators*** are CASE tools that enable the automatic generation of program and database definition code directly from the design documents, diagrams, forms, and reports stored in the repository.

Difficulty: Med   **Reference**: p. 111

124. An ***object*** is a chunk of program and data that is built to perform common functions within a system.

Difficulty: Med   **Reference**: pp. 111-112

125. ***Encapsulation*** is the process of grouping data and instructions together into a single object.

Difficulty: Med   **Reference**: p. 112

Matching Questions

Match each of the following terms with its definition.

       a. I- CASE
       b. upper CASE
       c. lower CASE
       d. cross life-cycle CASE
       e. CASE

126.   CASE tools designed to support the information planning and the project identification and selection, project initiation and planning, analysis, and design phases of the systems development life cycle.

               Answer: b   **Reference**: p. 99

127.   CASE tools designed to support activities that occur across multiple phases of the systems development life cycle.

               Answer: d   **Reference**: p. 99

128.   CASE tools designed to support the implementation and maintenance phases of the systems development life cycle.

               Answer: c   **Reference**: p. 99

129.   Software tools that provide automated support for some portion of the systems development process.

               Answer: e   **Reference**: p. 94

130.   An automated systems development environment that provides numerous tools to create diagrams, forms, and reports; provides analysis, reporting, and code generation facilities; and seamlessly shares and integrates data across and between tools.

               Answer: a   **Reference**: p. 106

Match each of the following terms with its definition.

      a.   information repository
      b.   repository
      c.   analysis tools
      d.   data dictionary
      e.   diagramming tools

131.   CASE tools that support the creation of graphical representations of various system elements such as process flow, data relationships, and program structures.

              Answer: e   **Reference:** p. 102

132.   Automated tools used to manage and control access to organizational business information and application portfolio as components within a comprehensive repository.

              Answer: a   **Reference:** p. 107

133.   The repository of all data definitions for all organizational applications.

              Answer: d   **Reference:** p. 107

134.   A centralized database that contains all diagrams, form and report definitions, data structure, data definitions, process flows and logic, and definitions of other organizational and system components; it provides a set of mechanisms and structures to achieve seamless data-to-tool and data-to-data integration.

              Answer: b   **Reference:** p. 106

135.   CASE tools that enable automatic checking for incomplete, inconsistent, or incorrect specifications in diagrams, forms, and reports.

              Answer: c   **Reference:** p. 105

Match each of the following types of CASE tools with its corresponding definition.

    a. code generators
    b. diagramming tools
    c. form and report generators
    d. analysis tools
    e. repositories
    f. documentation generators

136.   Help produce both technical and user documentation in standard formats.

        Answer: f   **Reference**: p. 110

137.   Help prototype how systems "look and feel" to users.

        Answer: c   **Reference**: p. 104

138.   Enable the automatic generation of program and database definition code directly from the design documents, diagrams, forms, and reports.

        Answer: a   **Reference**: p. 100

139.   Enable the integrated storage of specification, diagrams, reports, and project management information.

        Answer: e   **Reference**: p. 106

140.   Automatically check for incomplete, inconsistent, or incorrect specifications in diagrams, forms, and reports.

        Answer: d   **Reference**: p. 105

141.   Enable system process, data relationships, and program structures to be represented graphically.

        Answer: b   **Reference**: p. 102

Match each of the following terms with its corresponding definition.

    a.   object
    b.   encapsulation
    c.   visual development
    d.   intelligent agents
    e.   object-oriented development

142.   A chunk of program and data that is built to perform common functions within a system.

                    Answer: a   **Reference:** pp. 111-112

143.   Enables designers to draw a design using predefined objects.

                    Answer: c   **Reference:** pp. 113-114

144.   Its goal is to make software easier to create, simpler and more consistent to use, and more reliable.

                    Answer: e   **Reference:** p. 113

145.   Embedded artificial intelligence in development environments.

                    Answer: d   **Reference:** p. 117

146.   The process of grouping data and instructions together into a single object.

                    Answer: b   **Reference:** p. 112

Match each of the SDLC phases with its key activities.

   a. project identification and selection
   b. project initiation and planning
   c. analysis
   d. logical and physical design
   e. implementation
   f. maintenance

147. Develop project scope and feasibility

                          Answer: b   **Reference:** p. 101

148. Translate designs into an information system

                          Answer: e   **Reference:** p. 101

149. Create new systems designs

                          Answer: d   **Reference:** p. 101

150. Display and structure high-level organizational information

                          Answer: a   **Reference:** p. 101

151. Determine and structure requirements

                          Answer: c   **Reference:** p. 101

152. Evolve information systems

                          Answer: f   **Reference:** p. 101

Essay Questions

153. *Define CASE, upper CASE, lower CASE, cross life-cycle CASE, and I-CASE.*

   CASE can be defined as software tools that provide automated support for some portion of the systems
   development process. Upper CASE tools are designed to support the information planning and the
   project identification and selection, project initiation and planning, analysis, and design phases of the
   systems development life cycle. Lower CASE tools support the implementation and maintenance
   phases of the systems development life cycle. Cross life-cycle CASE tools are designed to support
   activities that occur across multiple phases of the systems development life cycle. I-CASE refers to an
   automated systems development environment that provides numerous tools to create diagrams, forms,
   and reports; provides analysis, reporting, and code generation facilities; and seamlessly shares and
   integrates data across and between tools.

154. *For each systems development life cycle phase, indicate the CASE tools that would be used to support that phase.*

During project identification and selection, CASE diagramming and matrix tools create and structure information. During project initiation and planning, repository and documentation generators develop project plans. During analysis, diagramming tools create process, logic, and data models. During logical and physical design, form and report generators prototype designs, and analysis and documentation generators define specifications. During implementation, code generators and analysis, form, and report generators develop the system, and documentation generators develop system and user documentation. All available CASE tools would be used during maintenance.

155. *Briefly identify the organizational forces for and against CASE.*

The driving forces for CASE include providing new systems with shorter development times, improving the productivity of the system development process, improving the quality of the systems development process, improving worker skills, improving the portability of new systems, and improving the management of the systems development process.

156. *Briefly identify the organizational forces against CASE.*

The opposing forces for CASE include the high cost of purchasing CASE, the high cost of training personnel, a low organizational confidence in the IS department to deliver high quality systems on time and within budget, a lack of methodology standards within the organization, viewing CASE as a threat to job security, and a lack of confidence in CASE products.

157. *What are the common impacts CASE has on individuals within organizations?*

CASE automates many routine tasks of the analyst, making communication skills critical. Programmers will see their role become more of maintaining designs rather than source code. Users will become more active in the systems development process through the use of upper CASE tools. Top managers will have a more active role in establishing priorities and strategic directions for IS. By using CASE to reengineer their business processes, functional managers will have a greater role in leading development projects. Greater control over development projects and resources will be afforded to IS project managers.

158. *Briefly identify the general types of CASE tools.*

The general types of CASE tools are diagramming tools, form and report generators, analysis tools, a central repository, documentation generators, and code generators. Diagramming tools enable system process, data, and control structures to be represented graphically. Form and report generators are used to help prototype how systems will "look and feel." Analysis tools can automatically check for incomplete, inconsistent, or incorrect specifications in diagrams, forms, and reports. A central repository provides for the integrated storage of specification, diagrams, reports, and project management information. Technical and user documentation in standard formats can be produced by document generators. The automatic generation of program and database definition code directly from the design documents, diagrams, forms, and reports is provided through code generators.

159. *Briefly describe three emerging systems development tools.*

Object-oriented, visual, and embedded artificial intelligence are three emerging systems development tools. Object-oriented development encapsulates instructions and data together, making programs easier to maintain. Visual development tools enable an analyst to "draw" the design, using predefined objects. By embedding artificial intelligence into development environments, analysts can request intelligent agents to perform functions.

160. *Besides using a single CASE repository, how can data be shared between CASE tools.*

Data can be shared by: (1) manually entering specifications contained in one repository into another repository; (2) converting repository contents into some neutral format and then importing these into another repository; (3) using third party utilities; and (4) allowing one CASE tool to directly read the repository of another CASE tool.

161. *What is a CASE repository? Identify three advantages of a CASE repository.*

A CASE repository is a centralized database that contains all diagrams, form and report definitions, data structure, data definitions, process flows and logic, and definitions of other organizational and system components. The repository provides a set of mechanisms and structures to achieve seamless data-to-tool and data-to-data integration. Specific tool integration, project management, and reusability are three advantages.

162. *Identify the components within a comprehensive CASE repository.*

A data dictionary and an information repository are the components within a CASE repository. A data dictionary is the repository of all data definitions for all organizational applications. An information repository refers to automated tools used to manage and control access to organizational business information and application portfolio as components within a comprehensive repository.

Chapter 5
Identifying and Selecting Systems
Development Projects

True-False Questions

1. Nonintegrated systems used in the past are being replaced with cooperative, integrated enterprise systems that can easily support information sharing.

   Answer: True   **Difficulty**: Easy   **Reference**: p. 134

2. Systems analysis is the first phase of the systems development life cycle.

   Answer: False   **Difficulty**: Easy   **Reference**: p. 135

3. During project identification and selection, all possible systems development projects that an organizational unit can undertake are identified and assessed.

   Answer: True   **Difficulty**: Med   **Reference**: p. 135

4. An IS manager, a formal planning group, a user department, and a development group are possible sources for information systems development projects.

   Answer: True   **Difficulty**: Med   **Reference**: p. 135

5. Requirements structuring is the first activity of the project identification and selection phase.

   Answer: False   **Difficulty**: Med   **Reference**: p. 136

6. Projects identified by top management have a cross-functional focus.

   Answer: False   **Difficulty**: Med   **Reference**: p. 136

7. The development group identifies projects based on the ease with which existing hardware and systems will integrate with the proposed project.

   Answer: True   **Difficulty**: Med   **Reference**: p. 137

8. When comparing alternative methods for making information systems identification and selection decisions, top management has the smallest system size and a cross-functional focus.

   Answer: False   **Difficulty**: Hard   **Reference**: p. 137

9. To maintain consistency, top management or a steering committee should classify and rank projects, not the IS group or individual business units.

   Answer: False   **Difficulty**: Hard   **Reference**: p. 138

10. The criteria used to evaluate projects will vary by organization.

    Answer: True   **Difficulty**: Easy   **Reference**: p. 138

11. Potential benefits are the process of analyzing an organization's activities to determine where value is added to products and/or services and the costs incurred for doing so; this process usually also includes a comparison with the activities, added value, and costs of other organizations for the purpose of making improvements in the organization's operations and performance.

     Answer: False   **Difficulty**: Hard   **Reference**: p. 138

12. When classifying and ranking projects, resource availability, potential benefits, and project size/duration are possible evaluation criteria.

     Answer: True   **Difficulty**: Med   **Reference**: p. 138

13. Project selection is a process of considering both short- and long-term projects and selecting those most likely to achieve business objectives.

     Answer: True   **Difficulty**: Med   **Reference**: p. 139

14. The Baseline Project Plan is the primary deliverable from the project identification and selection phase.

     Answer: False   **Difficulty**: Med   **Reference**: p. 140

15. A schedule of specific IS development projects is the primary deliverable from the project identification and selection phase.

     Answer: True   **Difficulty**: Med   **Reference**: p. 140

16. Due to the principle of incremental commitment, a selected project will result in a working system.

     Answer: False   **Difficulty**: Med   **Reference**: p. 140

17. When determining how to allocate IS resources, organizations have traditionally used a systematic planning process.

     Answer: False   **Difficulty**: Med   **Reference**: p. 141

18. "What information requirements will satisfy our business's decision-making needs today and well into the future?" is a question that might be asked by a planning-based approach to project identification and selection.

     Answer: True   **Difficulty**: Med   **Reference**: p. 141

19. A major disadvantage to the planning-based approach is that an organization's informational needs are more likely to change than its business processes.

     Answer: False   **Difficulty**: Med   **Reference**: p. 141

20. To benefit from a planning-based approach for identifying and selecting projects, an organization must analyze its information needs and plan its projects carefully.

     Answer: True   **Difficulty**: Med   **Reference**: p. 141

21. The rising costs of information systems is one reason why improved information systems project identification and selection is needed.

    Answer: True   **Difficulty**: Easy   **Reference**: p. 141

22. Data redundancy and users having little confidence in the quality of data are reasons why improved information systems project identification and selection is needed.

    Answer: True   **Difficulty**: Med   **Reference**: p. 142

23. A disciplined approach, driven by top management commitment, is a prerequisite to most effectively apply information systems in order to reach organizational objectives.

    Answer: True   **Difficulty**: Med   **Reference**: p. 142

24. Requirements determination and requirements structuring are two processes that can significantly improve the quality of project identification and selection decisions.

    Answer: False   **Difficulty**: Med   **Reference**: p. 142

25. Corporate analysis is an ongoing process that defines the mission, objectives, and strategies of an organization.

    Answer: False   **Difficulty**: Med   **Reference**: p. 142

26. During corporate strategic planning, executives typically develop a mission statement, statements of future corporate objectives, and strategies designed to help the organization reach its objectives.

    Answer: True   **Difficulty**: Med   **Reference**: p. 142

27. A business objective statement is a statement that makes it clear what business the company is in.

    Answer: False   **Difficulty**: Med   **Reference**: p. 142

28. "We are in the business of selling high-quality men's shoes" is an example of a mission statement.

    Answer: True   **Difficulty**: Med   **Reference**: p. 142

29. "Baker's Fitness Center will increase market share and profitability" is an example of a mission statement.

    Answer: False   **Difficulty**: Hard   **Reference**: p. 143

30. Objective statements are a series of statements that express an organization's qualitative and quantitative goals for reaching a desired future position.

    Answer: True   **Difficulty**: Med   **Reference**: p. 143

31. Mission statements are a series of statements that express an organization's qualitative and quantitative goals for reaching a desired future position.

    Answer: False   **Difficulty**: Med   **Reference**: p. 143

32. Mission statements are often referred to as critical success factors.

     Answer: False   **Difficulty**: Med   **Reference**: p. 143

33. A low-cost producer competitive strategy reflects competing in an industry on the basis of product or service cost to the consumer.

     Answer: True   **Difficulty**: Med   **Reference**: p. 144

34. The South Korean-produced Hyundai uses a product focus competitive strategy.

     Answer: False   **Difficulty**: Hard   **Reference**: p. 144

35. Promoting your product as having an ingredient that competing products do not, setting the product apart from the competition, best exemplifies the product differentiation competitive strategy.

     Answer: True   **Difficulty**: Med   **Reference**: p. 144

36. The product focus or niche competitive strategy is similar to both the low-cost and differentiation strategies, but with a much narrower market focus.

     Answer: True   **Difficulty**: Med   **Reference**: p. 144

37. A company should define its competitive strategy and then define its mission and objectives.

     Answer: False   **Difficulty**: Med   **Reference**: p. 144

38. A competitive strategy is the method by which an organization attempts to achieve its mission and objectives.

     Answer: True   **Difficulty**: Med   **Reference**: p. 144

39. To build the most effective information systems, an organization must clearly understand its mission, objectives, and strategy.

     Answer: True   **Difficulty**: Easy   **Reference**: p. 144

40. Systems requirements planning is an orderly means of assessing the information needs of an organization and defining the systems, databases, and technologies that will best satisfy those needs.

     Answer: False   **Difficulty**: Med   **Reference**: pp. 144-145

41. During ISP, the current and future organizational needs are modeled, and strategies and project plans to migrate the current information systems and technologies to their desired future state are developed.

     Answer: True   **Difficulty**: Med   **Reference**: p. 145

42. A location-to-function matrix identifies which organizational units are located in or interact with a specific business function.

     Answer: False   **Difficulty**: Med   **Reference**: p. 147

43. The systems planning and selection process for an Internet-based electronic commerce application is no different than the process followed for other applications.

     Answer: True   **Difficulty**: Med   **Reference**: p. 152

44. The Internet is a global network comprised of thousands of interconnected individual networks that communicate with each other through TCP/IP.

     Answer: True   **Difficulty**: Easy   **Reference**: p. 152

45. An Intranet refers to the use of the Internet between firms.

     Answer: False   **Difficulty**: Med   **Reference**: p. 152

46. EDI is the use of telecommunications technologies to transfer business documents directly between organizations.

     Answer: True   **Difficulty**: Med   **Reference**: p. 152

47. Organizations that have Intranets dictate what applications will run over the Intranet and the speed and quality of the hardware connected to the Intranet.

     Answer: True   **Difficulty**: Med   **Reference**: p. 152

48. An Extranet is Internet-based communication to support business-to-business activities.

     Answer: True   **Difficulty**: Med   **Reference**: p. 152

49. When developing either an Intranet or an Extranet, developers know who the users are, what applications will be used, the speed of the network connection, and the type of communication devices.

     Answer: True   **Difficulty**: Med   **Reference**: p. 153

50. When developing an Internet EC application, developers must deal with several unknown factors, including the user, connection speed, and access method.

     Answer: True   **Difficulty**: Med   **Reference**: p. 153

Multiple Choice Questions

51. Identification and assessment of all possible systems development projects that an organization unit can undertake is conducted during:

    a. project identification and selection
    b. project initiation and planning
    c. physical design
    d. analysis

    Answer: a   **Difficulty**: Med   **Reference**: p. 135

52. Which of the following is one of the three primary activities associated with identifying and selecting IS development projects?

    a. preliminary investigation of the system problem or opportunity
    b. identification of potential development projects
    c. requirements determination
    d. generating alternative initial designs

    Answer: b   **Difficulty**: Med   **Reference**: p. 136

53. A department head deciding which project requests to submit is an example of:

    a. a preliminary investigation of the system problem or opportunity
    b. identifying potential development projects
    c. requirements determination
    d. generating alternative initial designs

    Answer: b   **Difficulty**: Med   **Reference**: p. 136

54. Research has found that projects identified by top management more often:

    a. have a narrow, tactical focus
    b. reflect diversity and have a cross-functional focus
    c. have a strategic, organizational focus
    d. will integrate easily with existing hardware and systems

    Answer: c   **Difficulty**: Med   **Reference**: p. 136

55. Research has found that projects identified by individual departments or business units most often:

    a. have a narrow, tactical focus
    b. reflect diversity and have a cross-functional focus
    c. have a strategic, organizational focus
    d. will integrate easily with existing hardware and systems

    Answer: a   **Difficulty**: Med   **Reference**: p. 136

56.   Potential development projects can be identified by:

    a.   a steering committee
    b.   top management
    c.   a senior IS manager
    d.   all of the above

Answer: d   **Difficulty**: Med   **Reference**: p. 136

57.   Which of the following possible project sources most often reflects the broader needs of the organization?

    a.   user department
    b.   development group
    c.   IS manager
    d.   top management

Answer: d   **Difficulty**: Med   **Reference**: p. 137

58.   Which of the following characteristics is associated with the steering committee selection method?

    a.   greater strategic focus
    b.   greater organizational change
    c.   fewer users, management layers, and business functions
    d.   less concern on cost-benefit analysis

Answer: b   **Difficulty**: Hard   **Reference**: p. 137

59.   Which of the following is a way projects can be identified?

    a.   bottom-up initiative
    b.   upper-echelon initiative
    c.   top-down initiative
    d.   both a and c

Answer: d   **Difficulty**: Easy   **Reference**: p. 137

60.   The extent to which the project is viewed as improving profits, customer service, etc., and the duration of these benefits best defines which of the following evaluation criteria?

    a.   potential benefits
    b.   resource availability
    c.   technical difficulty or risks
    d.   strategic alignment

Answer: a   **Difficulty**: Med   **Reference**: p. 138

61. The extent to which the project is viewed as helping the organization achieve its strategic objectives and long-term goals describes:

    a. potential benefits
    b. resource availability
    c. technical difficulty or risks
    d. strategic alignment

    Answer: d   **Difficulty**: Med   **Reference**: p. 138

62. Analyzing an organization's activities to determine where value is added to products and/or services and the costs incurred best describes:

    a. affinity clustering
    b. business process reengineering
    c. value chain analysis
    d. technical difficulty or risks

    Answer: c   **Difficulty**: Med   **Reference**: p. 138

63. If the project team and organizational officials reassess the project after each subsequent SDLC phase to determine if the business conditions have changed or if a more detailed understanding of a system's costs, benefits, and risks suggest that the project is not as worthy as previously thought, they are:

    a. adhering to the incremental commitment principle
    b. overly cautious
    c. using a CASE methodology
    d. adhering to a bottom-up commitment principle

    Answer: a   **Difficulty**: Med   **Reference**: pp. 140-141

64. Which of the following is a true statement regarding a planning-based approach?

    a. An emphasis is placed on identifying the procedure that is required to solve a particular problem as it exists today.
    b. The difficulty with this approach is that the required organizational procedures are likely to change over time as the environment changes.
    c. A major advantage of this approach is that an organization's informational needs are less likely to change (or will change more slowly) than its business processes.
    d. One of the benefits of this plan is that an organization does not need to analyze its information needs and plan its projects carefully.

    Answer: c   **Difficulty**: Hard   **Reference**: p. 141

65. Which of the following is a need for improved information systems project identification and selection?

    a. The costs of information systems are steadily decreasing.
    b. Many systems can handle applications that cross organization boundaries.
    c. Data redundancy is often out of control, and users may have little confidence in the quality of the data.
    d. Systems maintenance costs are well under control.

    Answer: c   **Difficulty**: Med   **Reference**: pp. 141-142

66. Gaining a clear idea of where an organization is, its vision of where it wants to be in the future, and a plan of how to make the transition to its desired state is:

    a. the third activity in the analysis phase
    b. a prerequisite to making effective project selection decisions
    c. the first step in a bottom-up approach
    d. not necessary if one is using a CASE product

    Answer: b   **Difficulty**: Med   **Reference**: p. 142

67. An ongoing process that defines the mission, objectives, and strategies of an organization refers to:

    a. corporate strategic planning
    b. analysis
    c. goal setting
    d. information systems planning

    Answer: a   **Difficulty**: Med   **Reference**: p. 142

68. A statement that makes it clear what business a company is in is called a:

    a. business statement
    b. corporate policy statement
    c. goal statement
    d. mission statement

    Answer: d   **Difficulty**: Med   **Reference**: p. 142

69. "We are in the business of designing, fabricating, and selling to retail stores high-quality wood furniture" is what kind of statement?

    a. business statement
    b. mission statement
    c. goal statement
    d. corporate policy

    Answer: b   **Difficulty**: Med   **Reference**: p. 143

70. A series of statements that express an organization's qualitative and quantitative goals for reaching a desired future position best defines:

    a. objective statements
    b. information systems plan
    c. competitive strategy
    d. business policy

    Answer: a   **Difficulty**: Med   **Reference**: p. 143

71. Once a company has defined its mission and objectives:

    a. goals can be established
    b. an information architecture can be developed
    c. project analysis can begin
    d. a competitive strategy can be formulated

    Answer: d   **Difficulty**: Med   **Reference**: p. 144

72. The method by which an organization attempts to achieve its mission and objectives best defines:

    a. critical success factors
    b. competitive strategy
    c. business policy
    d. information systems plan

    Answer: b   **Difficulty**: Med   **Reference**: p. 144

73. Which of the following is a strategy for a low-cost producer?

    a. competing in an industry on the basis of product quality
    b. capitalizing on a key product criteria requested by the market
    c. competing in an industry on the basis of product or service cost to the consumer
    d. competing in an industry on the basis of product quantity

    Answer: c   **Difficulty**: Med   **Reference**: p. 144

74. Which of the following describes the product differentiation strategy?

    a. competing in an industry on the basis of product quality
    b. competing in an industry on the basis of product quantity
    c. competing in an industry on the basis of product or service cost to the consumer
    d. capitalizing on a key product criteria requested by the market

    Answer: d   **Difficulty**: Med   **Reference**: p. 144

75. Which of the following is a competitive strategy?

    a. low-cost producer
    b. product differentiation
    c. product focus
    d. all of the above

    Answer: d   **Difficulty**: Easy   **Reference**: p. 144

76. If GEO is attempting to achieve its mission and objectives by providing a low-priced line of cars, this is referred to as its:

    a. competitive strategy
    b. business policy
    c. information systems plan
    d. objective statement

    Answer: a   **Difficulty**: Med   **Reference**: p. 144

77. The second planning process that can play a significant role in the quality of project identification and selection decisions is called:

   a.   strategic alignment
   b.   cost/benefit analysis
   c.   information systems planning
   d.   incremental commitment

   Answer: c   **Difficulty**: Med   **Reference**: p. 144

78. Which of the following is a true statement regarding ISP?

   a.   During ISP, the current and future information needs of an organization are modeled.
   b.   Strategies and project plans to migrate the current information systems and technologies to their desired future state are developed.
   c.   ISP is a top-down process that takes into account the outside forces (industry, economic, relative size, geographic region, etc. . .)
   d.   all of the above

   Answer: d   **Difficulty**: Med   **Reference**: p. 145

79. An orderly means of assessing the information needs of an organization and defining the systems, databases, and technologies that will best satisfy those needs best defines:

   a.   information systems planning
   b.   mission statement
   c.   objective statement
   d.   competitive strategy

   Answer: a   **Difficulty**: Med   **Reference**: pp. 144-145

80. Which of the following is the first ISP step?

   a.   Develop target blueprints
   b.   Assess current IS-related assets
   c.   Define a series of scheduled projects
   d.   Assign resources

   Answer: b   **Difficulty**: Med   **Reference**: p. 145

81. A generic information systems planning methodology that attempts to gain a broad understanding of the information system needs of the entire organization defines:

   a.   bottom-up planning
   b.   top-down planning
   c.   democratic planning
   d.   foundation planning

   Answer: b   **Difficulty**: Med   **Reference**: p. 146

82. This approach begins by conducting an extensive analysis of the organization's mission, objectives, and strategy and determining the information requirements needed to meet each objective:

    a. foundation planning
    b. democratic planning
    c. top-down planning
    d. bottom-up planning

    Answer: c   **Difficulty**: Med   **Reference**: p. 146

83. This approach requires the identification of business problems and opportunities used to define projects:

    a. foundation planning
    b. democratic planning
    c. top-down planning
    d. bottom-up planning

    Answer: d   **Difficulty**: Med   **Reference**: p. 146

84. A generic information systems planning methodology that identifies and defines IS development projects based on solving operational business problems or taking advantage of some business opportunities defines:

    a. democratic planning
    b. bottom-up planning
    c. top-down planning
    d. foundation planning

    Answer: b   **Difficulty**: Med   **Reference**: p. 146

85. Which of the following is an advantage to the top-down planning approach over other planning approaches?

    a. broader perspective
    b. improved integration
    c. better understanding
    d. all of the above

    Answer: d   **Difficulty**: Med   **Reference**: p. 146

86. Which of the following best describes the top-down planning approach advantage, improved integration?

    a. If not viewed from the top, totally new management information systems may be implemented rather than planning how to evolve existing systems.
    b. If not viewed from the top, planners may lack sufficient management acceptance of the role of information systems in helping them achieve business objectives.
    c. If not viewed from the top, planners may lack the understanding necessary to implement information systems across the entire business rather than simply to individual operating units.
    d. If not viewed from the top, information systems may be implemented without first understanding the business from general management's viewpoint.

    Answer: a   **Difficulty**: Hard   **Reference**: p. 146

87. Which of the following best describes the top-down planning approach advantage, better understanding?

    a. If not viewed from the top, totally new management information systems may be implemented rather than planning how to evolve existing systems.
    b. If not viewed from the top, planners may lack sufficient management acceptance of the role of information systems in helping them achieve business objectives.
    c. If not viewed from the top, planners may lack the understanding necessary to implement information systems across the entire business rather than simply to individual operating units.
    d. If not viewed from the top, information systems may be implemented without first understanding the business from general management's viewpoint.

    Answer: c   **Difficulty**: Hard   **Reference**: p. 146

88. An advantage of the bottom-up approach is:

    a. identifying pressing organizational problems
    b. broader perspective
    c. improved integration
    d. better understanding

    Answer: a   **Difficulty**: Med   **Reference**: p. 147

89. Which of the following is an advantage of the bottom-up approach?

    a. By using the bottom-up approach, a broader perspective can be achieved.
    b. IS plans can be created faster and are less costly to develop than using the top-down approach.
    c. By using the bottom-up approach, planners may gain the understanding necessary to implement information systems across the entire business.
    d. By using the bottom-up approach, planners will have sufficient management acceptance of the role of information systems in helping them achieve business objectives.

    Answer: b   **Difficulty**: Hard   **Reference**: p. 147

90. This matrix identifies the relationships between organizational entities and each business function.

    a. unit-to-function
    b. location-to-unit
    c. function-to-process
    d. entity-to-process

    Answer: a   **Difficulty**: Hard   **Reference**: p. 148

91. This matrix identifies which data are created, updated, accessed, or deleted in each system.

    a. data entity-to-information system
    b. process-to-information system
    c. information system-to-objective
    d. process-to-data entity

    Answer: a   **Difficulty**: Med   **Reference**: p. 148

92. The process of arranging planning matrix information so that clusters of information with some predetermined level or type of affinity are placed next to each other on a matrix report defines:

    a. grouping
    b. isolating
    c. affinity clustering
    d. trend analysis

    Answer: c   **Difficulty**: Med   **Reference**: p. 149

93. Matrices of the target or "future" situation are sometimes called:

    a. forward-looking matrices
    b. "to be" matrices
    c. candidate matrices
    d. proposed matrices

    Answer: b   **Difficulty**: Med   **Reference**: p. 149

94. Which of the following is a CASE tool feature that can help you make sense out of matrices?

    a. management of information
    b. matrix construction
    c. matrix analysis
    d. all of the above

    Answer: d   **Difficulty**: Med   **Reference**: p. 149

95. The third activity in the ISP process is:

    a. describe the target situation, trends, and constraints
    b. describe the current situation
    c. developing a transition strategy and plans
    d. develop the logical design

    Answer: c   **Difficulty**: Med   **Reference**: p. 150

96. The second activity in the ISP process is:

    a. describe the target situation, trends, and constraints
    b. describe the current situation
    c. develop a transition strategy and plans
    d. develop the logical design

    Answer: a   **Difficulty**: Med   **Reference**: p. 150

97.   Which of the following is a true statement regarding the IS plan?

a.   The short- and long-term development needs identified in the plan are typically expressed as a series of projects.
b.   Projects from the long-term plan tend to build a foundation for later projects.
c.   Projects from the short-term plan are specific steps to fill the gap between current and desired systems or respond to dynamic business conditions.
d.   all of the above

Answer: d   **Difficulty**: Med   **Reference**: p. 150

98.   Which of the following is not a component on the typical information systems plan?

a.   corporation history
b.   constraints on IS development
c.   informational inventory
d.   the short-term plan

Answer: a   **Difficulty**: Med   **Reference**: p. 151

99.   The use of telecommunications technologies to transfer business documents directly between organizations best defines:

a.   electronic delivery
b.   computer conferencing
c.   extranet exchange
d.   electronic data interchange

Answer: d   **Difficulty**: Med   **Reference**: p. 152

100.   An Internet-based communication that supports business-to-business activities best describes:

a.   Internet
b.   electronic commerce
c.   electronic data interchange
d.   Extranet

Answer: d   **Difficulty**: Med   **Reference**: p. 152

Fill In the Blanks

101.   *Value chain analysis* refers to analyzing an organization's activities to determine where value is added to products and/or services and the costs incurred for doing so; usually also includes a comparison with the activities, added value, and costs of other organizations for the purpose of making improvements in the organization's operations and performance.

Difficulty: Hard   **Reference**: p. 138

102.   *Strategic alignment* is the extent to which the project is viewed as helping the organization achieve its strategic objectives and long-term goals.

Difficulty: Med   **Reference**: p. 138

103. *Potential benefits* are the extent to which the project is viewed as improving profits, customer service, and so forth and the duration of these benefits.

Difficulty: Med   **Reference**: p. 138

104. *Resource availability* is the amount and type of resources the project requires and their availability.

Difficulty: Easy   **Reference**: p. 138

105. *Project/size duration* refers to the number of individuals and the length of time needed to complete the project.

Difficulty: Med   **Reference**: p. 138

106. *Technical difficulty/risks* refers to the level of technical difficulty to successfully complete the project within given time and resource constraints.

Difficulty: Med   **Reference**: p. 138

107. *Incremental commitment* is a strategy in systems analysis and design in which the project is reviewed after each phase and continuation of the project is rejustified in each of these reviews.

Difficulty: Med   **Reference**: p. 140

108. *Corporate strategic planning* is an ongoing process that defines the mission, objectives, and strategies of an organization.

Difficulty: Med   **Reference**: p. 142

109. A *mission statement* is a statement that makes it clear what business a company is in.

Difficulty: Med   **Reference**: p. 142

110. *Objective statements* are a series of statements that express an organization's qualitative and quantitative goals for reaching a desired future position.

Difficulty: Med   **Reference**: p. 143

111. A *competitive strategy* is the method by which an organization attempts to achieve its mission and objectives.

Difficulty: Med   **Reference**: p. 144

112. *Low-cost producer* is the competitive strategy that reflects competing in an industry on the basis of product or service cost to the consumer.

Difficulty: Med   **Reference**: p. 144

113. *Product differentiation* is the competitive strategy that reflects capitalizing on a key product criterion requested by the market.

Difficulty: Med   **Reference**: p. 144

114. ***Product focus or niche*** is the competitive strategy that is similar to both low-cost and differentiation strategies but with a much narrower market focus.

Difficulty: Med   **Reference**: p. 144

115. ***Information systems planning*** is an orderly means of assessing the information needs of an organization and defining the systems, databases, and technologies that will best satisfy those needs.

Difficulty: Med   **Reference**: p. 144

116. ***Top-down planning*** is a generic information systems planning methodology that attempts to gain a broad understanding of the information system needs of the entire organization.

Difficulty: Med   **Reference**: p. 146

117. ***Bottom-up planning*** is a generic information systems planning methodology that identifies and defines IS development projects based upon solving operational business problems or taking advantage of some business opportunities.

Difficulty: Med   **Reference**: p. 146

118. ***Process-to-data entity*** is a matrix that identifies which data are captured, used, updated, or deleted within each process.

Difficulty: Hard   **Reference**: p. 148

119. ***Affinity clustering*** is the process of arranging planning matrix information so the clusters of information with some predetermined level or type of affinity are placed next to each other on a matrix report.

Difficulty: Hard   **Reference**: p. 149

120. The ***Internet*** is a large worldwide network of networks that use a common protocol to communicate with each other.

Difficulty: Easy   **Reference**: p. 152

121. ***Electronic commerce*** refers to Internet-based communication to support day-to-day business activities.

Difficulty: Easy   **Reference**: p. 152

122. ***Internets***, ***Extranets***, and ***Intranets*** are the three general classes of Internet EC applications.

Difficulty: Med   **Reference**: p. 152

123. An ***Intranet*** is the use of the Internet within the same business.

Difficulty: Med   **Reference**: p. 152

124. ***Electronic data interchange*** is the use of telecommunications technologies to directly transfer business documents between organizations.

Difficulty: Med   **Reference**: p. 152

125. *User*, *connection speed*, and *access method* are the three unknowns that must be dealt with when designing and building Internet applications.

Difficulty: Hard   **Reference**: p. 153

Matching Questions

Match each of the following terms with its definition.

   a. mission statement
   b. information systems planning
   c. top-down planning
   d. bottom-up planning
   e. objective statements

126. A generic information systems planning methodology that identifies and defines IS development projects based on solving operational business problems or taking advantage of some business opportunities.

Answer: d   **Reference**: p. 146

127. A generic information systems planning methodology that attempts to gain a broad understanding of the information system needs of the entire organization.

Answer: c   **Reference**: p. 146

128. An orderly means of assessing the information needs of an organization and defining the systems, databases, and technologies that will best satisfy those needs.

Answer: b   **Reference**: p. 144

129. A statement that makes it clear what business a company is in.

Answer: a   **Reference**: p. 142

130. A series of statements that express an organization's qualitative and quantitative goals for reaching a desired future position.

Answer: e   **Reference**: p. 143

Match each of the following selection methods with its related characteristic. (Answers may occur more than once.)

    a. top management
    b. steering committee
    c. user department
    d. development group

131.   Narrow/non-strategic focus

              Answer: c   **Reference:** p. 137

132.   Integration with existing systems focus

              Answer: d   **Reference:** p. 137

133.   Largest project size

              Answer: a   **Reference:** p. 137

134.   Greater organizational change

              Answer: b   **Reference:** p. 137

135.   Less concern on cost-benefit analysis

              Answer: d   **Reference:** p. 137

136.   Fewer users, management layers, and business functions

              Answer: c   **Reference:** p. 137

137.   Longest project duration

              Answer: a   **Reference:** p. 137

138.   Formal cost-benefit analysis

              Answer: b   **Reference:** p. 137

Match each of the following types of matrices with its corresponding definition.

      a.   function-to-process
      b.   function-to-data entity
      c.   process-to-data entity
      d.   function-to-objective
      e.   unit-to-function

139.   Identifies the relationships between organizational entities and each business function.

                 Answer: e   **Reference:** p. 148

140.   Identifies which processes are used to support each business function.

                 Answer: a   **Reference:** p. 148

141.   Identifies which data are captured, used, updated, or deleted within each process.

                 Answer: c   **Reference:** p. 148

142.   Identifies which functions are essential or desirable in achieving each organizational objective.

                 Answer: d   **Reference:** p. 148

143.   Identifies which business functions utilize which data entities.

                 Answer: b   **Reference:** p. 148

Match each of the following types of matrices with its description.

    a.   process-to-information system
    b.   data entity-to-information system
    c.   location-to-function
    d.   information system-to-objective
    e.   location-to-unit

144.   Identifies which business functions are being performed at various organizational locations.

               Answer: c   **Reference**: p. 147

145.   Identifies which organizational units are located or interact with a specific business location.

               Answer: e   **Reference**: p. 147

146.   Identifies which information systems are used to support each process.

               Answer: a   **Reference**: p. 148

147.   Identifies which data are created, updated, accessed, or deleted in each system.

               Answer: b   **Reference**: p. 148

148.   Identifies which information systems support each business objective as identified during organizational planning.

               Answer: d   **Reference**: p. 148

Match the following typical components of an information system plan with its description.

       a.   Organizational Mission, Objectives, and Strategy
       b.   Informational Inventory
       c.   Mission and Objectives of Information Systems
       d.   Constraints on IS Development
       e.   Overall Systems Needs and Long-Range IS Strategies
       f.   The Short-Term Plan
       g.   Conclusions

149.   Description of the primary role IS will play in the organization to transform the enterprise from its current to future state.

                   Answer: c   **Reference**: p. 151

150.   This section provides a summary of the various business processes, functions, data entities, and information needs of the enterprise.

                   Answer: b   **Reference**: p. 151

151.   Briefly describes the mission, objectives, and strategy of the organization.

                   Answer: a   **Reference**: p. 151

152.   Briefly describes limitations imposed by technology and the current level of resources within the company.

                   Answer: d   **Reference**: p. 151

153.   Presents a summary of the overall systems needed within the company and the set of long-range (2-5 years) strategies chosen by the IS department to fill the needs.

                   Answer: e   **Reference**: p. 151

154.   Contains likely but not-yet-certain events that may affect the plan, an inventory of business change elements as presently known, and a description of their estimated impact on the plan.

                   Answer: g   **Reference**: p. 151

155.   Shows a detailed inventory of present projects and systems, and a detailed plan of projects to be developed or advanced during the current year.

                   Answer: f   **Reference**: p. 151

Essay Questions

156. *List and briefly identify the three primary activities of the project identification and selection phase.*

The first phase of the SDLC is project identification and selection. During this phase, all possible systems development projects are identified and assessed. Project identification and selection consists of three primary activities: identify potential development projects, classifying and ranking projects, and selecting projects for development. During the first activity, projects can be identified by a variety of sources. A key member of top-management, a steering committee, user departments, and the development group are possible sources. Classifying and ranking IS development projects, the second major activity, focuses on assessing the relative merit of potential projects. Various criteria (strategic alignment, potential benefits, resource availability, project size/duration, and technical difficulty/risks) can be used to evaluate the projects. The last activity, selecting IS development projects, is the actual selection of projects for further development. Consideration is given to both short- and long-term projects. Projects most likely to achieve business objectives are selected. Numerous factors (perceived organizational needs, existing systems and ongoing projects, resource availability, evaluation criteria, current business conditions, and decision maker perceptions) impact the selection process. Acceptance, rejection, and conditional acceptance are possible outcomes for this activity.

157. *Define and briefly discuss corporate strategic planning.*

To make effective project selection decisions, a corporation must know where it is, where it is going, and the path it will take to get there. Corporate strategic planning is based on this premise. Corporate strategic planning can be viewed as a three step process: (1) current enterprise, (2) future enterprise, and (3) strategic plan. During corporate strategic planning, mission statements, statements of future corporate objectives, and strategies are developed.

158. *Define and briefly discuss information systems planning.*

ISP is an orderly means of assessing the information needs of an organization, and defining the systems, databases, and technologies that will best satisfy those needs. During ISP, current and future organization informational needs will be modeled. Also, strategies and project plans to move the current information system and technologies to their desired future state will be developed. ISP looks at information systems and technologies in terms of how they can help the business achieve its objectives defined during corporate planning. ISP includes three key activities. The first activity involves assessing current IS-related assets; the second step involves developing target blueprints of the resources; a series of scheduled projects is defined in the third step.

159. *Define top-down planning and bottom-up planning.*

Top-down planning is a generic information systems planning methodology that attempts to gain a broad understanding of the information system needs of the entire organization. Bottom-up planning is a generic information systems planning methodology that identifies and defines IS development projects based upon solving operational business problems or taking advantage of some business opportunities.

160. *What is incremental commitment? Does it always result in a working system? Why or why not?*

Incremental commitment is a systems analysis and design strategy in which the project is reviewed after each phase and continuation of the project is rejustified in each of these reviews. Incremental commitment does not always result in a working system. Incremental commitment permits management and the project team to reevaluate the system's costs, benefits, and risks in light of changing business conditions. If business conditions, system costs, system benefits, and/or risks have changed, the project may be cancelled.

161. *Identify six reasons why improved information systems project identification and selection is needed.*

Information systems costs continue to rise, the inability of systems to handle applications that cross organizational boundaries, systems not addressing the critical problems of the business as a whole nor supporting strategic planning applications, data redundancy and lack of user confidence in the quality of data, out-of-control system maintenance costs, and lengthy application backlogs are six reasons why improvements in the information systems project identification and selection process are necessary.

162. *Briefly discuss three generic competitive strategies. Provide an example of each.*

Low-cost producer, product differentiation, and product focus or niche are three generic competitive strategies. A low-cost producer strategy reflects competing in an industry on the basis of product or service cost to the consumer. South Korean-produced Hyundai is the example mentioned in the textbook. The product differentiation strategy reflects capitalizing on a key product criterion requested by the market. An example is an automobile manufacturer suggesting that its line of trucks provides the quietest and most comfortable ride. The product focus or niche strategy is similar to both the low-cost and differentiation strategies but with a much narrower market focus. An example of this strategy is a fitness center that caters exclusively to women.

163. *What is a top-down planning approach? Identify four advantages to the top-down planning approach over other planning approaches.*

A top-down planning approach is a generic information systems planning methodology that attempts to gain a broad understanding of the information system needs of the entire organization. Broader perspective, improved integration, improved management support, and better understanding are four advantages.

164. *Using any business as an example, provide one example each for its organizational locations, units, functions, processes, and information systems.*

A national insurance company is a good example. Organizational locations include the home office and its various branch locations. Most finance and accounting functions are handled at the home office, while the local branches are responsible, to some degree, for marketing and sales. Customer enrollment and billing are processes. Payroll processing, accounts payable, and accounts receivable are information systems. The insurance company would keep information about its customers, branch locations, and insurance plans.

165. *Briefly describe three of the ten types of matrices that are beneficial during information systems planning.*

Location-to-function, location-to-unit, and unit to function are three of the ten types of matrices. The location-to-function matrix identifies which business functions are being performed at various organizational locations. The location-to-unit matrix identifies which organizational units are located in or interact with a specific function. The unit-to-function matrix identifies the relationships between organizational entities and each business function. Additional matrices are mentioned in the textbook.

Chapter 6
Initiating and Planning Systems
Development Projects

True-False Questions

1. Proper and insightful project planning, including determining project scope as well as identifying project activities, can easily reduce time in later project phases.

    Answer: True   **Difficulty**: Med   **Reference**: p. 164

2. The objective of project initiation and planning is to transform a vague system request document into a tangible project description.

    Answer: True   **Difficulty**: Hard   **Reference**: p. 164

3. Project initiation focuses on activities that will help organize a team to conduct project planning.

    Answer: True   **Difficulty**: Med   **Reference**: p. 165

4. Project planning focuses on defining clear, discrete tasks and the work needed to complete each task.

    Answer: True   **Difficulty**: Med   **Reference**: p. 166

5. The objective of the project planning process is the development of a Baseline Project Plan and a Statement of Work.

    Answer: True   **Difficulty**: Med   **Reference**: p. 166

6. The Statement of Work clearly outlines the objectives and constraints of the project for the development group.

    Answer: False   **Difficulty**: Med   **Reference**: p. 166

7. The major outcomes and deliverables from project initiation and planning are the Baseline Project Plan and the Statement of Work.

    Answer: True   **Difficulty**: Med   **Reference**: p. 166

8. The Systems Service Request reflects the best estimate of the project's scope, benefits, costs, risks, and resource requirements, given the current understanding of the project.

    Answer: False   **Difficulty**: Med   **Reference**: p. 166

9. The Explanation of Services is a short document prepared for the customer that describes what the project will deliver and outlines all work required to complete the project.

    Answer: False   **Difficulty**: Med   **Reference**: p. 167

10. The Statement of Work is a document prepared for the customer during project initiation and planning that describes what the project will deliver and outlines generally at a high level all work required to complete the project.

    Answer: True   **Difficulty**: Med   **Reference**: p. 167

11. The Statement of Work can be used as the basis of a formal contractual agreement outlining firm deadlines, costs, and specifications.

    Answer: True   **Difficulty**: Easy   **Reference**: p. 167

12. Assessing project feasibility is a required activity for all information systems projects.

    Answer: True   **Difficulty**: Easy   **Reference**: p. 168

13. The culmination of the feasibility analyses form the business case that justifies the expenditure of resources on the project.

    Answer: True   **Difficulty**: Med   **Reference**: p. 168

14. Economic feasibility is the process of identifying the financial benefits and costs associated with a development project.

    Answer: True   **Difficulty**: Easy   **Reference**: p. 168

15. During project initiation and planning, you should be able to precisely define all benefits and costs related to a particular project.

    Answer: False   **Difficulty**: Med   **Reference**: p. 168

16. Opening new markets and increasing sales opportunities is a tangible benefit.

    Answer: True   **Difficulty**: Med   **Reference**: p. 170

17. Increased flexibility is an intangible benefit.

    Answer: False   **Difficulty**: Med   **Reference**: p. 170

18. Improvement of management planning and control is a tangible benefit.

    Answer: True   **Difficulty**: Med   **Reference**: p. 170

19. Competitive necessity, more timely information, and improved organizational planning are intangible benefits.

    Answer: True   **Difficulty**: Med   **Reference**: p. 171

20. Site preparation is an example of a one-time cost.

    Answer: True   **Difficulty**: Easy   **Reference**: p. 171

21. During project initiation and planning, potential tangible benefits may have to be considered intangible.

    Answer: True   **Difficulty**: Med   **Reference**: p. 171

22. Intangible benefits are benefits associated with project start-up, development, or system start-up.

    Answer: False   **Difficulty**: Med   **Reference**: p. 171

23. Variable costs are costs resulting from the ongoing evolution and use of a system.

    Answer: False   **Difficulty**: Med   **Reference**: p. 172

24. Disruption to the rest of the organization is an example of a procurement cost.

    Answer: False   **Difficulty**: Hard   **Reference**: p. 172

25. Management, operation, and planning personnel are examples of start-up costs.

    Answer: False   **Difficulty**: Hard   **Reference**: p. 172

26. Fixed costs are costs that are billed or incurred at a regular interval and usually at a fixed rate.

    Answer: True   **Difficulty**: Easy   **Reference**: p. 172

27. Anticipating and controlling user changes is a guideline for better cost estimating.

    Answer: True   **Difficulty**: Med   **Reference**: p. 172

28. The time value of money compares present cash outlays to future expected returns.

    Answer: True   **Difficulty**: Med   **Reference**: p. 174

29. Because many projects may be competing for the same investment dollars and may have different useful life expectancies, all costs and benefits must be viewed in relation to their present rather than future value when comparing investment options.

    Answer: True   **Difficulty**: Hard   **Reference**: p. 174

30. Using a discount rate of 10 percent, the present value of a $2,500 benefit received 5 years from now is $1,552.30.

    Answer: True   **Difficulty**: Med   **Reference**: p. 174

31. Using a discount rate of 14 percent, the present value of a $10,000 benefit received 5 years from now is $5,500.49.

    Answer: False   **Difficulty**: Med   **Reference**: p. 174

32. Using a discount rate of 12 percent, the present value of a $50,500 benefit received 2 years from now is $39,859.69.

    Answer: False   **Difficulty**: Med   **Reference**: p. 174

33. The objective of ROI analysis is to discover at what point cumulative benefits equal costs.

    Answer: False   **Difficulty**: Med   **Reference**: p. 175

34. If the NPV of all costs is $100,000 and the NPV of all benefits is $170,000, then the ROI would be 35 percent.

   Answer: False   **Difficulty**: Med   **Reference**: p. 175

35. If the NPV of all benefits is $150,000 and the NPV of all costs is $125,000, then the ROI is 15 percent.

   Answer: False   **Difficulty**: Med   **Reference**: p. 175

36. If the NPV of all benefits is $2,500,000 and the NPV of all costs are $1,000,000 then the ROI is 10 percent.

   Answer: False   **Difficulty**: Med   **Reference**: p. 175

37. Most techniques for analyzing economic feasibility employ the time value of money concept.

   Answer: True   **Difficulty**: Med   **Reference**: p. 176

38. Fulfillment feasibility is the process of examining the likelihood that the project will attain its desired objectives.

   Answer: False   **Difficulty**: Med   **Reference**: p. 180

39. The goal of operational feasibility is to understand the degree to which a proposed system will likely solve the business problems or take advantage of opportunities.

   Answer: True   **Difficulty**: Med   **Reference**: p. 180

40. Generally speaking, legal and contractual feasibility is a greater consideration if your organization has historically used an outside organization for specific systems or services that you now are considering handling yourself.

   Answer: True   **Difficulty**: Med   **Reference**: p. 181

41. The construction of an information system can have political ramifications.

   Answer: True   **Difficulty**: Easy   **Reference**: p. 181

42. All information collected during project initiation and planning is collected and organized into a document called the Baseline Project Plan.

   Answer: True   **Difficulty**: Med   **Reference**: p. 181

43. Referencing the Management Issues section of the Baseline Project Plan, the communication plan provides a description of the team member roles and reporting relationships.

   Answer: False   **Difficulty**: Hard   **Reference**: p. 182

44. A walkthrough is a peer group review of any product created during the systems development process.

   Answer: True   **Difficulty**: Med   **Reference**: p. 185

45. Referencing a walkthrough, the maintenance oracle ensures that the work product adheres to organizational technical standards.

    Answer: False   **Difficulty**: Hard   **Reference**: p. 186

46. Referencing a walkthrough, the coordinator reviews the work product in terms of future maintenance activities.

    Answer: False   **Difficulty**: Med   **Reference**: p. 186

47. Referencing a walkthrough, the user makes sure that the work product meets the needs of the project's customers.

    Answer: True   **Difficulty**: Easy   **Reference**: p. 186

48. The project initiation and planning process for an Internet-based electronic commerce application is similar to the process followed for other applications.

    Answer: True   **Difficulty**: Med   **Reference**: p. 189

49. Web-based system costs include platform costs, content and service, and marketing.

    Answer: True   **Difficulty**: Med   **Reference**: p. 189

50. A firewall server is an example of a content and service web-based system cost.

    Answer: False   **Difficulty**: Med   **Reference**: p. 189

Multiple Choice Questions

51. As a rule of thumb estimate, what percentage of the entire development effort should be devoted to the project initiation and planning process?

    a. between 10 and 20 percent
    b. less than 5 percent
    c. less than 10 percent
    d. between 20 and 30 percent

    Answer: a   **Difficulty**: Med   **Reference**: p. 164

52. Activities designed to assist in organizing a team to conduct project planning is the focus of:

    a. project planning
    b. project identification and selection
    c. project initiation
    d. analysis

    Answer: c   **Difficulty**: Med   **Reference**: p. 165

53. Which of the following is not an element of project initiation?

a. establishing management procedures
b. dividing the project into manageable tasks
c. establishing a relationship with the customer
d. establishing the project initiation team

Answer: b   **Difficulty**: Med   **Reference**: p. 166

54. How is project planning distinct from general information systems planning?

a. General information systems planning focuses on assessing the information systems needs of the entire organization.
b. Project planning focuses on assessing the information systems needs of the entire organization.
c. General information systems planning focuses on defining clear, discrete activities and the work needed to complete each activity within a single project.
d. Project planning focuses on defining discrete activities needed to complete all projects.

Answer: a   **Difficulty**: Med   **Reference**: p. 166

55. The objective of the project planning process is:

a. the development of a Baseline Project Plan and Statement of Work
b. the development of a Systems Service Request
c. the development of entity relationship diagrams
d. the development of transitional operations plans

Answer: a   **Difficulty**: Med   **Reference**: p. 166

56. Which of the following is an element of project planning?

a. establishing management procedures
b. establishing a relationship with the customer
c. estimating resources and creating a resource plan
d. establishing the project management environment and project workbook

Answer: b   **Difficulty**: Med   **Reference**: p. 166

57. The Baseline Project Plan:

a. contains all information collected and analyzed during project initiation and planning
b. specifies detailed project activities for the next life cycle phase, analysis, and less detail for subsequent project phases
c. is used by the project selection committee to help decide if the project should be accepted, redirected, or canceled
d. all of the above

Answer: d   **Difficulty**: Med   **Reference**: p. 166

58. A major outcome and deliverable from the project initiation and planning phase that contains the best estimate of a project's scope, benefits, costs, risks, and resource requirements defines the:

     a. Baseline Project Plan
     b. Information Systems Plan
     c. Mission Statement
     d. Statement of Work

     Answer: a   **Difficulty:** Med   **Reference:** p. 166

59. The justification for an information system, presented in terms of the tangible and intangible economic benefits and costs, and the technical and organizational feasibility of the proposed system best defines:

     a. Baseline Project Plan
     b. Information Systems Plan
     c. Business Case
     d. Statement of Work

     Answer: c   **Difficulty:** Med   **Reference:** p. 166

60. The Statement of Work:

     a. is a short document prepared for the customer that describes what the project will deliver and outlines all work required to complete the project
     b. is useful for ensuring that both you and your customer gain a common understanding of the project
     c. is a very easy document to create because it typically consists of a high-level summary of the BPP information
     d. all of the above

     Answer: d   **Difficulty:** Med   **Reference:** p. 167

61. A document prepared for the customer during project initiation and planning that describes what the project will deliver and outlines generally at a high level all work required to complete the project is the:

     a. Information Systems Plan
     b. Statement of Work
     c. Mission Statement
     d. Baseline Project Plan

     Answer: b   **Difficulty:** Med   **Reference:** p. 167

62. To identify the financial benefits and costs associated with the development project is the purpose of:

     a. economic feasibility
     b. technical feasibility
     c. operational feasibility
     d. schedule feasibility

     Answer: a   **Difficulty:** Med   **Reference:** p. 168

63. Tangible benefits would include:

a. improved organizational planning
b. ability to investigate more alternatives
c. improved asset control
d. lower transaction costs

Answer: d   **Difficulty**: Med   **Reference**: p. 170

64. Cost reduction and avoidance, error reduction, and increased flexibility are examples of:

a. intangible benefits
b. qualitative benefits
c. tangible benefits
d. legal and contractual benefits

Answer: c   **Difficulty**: Med   **Reference**: p. 170

65. A savings of $3,000 resulting from a data entry error correction would most likely be classified as a(n):

a. intangible benefit
b. qualitative benefit
c. tangible benefit
d. operational benefit

Answer: c   **Difficulty**: Med   **Reference**: p. 170

66. A benefit derived from the creation of an information system that can be measured in dollars and with certainty is a(n):

a. intangible benefit
b. qualitative benefit
c. tangible benefit
d. operational benefit

Answer: c   **Difficulty**: Med   **Reference**: p. 170

67. The reduction of waste creation is an example of a(n):

a. intangible benefit
b. qualitative benefit
c. tangible benefit
d. operational benefit

Answer: a   **Difficulty**: Med   **Reference**: p. 171

68. A cost associated with an information system that can be measured in dollars and with certainty is referred to as a(n):

    a. economic cost
    b. tangible cost
    c. intangible cost
    d. one-time cost

    Answer: b   **Difficulty**: Med   **Reference**: p. 171

69. Which of the following would be classified as a tangible cost?

    a. loss of customer goodwill
    b. cost of hardware
    c. employee morale
    d. operational inefficiency

    Answer: b   **Difficulty**: Med   **Reference**: p. 171

70. Capital costs, management and staff time, and consulting costs are examples of:

    a. project-related costs
    b. operating costs
    c. start-up costs
    d. procurement costs

    Answer: d   **Difficulty**: Hard   **Reference**: p. 172

71. Rental of space and equipment, system maintenance costs, and asset depreciation are examples of:

    a. project-related costs
    b. operating costs
    c. start-up costs
    d. procurement costs

    Answer: b   **Difficulty**: Hard   **Reference**: p. 172

72. Which of the following would be classified as an intangible cost?

    a. hardware costs
    b. labor costs
    c. employee morale
    d. operational costs

    Answer: c   **Difficulty**: Med   **Reference**: p. 171

73. A cost associated with project startup and development or system startup refers to a(n):

    a. recurring cost
    b. one-time cost
    c. incremental cost
    d. infrequent cost

    Answer: b   **Difficulty**: Med   **Reference**: p. 171

74. A cost associated with an information system that cannot be easily measured in terms of dollars or with certainty refers to:

    a. economic cost
    b. tangible cost
    c. intangible cost
    d. one-time cost

    Answer: c   **Difficulty**: Med   **Reference**: p. 171

75. A cost resulting from the ongoing evolution and use of a system refers to a(n):

    a. recurring cost
    b. one-time cost
    c. incremental cost
    d. frequent cost

    Answer: a   **Difficulty**: Med   **Reference**: p. 172

76. Application software maintenance, new software and hardware leases, and incremental communications are examples of:

    a. recurring costs
    b. one-time costs
    c. incremental costs
    d. frequent costs

    Answer: a   **Difficulty**: Med   **Reference**: p. 172

77. The concept of comparing present cash outlays to future expected returns best defines:

    a. cost/benefit analysis
    b. internal rate of return
    c. time value of money
    d investment return analysis

    Answer: c   **Difficulty**: Med   **Reference**: p. 174

78. The rate of return used to compute the present value of future cash flows refers to:

    a. discount rate
    b. investment rate
    c. transfer rate
    d. future cash flow rate

    Answer: a   **Difficulty**: Med   **Reference**: p. 174

79. The current value of a future cash flow is referred to as its:

    a. future value
    b. present value
    c. investment value
    d. discount rate

    Answer: b   **Difficulty**: Med   **Reference**: p. 174

80. The analysis technique that uses a discount rate determined from the company's cost of capital to establish the present value of a project is commonly called:

    a. return on investment (ROI)
    b. break-even analysis (BEA)
    c. net present value (NPV)
    d. future value (FV)

    Answer: c   **Difficulty**: Med   **Reference**: p. 177

81. The ratio of the net cash receipts of the project divided by the cash outlays of the project, enabling tradeoff analysis to be made between competing projects is often referred to as:

    a. return on investment (ROI)
    b. break-even analysis (BEA)
    c. net present value (NPV)
    d. future value (FV)

    Answer: a   **Difficulty**: Med   **Reference**: p. 177

82. The analysis technique that finds the amount of time required for the cumulative cash flow from a project to equal its initial and ongoing investment is referred to as:

    a. return on investment (ROI)
    b. break-even analysis (BEA)
    c. net present value (NPV)
    d. future value (FV)

    Answer: b   **Difficulty**: Med   **Reference**: p. 177

83. To gain an understanding of the organization's ability to construct the proposed system is the purpose of:

    a. operational feasibility
    b. schedule feasibility
    c. technical feasibility
    d. political feasibility

    Answer: c   **Difficulty**: Med   **Reference**: p. 177

84. An assessment of the development group's understanding of the possible target hardware, software, and operating environments, system size, complexity, and the group's experience with similar systems should be included as part of:

    a. technical feasibility
    b. political feasibility
    c. operational feasibility
    d. schedule feasibility

    Answer: a   **Difficulty**: Med   **Reference**: p. 177

85. When conducting a technical risk assessment, which of the following is true?

    a. A project has a greater likelihood of experiencing unforeseen technical problems when the development group lacks knowledge related to some aspect of the technology environment.
    b. Large projects are riskier than small projects.
    c. Successful IS projects require active involvement and cooperation between the user and development groups.
    d. all of the above

    Answer: d   **Difficulty**: Med   **Reference**: pp. 178-179

86. Which of the following is an example of a web-based content and service cost?

    a. web project manager
    b. firewall server
    c. advertising sales staff
    d. promotions

    Answer: a   **Difficulty**: Hard   **Reference**: p. 189

87. A new system or the renovation of existing systems, user perceptions, and management commitment to the system are examples of which of the following risk factors?

    a. development group
    b. project structure
    c. project size
    d. user group

    Answer: b   **Difficulty**: Hard   **Reference**: p. 178

88. The number of members on the project team, project duration, and the number of organizational departments involved in the project are examples of which of the following risk factors?

    a. development group
    b. project structure
    c. project size
    d. user group

    Answer: c   **Difficulty**: Med   **Reference**: p. 178

89. To gain an understanding of the likelihood that all potential time frame and completion date schedules can be met and that meeting these dates will be sufficient for dealing with the needs of the organization is the purpose of:

    a. schedule feasibility
    b. operational feasibility
    c. technical feasibility
    d. political feasibility

    Answer: a   **Difficulty**: Med   **Reference**: p. 180

90. The process of assessing potential legal and contractual ramifications due to the construction of a system refers to:

    a. technical feasibility
    b. legal and contractual feasibility
    c. economic feasibility
    d. operational feasibility

    Answer: b   **Difficulty**: Med   **Reference**: p. 180

91. To gain an understanding of how key stakeholders within the organization view the proposed system is the purpose of:

    a. technical feasibility
    b. legal and contractual feasibility
    c. political feasibility
    d. operational feasibility

    Answer: c   **Difficulty**: Med   **Reference**: p. 181

92. During project initiation and planning, the most crucial element of the design strategy is:

    a. the physical design statement
    b. the system's scope
    c. the identification of the business mission
    d. the logical design statement

    Answer: b   **Difficulty**: Med   **Reference**: p. 183

93. A peer group review of any product created during the system development process refers to:

    a. walkthrough
    b. feasibility assessment
    c. joint application discussion
    d. product evaluation

    Answer: a   **Difficulty**: Med   **Reference**: p. 185

94. At a walkthrough meeting, the person who plans the meetings and facilitates a smooth meeting process is referred to as the:

    a. presenter
    b. coordinator
    c. standards bearer
    d. maintenance oracle

    Answer: b   **Difficulty**: Med   **Reference**: p. 186

95. At a walkthrough meeting, the person (or group) who ensures that the work product meets the needs of the project's customers is referred to as the:

    a. coordinator
    b. user
    c. maintenance oracle
    d. standards bearer

    Answer: b   **Difficulty**: Med   **Reference**: p. 186

96. At a walkthrough meeting, the person who ensures that the work product adheres to organizational technical standards is referred to as the:

    a. coordinator
    b. user
    c. maintenance oracle
    d. standards bearer

    Answer: d   **Difficulty**: Med   **Reference**: p. 186

97. At a walkthrough meeting, the person who reviews the work product in terms of future maintenance activities is referred to as the:

    a. coordinator
    b. user
    c. maintenance oracle
    d. standards bearer

    Answer: c   **Difficulty**: Med   **Reference**: p. 186

98. Which of the following is an example of a web-based platform cost?

    a. ongoing design fees
    b. server software
    c. direct mail
    d. training and travel

    Answer: b   **Difficulty**: Hard   **Reference**: p. 189

99. Which of the following is an example of a web-based marketing cost?

    a. support staff
    b. web-hosting service
    c. graphics staff
    d. paid links to other Web sites

    Answer: d   **Difficulty**: Med   **Reference**: p. 189

100. The process of assessing the degree to which a proposed system solves business problems or takes advantage of business opportunities refers to:

    a.   schedule feasibility
    b.   operational feasibility
    c.   technical feasibility
    d.   political feasibility

    Answer: b   **Difficulty**: Med   **Reference**: p. 180

Fill In the Blanks

101. A *business case* is a written report that outlines the justification for an information system; this report highlights economic benefits and costs and the technical and organizational feasibility of the proposed system.

    Difficulty: Med   **Reference**: p. 166

102. The *Baseline Project Plan* is the major outcome and deliverable from the project initiation and planning phase and contains an estimate of the project's scope, benefits, costs, risks, and resource requirements.

    Difficulty: Med   **Reference**: p. 166

103. The *Statement of Work* is a document prepared for the customer during project initiation and planning that describes what the project will deliver and outlines generally at a high level all work required to complete the project.

    Difficulty: Med   **Reference**: p. 167

104. *Economic feasibility* is the process of identifying the financial benefits and costs associated with a development project.

    Difficulty: Easy   **Reference**: p. 168

105. A *tangible benefit* is a benefit derived from the creation of an information system that can be measured in dollars and with certainty.

    Difficulty: Easy   **Reference**: p. 170

106. An *intangible benefit* is a benefit derived from the creation of an information system that cannot be easily measured in dollars or with certainty.

    Difficulty: Easy   **Reference**: p. 171

107. A *tangible cost* is a cost associated with an information system that can be easily measured in dollars and with certainty.

    Difficulty: Easy   **Reference**: p. 171

108. An ***intangible cost*** is a cost associated with an information system that cannot be easily measured in terms of dollars or with certainty.

Difficulty: Easy   **Reference**: p. 171

109. ***One-time costs*** are costs associated with project start-up and development, or system start-up.

Difficulty: Med   **Reference**: p. 171

110. ***Recurring costs*** are costs resulting from the ongoing evolution and use of a system.

Difficulty: Med   **Reference**: p. 172

111. The ***time value of money*** refers to the process of comparing present cash outlays to future expected returns.

Difficulty: Med   **Reference**: p. 174

112. The ***discount rate*** is the rate of return used to compute the present value of future cash flows.

Difficulty: Med   **Reference**: p. 174

113. ***Present value*** is the current value of a future cash flow.

Difficulty: Med   **Reference**: p. 174

114. ***Break-even analysis*** finds the amount of time required for the cumulative cash flow from a project to equal its initial and ongoing investment.

Difficulty: Med   **Reference**: p. 177

115. ***Return on investment*** is the ratio of the net cash receipts of the project divided by the cash outlays of the project.

Difficulty: Hard   **Reference**: p. 177

116. ***Net present value*** uses a discount rate determined from the company's cost of capital to establish the present value of the project.

Difficulty: Med   **Reference**: p. 177

117. ***Technical feasibility*** is the process of assessing the development organization's ability to construct a proposed system.

Difficulty: Med   **Reference**: p. 177

118. ***Operational feasibility*** is the process of assessing the degree to which a proposed system solves business problems or takes advantage of business opportunities.

Difficulty: Med   **Reference**: p. 180

119. **_Schedule feasibility_** is the process of assessing the degree to which the potential time frame and completion dates for all major activities within a project meet organizational deadlines and constraints for affecting change.

    Difficulty: Med   **Reference**: p. 180

120. **_Legal and contractual feasibility_** is the process of assessing potential legal and contractual ramifications due to the construction of a system.

    Difficulty: Easy   **Reference**: p. 180

121. **_Political feasibility_** is the process of evaluating how key stakeholders within the organization view the proposed system.

    Difficulty: Med   **Reference**: p. 181

122. A **_walkthrough_** is a peer group review of any product created during the systems development process.

    Difficulty: Med   **Reference**: p. 185

123. Referencing a walkthrough meeting, the **_coordinator_** plans the meeting and facilitates a smooth meeting process.

    Difficulty: Hard   **Reference**: p. 186

124. Referencing a walkthrough meeting, the **_standards bearer_** ensures that the work product adheres to organizational technical standards.

    Difficulty: Hard   **Reference**: p. 186

125. Referencing a walkthrough meeting, the **_maintenance oracle_**, reviews the work product in terms of future maintenance activities.

    Difficulty: Hard   **Reference**: p. 186

Matching Questions

Match each of the following terms with its definition.

    a.   economic feasibility
    b.   legal and contractual feasibility
    c.   operational feasibility
    d.   political feasibility
    e.   schedule feasibility
    f.   technical feasibility

126.   A process of identifying the financial benefits and costs associated with a development project.

        Answer: a   **Reference:** p. 168

127.   The process of assessing the degree to which the potential time frame and completion dates for all major activities within a project meet organizational deadlines and constraints for affecting change.

        Answer: e   **Reference:** p. 180

128.   The process of evaluating how key stakeholders within the organization view the proposed system.

        Answer: d   **Reference:** p. 181

129.   The process of assessing the degree to which a proposed system solves business problems or takes advantage of business opportunities.

        Answer: c   **Reference:** p. 180

130.   The process of assessing potential legal and contractual ramifications due to the construction of a system.

        Answer: b   **Reference:** p. 180

131.   A process of assessing the development organization's ability to construct a proposed system.

        Answer: f   **Reference:** p. 177

Match each of the following terms with its definition.

    a.   intangible benefit
    b.   intangible cost
    c.   one-time cost
    d.   recurring cost
    e.   tangible benefit
    f.   tangible cost

132.   A cost associated with an information system that can be measured in dollars and with certainty.

                Answer: f   **Reference**: p. 171

133.   A benefit derived from the creation of an information system that can be measured in dollars and with certainty.

                Answer: e   **Reference**: p. 170

134.   A cost resulting from the ongoing evolution and use of a system.

                Answer: d   **Reference**: p. 172

135.   A cost associated with project startup and development, or system startup.

                Answer: c   **Reference**: p. 171

136.   A cost associated with an information system that cannot be easily measured in terms of dollars or with certainty.

                Answer: b   **Reference**: p. 171

137.   A benefit derived from the creation of an information system that cannot be easily measured in dollars or with certainty.

                Answer: a   **Reference**: p. 171

Match each of the following terms with its definition.

    a.   Baseline Project Plan
    b.   discount rate
    c.   economic feasibility
    d.   intangible benefit
    e.   intangible cost
    f.   legal and contractual feasibility
    g.   operational feasibility
    h.   one-time cost
    i.   political feasibility
    j.   present value
    k.   recurring cost
    l.   schedule feasibility
    m.   Statement of Work
    n.   tangible benefit
    o.   tangible cost
    p.   technical feasibility
    q.   walkthrough

138.   The rate of return used to compute the present value of future cash flows.

             Answer: b   **Reference:** p. 174

139.   A major outcome and deliverable from the project initiation and planning phase that contains the best estimate of a project's scope, benefits, costs, risks, and resource requirements.

             Answer: a   **Reference:** p. 166

140.   A peer group review of any product created during the system development process.

             Answer: q   **Reference:** p. 185

141.   The current value of a future cash flow.

             Answer: j   **Reference:** p. 174

142.   A cost associated with an information system that can be measured in dollars and with certainty.

             Answer: o   **Reference:** p. 171

143.   A benefit derived from the creation of an information system that can be measured in dollars and with certainty.

             Answer: n   **Reference:** p. 170

144.   A cost resulting from the ongoing evolution and use of a system.

             Answer: k   **Reference:** p. 172

145.   A cost associated with project startup and development, or system startup.

             Answer: h   **Reference:** p. 171

146.   A cost associated with an information system that cannot be easily measured in terms of dollars or with certainty.

                    Answer: e   **Reference**: p. 171

147.   A benefit derived from the creation of an information system that cannot be easily measured in dollars or with certainty.

                    Answer: d   **Reference**: p. 171

148.   A document prepared for the customer during project initiation and planning that describes what the project will deliver and outlines generally at a high level all work required to complete the project.

                    Answer: m   **Reference**: p. 167

149.   A process of identifying the financial benefits and costs associated with a development project.

                    Answer: c   **Reference**: p. 168

150.   The process of assessing the degree to which the potential time frame and completion dates for all major activities within a project meet organizational deadlines and constraints for affecting change.

                    Answer: l   **Reference**: p. 180

151.   The process of evaluating how key stakeholders within the organization view the proposed system.

                    Answer: i   **Reference**: p. 181

152.   The process of assessing the degree to which a proposed system solves business problems or takes advantage of business opportunities.

                    Answer: g   **Reference**: p. 180

153.   The process of assessing potential legal and contractual ramifications due to the construction of a system.

                    Answer: f   **Reference**: p. 180

154.   A process of assessing the development organization's ability to construct a proposed system.

                    Answer: p   **Reference**: p. 177

For each of the following walkthrough roles, match it with its description.

- a. coordinator
- b. maintenance oracle
- c. presenter
- d. secretary
- e. standards bearer
- f. user

155. This person reviews the work product in terms of future maintenance activities.

   Answer: b   **Reference:** p. 186

156. This person ensures that the work product adheres to organizational standards.

   Answer: e   **Reference:** p. 186

157. This person plans the meeting and facilitates a smooth meeting process.

   Answer: a   **Reference:** p. 186

158. This person describes the work product to the group.

   Answer: c   **Reference:** p. 186

159. This person ensures that the work product meets the needs of the project's customers.

   Answer: f   **Reference:** p. 186

160. This person takes notes and records decisions or recommendations made by the group.

   Answer: d   **Reference:** p. 186

Match each of the following feasibility criteria with its purpose.

    a. economic
    b. legal and contractual
    c. operational
    d. political
    e. schedule
    f. technical

161. To gain an understanding of the degree to which the proposed system will likely solve the business problems or take advantage of the opportunities outlined in the systems service request or project identification study.

          Answer: c   **Reference:** p. 180

162. To gain an understanding of the organization's ability to construct the proposed system.

          Answer: f   **Reference:** p. 177

163. To provide an understanding of any potential legal ramifications due to the construction of the system.

          Answer: b   **Reference:** p. 180

164. To evaluate how key stakeholders within the organization view the proposed system.

          Answer: d   **Reference:** p. 181

165. To provide an understanding of the likelihood that all potential time frames and completion date schedules can be met, and that meeting these dates will be sufficient for dealing with the needs of the organization.

          Answer: e   **Reference:** p. 180

166. To identify the financial benefits and costs associated with the development project.

          Answer: a   **Reference:** p. 168

Essay Questions

167. *Briefly identify and define the six major categories of feasibility.*

The six feasibility categories are economic, technical, operational, schedule, legal and contractual, and political. The specifics of a particular project will determine the emphasis placed on each of the feasibility criteria. Economic feasibility seeks to identify the financial benefits and costs associated with the project. Technical feasibility seeks to determine if the organization is capable of developing the new system. Operational feasibility examines the degree of likelihood that the candidate system will be able to solve the business problem or take advantage of opportunities. Schedule feasibility examines the likelihood that all potential time frame and completion date schedules can be met. Legal and contractual feasibility tries to assess the potential legal ramifications due to the construction of the new system. Determining stakeholder's views of the candidate system is the intent of political feasibility.

168. *Briefly identify three commonly used economic cost-benefit analysis techniques.*

Break-even analysis (BEA) is the process of finding the amount of time required for the cumulative cash flow from a project to equal its initial and ongoing investment. Net present value (NPV) uses a discount rate determined from the company's cost of capital to establish the present value of a project. Return on investment (ROI) is the ratio of the net cash receipts of the project divided by the cash outlays of the project. A tradeoff analysis can be made between competing projects.

169. *What is a Statement of Work and Baseline Project Plan? How are they different?*

The Baseline Project Plan and the Statement of Work are the major outcomes and deliverables for the project initiation and planning phase. All information collected and analyzed during this phase is contained in the BP. This plan reflects the best estimate of the project's scope, benefits, costs, risks, and resource requirements. It also specifies detailed project activities for the following phase and more general specifications for the remaining phases. The BPP can be used by the project selection committee to determine the project worth--accept, reject, or modify. The Statement of Work is a document prepared for the customer during project initiation and planning that describes what the project will deliver and outlines generally at a high level all work required to complete the project. The SOW consists of a high-level summary of the BP. While the actual role of the SOW can vary, the SOW can be used by the analyst and the customer to gain an understanding of the project.

170. *Describe the differences between tangible and intangible benefits and costs, and between one-time and recurring benefits and costs.*

A tangible benefit refers to a benefit derived from the creation of an information system that can be measured in dollars and with certainty. Examples include reduced personnel expenses, lower transaction costs, and higher profit margins. Intangible benefit refers to a benefit derived from the creation of an information system that cannot be easily measured in dollars or with certainty. Examples include competitive necessity, promotion of organizational learning and understanding, and improved asset utilization. While tangible costs are costs associated with an information system that can be measured in dollars and with certainty, intangible costs are costs associated with an information system that cannot be easily measured in terms of dollars or with certainty. Hardware costs, labor costs, and operational costs are tangible costs. Loss of customer goodwill, employee morale, and operational inefficiency are intangible costs. One-time costs are costs associated with project startup and development or system startup. This type of cost includes hardware and software purchases, user training, and site preparation. Recurring costs are costs resulting from the ongoing evolution and use of a system. New software and hardware leases, incremental communications, and incremental data storage expense are recurring costs.

171. *Briefly define walkthrough and describe the role of each participant.*

A walkthrough is a peer group review of any product created during the systems development process. During the review users, management, and the development group participate through various roles. These roles are coordinator, presenter, user, secretary, standards bearer, and maintenance oracle. The coordinator is the person who plans the meeting and facilitates a smooth meeting process. The presenter is the individual who describes the work product to the group. Ensuring that the work product meets the needs of the project's customers is the role fulfilled by the user. The person taking notes and recording decisions or recommendations made by the group is the secretary. The standards bearer role is to ensure that the work product adheres to organizational technical standards. The maintenance oracle is the individual who reviews the work product in terms of future maintenance activities.

172. *Assume a proposed system has a useful life of 5 years, one-time costs of $50,000, recurring costs of $25,000 per year, and tangible benefits of $45,000 per year. If the cost of capital is 10 percent, what is the overall NPV? Overall ROI? Break-even point?*

The overall NPV is $25,816; the overall ROI is .18, and break-even occurs in year 4.

173. *Assume a proposed system has a useful life of 5 years, one-time costs of $250,000, recurring costs of $80,000 per year, and tangible benefits of $175,000 per year. If the cost of capital is 12 percent, what is the overall NPV? Overall ROI? Break-even point?*

The overall NPV is $92,454; the overall ROI is .17, and break-even occurs in year 4.

174. *Assume a proposed system has a useful life of 5 years, one-time costs of $1,000,000, recurring costs of $250,000 per year, and tangible benefits of $750,000 per year. If the cost of capital is 10 percent, what is the overall NPV? Overall ROI? Break-even point?*

The overall NPV is $895,393; the overall ROI is .46, and break-even occurs in year 3.

175. *Assume a proposed system has a useful life of 5 years, one-time costs of $50,000, recurring costs of $25,000 per year ,and tangible benefits of $35,000 per year. If the cost of capital is 10 percent, what is the overall NPV? Overall ROI? Break-even point?*

The overall NPV is ($12,092), and the overall ROI is negative. Based on the information given, this project will not break-even during its useful life.

176. *Assume a proposed system has a useful life of 5 years, one-time costs of $1,000,000, recurring costs of $250,000 per year, and tangible benefits of $750,000 per year. If the cost of capital is 10 percent, what is the overall NPV? Overall ROI? Break-even point?*

The overall NPV is $895,393 and the overall ROI is .46. The project breaks even in year 3.

Chapter 7
Determining System Requirements

True-False Questions

1. Requirements determination, requirements structuring, and alternative generation and choice are the three parts to analysis.

    Answer: True   **Difficulty**: Med   **Reference**: p. 202

2. During requirements determination, information can be gathered from users of the current system, forms, reports, and procedures.

    Answer: True   **Difficulty**: Med   **Reference**: p. 204

3. Challenging yourself to look at the organization in new ways describes the impertinence characteristic that a systems analyst should exhibit during the requirements determination phase.

    Answer: False   **Difficulty**: Hard   **Reference**: p. 204

4. Assuming anything is possible and eliminating the infeasible describes the reframing characteristic that a systems analyst should exhibit during the requirements determination phase.

    Answer: False   **Difficulty**: Hard   **Reference**: p. 204

5. Finding the best solution to a business problem or opportunity describes the attention to details characteristic that a systems analyst should exhibit during the requirements determination phase.

    Answer: False   **Difficulty**: Hard   **Reference**: p. 204

6. Requirements creep is a term used to describe a project that has bogged down in an abundance of analysis work.

    Answer: False   **Difficulty**: Med   **Reference**: p. 205

7. Joint Application Design and prototyping can help keep the analysis effort at a minimum yet still effective.

    Answer: True   **Difficulty**: Med   **Reference**: p. 205

8. Collection of information is at the core of systems analysis.

    Answer: True   **Difficulty**: Easy   **Reference**: p. 205

9. Contrary to popular belief, interviewing is not one of the primary ways analysts gather information about an information systems project.

    Answer: False   **Difficulty**: Med   **Reference**: p. 206

10. In order to promote more truthful responses, the general nature of the interview should not be explained to the interviewee in advance.

    Answer: False   **Difficulty**: Med   **Reference**: p. 206

11. Neutrality is a guideline for effective interviewing.

    Answer: True   **Difficulty**: Med   **Reference**: p. 206

12. As a general guideline, you should prepare an agenda with approximate time limits for different sections of the interview.

    Answer: True   **Difficulty**: Med   **Reference**: p. 207

13. Unstructured questions are questions in interviews and on questionnaires that have no prespecified answers.

    Answer: False   **Difficulty**: Med   **Reference**: p. 208

14. Open-ended questions are usually used to probe for information when you cannot anticipate all possible responses or when you do not know the precise question to ask.

    Answer: True   **Difficulty**: Med   **Reference**: p. 208

15. Open-ended questions can put the interviewee at ease because she can respond in her own words using her own structure.

    Answer: True   **Difficulty**: Med   **Reference**: p. 208

16. Open-ended questions put the interviewee at ease, are easily summarized, and save time.

    Answer: False   **Difficulty**: Med   **Reference**: p. 208

17. Closed-ended questions work well when the major answers to the questions are known.

    Answer: True   **Difficulty**: Med   **Reference**: p. 208

18. A major disadvantage of closed-ended questions is that useful information that does not quite fit the defined answers may be overlooked as the respondent tries to make a choice instead of providing his or her best answer.

    Answer: True   **Difficulty**: Med   **Reference**: p. 209

19. Multiple choice, rating, and ranking are types of closed-ended questions.

    Answer: True   **Difficulty**: Easy   **Reference**: p. 209

20. You should use the interview process to set expectations about the new or replacement system.

    Answer: False   **Difficulty**: Med   **Reference**: p. 209

21. Compared to interviews, questionnaires are time-consuming and expensive to conduct.

    Answer: False   **Difficulty**: Med   **Reference**: p. 210

22. Random, stratified, classified, and concentrated are four methods for choosing questionnaire respondents.

    Answer: False   **Difficulty**: Med   **Reference**: p. 210

23. Using a stratified sample, you specify only the people who satisfy certain criteria, such as users of the system for less than one year.

    Answer: False   **Difficulty**: Hard   **Reference**: p. 210

24. Using a purposeful sample, you would obtain a list of all current system users, and choose every *nth* person on the list.

    Answer: False   **Difficulty**: Hard   **Reference**: p. 210

25. Nonresponse bias is a systematic bias in the results because those who responded are different from those who did not respond.

    Answer: True   **Difficulty**: Med   **Reference**: p. 210

26. In general, questionnaires take less time to complete than interviews structured to obtain the same information.

    Answer: True   **Difficulty**: Med   **Reference**: p. 210

27. When designing a questionnaire, open-ended questions are preferable to closed-ended questions because they are easier to complete.

    Answer: False   **Difficulty**: Med   **Reference**: p. 210

28. One of the primary advantages to questionnaires is that they provide a direct means by which to ask follow-up questions.

    Answer: False   **Difficulty**: Med   **Reference**: p. 211

29. Questionnaires are most useful in the requirements determination process when used for very specific purposes rather than for more general information gathering.

    Answer: True   **Difficulty**: Med   **Reference**: p. 212

30. When comparing interviews with questionnaires, the information richness of an interview would be rated as moderate to low.

    Answer: False   **Difficulty**: Med   **Reference**: p. 212

31. When comparing interviews with questionnaires, the time required for an interview would be rated as moderate.

    Answer: False   **Difficulty**: Hard   **Reference**: p. 212

32. Since observations are unbiased, they are preferable to other requirements determination techniques.

    Answer: False   **Difficulty**: Med   **Reference**: p. 215

33. While being observed, employees may follow exact procedures more carefully than they typically do.

    Answer: True   **Difficulty**: Easy   **Reference**: p. 215

34. When performing observations, it is best to select typical people and sites as opposed to atypical people and sites.

    Answer: False   **Difficulty**: Med   **Reference**: p. 215

35. In documents you can find information about the values of the organization or individuals who can help determine priorities for different capabilities desired by different users.

    Answer: True   **Difficulty**: Med   **Reference**: p. 216

36. In documents you can find information about special information processing circumstances that occur irregularly.

    Answer: True   **Difficulty**: Med   **Reference**: p. 216

37. As a systems analyst, it is part of your job to create a document for a missing work procedure.

    Answer: False   **Difficulty**: Med   **Reference**: p. 216

38. If you encounter contradictory information about procedures from interviews, questionnaires, or observations, you should reconcile the contradictions before proceeding to other analysis tasks.

    Answer: False   **Difficulty**: Hard   **Reference**: p. 217

39. Informal systems develop because of inadequacies of formal procedures, individual work habits and preferences, and resistance to control.

    Answer: True   **Difficulty**: Med   **Reference**: p. 218

40. When gathering system requirements, document analysis and observation are used the least.

    Answer: False   **Difficulty**: Med   **Reference**: p. 220

41. When comparing observations and document analysis, the expense of observations is rated moderate.

    Answer: False   **Difficulty**: Hard   **Reference**: p. 220

42. When comparing observations and document analysis, the chances for follow-up and probing with document analysis are rated high to excellent.

    Answer: False   **Difficulty**: Hard   **Reference**: p. 220

43. When comparing observations and document analysis, the time required for document analysis is rated as low to moderate.

    Answer: True   **Difficulty**: Hard   **Reference**: p. 220

44. The primary purpose of using JAD in the analysis phase is to collect systems requirements simultaneously from the key people involved with the system.

    Answer: True   **Difficulty**: Med   **Reference**: p. 221

45. A JAD is an inexpensive, popular requirements determination technique.

    Answer: False   **Difficulty**: Med   **Reference**: p. 221

46. Referencing a JAD session, the sponsor is the individual responsible for organizing and running a JAD session.

    Answer: False   **Difficulty**: Med   **Reference**: p. 222

47. A first step in any BPR effort is to understand what processes need to change.

    Answer: True   **Difficulty**: Med   **Reference**: p. 227

48. BPR efforts often result in the development of information systems maintenance requests or requests for systems maintenance.

    Answer: True   **Difficulty**: Med   **Reference**: p. 227

49. Disruptive technologies enable the breaking of long-held business rules that inhibit organizations from making radical business changes.

    Answer: True   **Difficulty**: Med   **Reference**: p. 228

50. Determining systems requirements for an Internet-based electronic commerce application is no different than the process followed for other applications.

    Answer: True   **Difficulty**: Med   **Reference**: p. 229

Multiple Choice Questions

51. The first sub-phase of analysis is:

    a. alternative generation and choice
    b. requirements structuring
    c. requirements determination
    d. project identification and selection

    Answer: c   **Difficulty**: Med   **Reference**: p. 202

52. The impertinence characteristic of a good systems analyst is represented by which of the following statements?

    a. You must challenge yourself to look at the organization in new ways.
    b. Every fact must fit with every other fact.
    c. Assume anything is possible, and eliminate the infeasible.
    d. You should question everything.

    Answer: d   **Difficulty**: Hard   **Reference**: p. 204

53. The reframing characteristic of a good systems analyst is represented by which of the following statements?

   a. You must challenge yourself to look at the organization in new ways.
   b. Every fact must fit with every other fact.
   c. Assume anything is possible, and eliminate the infeasible.
   d. You should question everything.

   Answer: a   **Difficulty**: Hard   **Reference**: p. 204

54. The impartiality characteristic of a good systems analyst is represented by which of the following statements?

   a. You must challenge yourself to look at the organization in new ways.
   b. Your role is to find the best solution to a business problem or opportunity.
   c. Assume anything is possible, and eliminate the infeasible.
   d. You should question everything.

   Answer: b   **Difficulty**: Hard   **Reference**: p. 204

55. The primary deliverables from requirements determination include:

   a. analyzed responses from questionnaires
   b. transcripts of interviews
   c. notes from observation and from analysis documents
   d. all of the above

   Answer: d   **Difficulty**: Easy   **Reference**: p. 204

56. The term used to refer to systems development projects bogged down in an abundance of analysis work is:

   a. information overload
   b. analysis paralysis
   c. analysis overload
   d. information abundance

   Answer: b   **Difficulty**: Med   **Reference**: p. 205

57. Techniques developed to keep the analysis effort minimal, yet still effective include:

   a. JAD
   b. interviewing
   c. observations
   d. quiz sessions

   Answer: a   **Difficulty**: Med   **Reference**: p. 205

58. Traditional methods of collecting systems requirements include:

    a. individually interview people
    b. survey people via questionnaires
    c. interview groups of people
    d. all of the above

    Answer: d   **Difficulty:** Easy   **Reference:** p. 206

59. Which of the following is a traditional method of collecting systems requirements?

    a. group support systems
    b. interview groups of people
    c. Joint Application Design
    d. Rapid Application Development

    Answer: b   **Difficulty:** Med   **Reference:** p. 206

60. Questions in interviews and on questionnaires that have no pre-specified answers are:

    a. nonspecific questions
    b. closed-ended questions
    c. open-ended questions
    d. investigative questions

    Answer: c   **Difficulty:** Med   **Reference:** p. 208

61. One advantage of open-ended questions in an interview is:

    a. a significant amount of time can be devoted to each interviewee
    b. the interviewee is restricted to providing just a few answers
    c. previously unknown information can result
    d. they work well when the answers to the questions are well known

    Answer: c   **Difficulty:** Med   **Reference:** p. 208

62. Questions in interviews and on questionnaires asking those responding to choose from among a set of specified responses are:

    a. specific questions
    b. closed-ended questions
    c. open-ended questions
    d. structured questions

    Answer: b   **Difficulty:** Med   **Reference:** p. 208

63. Which of the following is an advantage of closed-ended questions?

a. Interviews based on closed-ended questions do not necessarily require a large time commitment, so more topics can be covered.
b. Closed-ended questions enable the analysts to explore information that does not quite fit defined answers.
c. The analyst can obtain previously unknown information.
d. Closed-ended questions often put the interviewee at ease.

Answer: a   **Difficulty**: Med   **Reference**: p. 208

64. Rating a response or idea on some scale, say from strongly agree to strongly disagree, would be classified as a(n):

a. open-ended question
b. JAD question
c. closed-ended question
d. rating question

Answer: c   **Difficulty**: Med   **Reference**: p. 209

65. Good interview guidelines consist of:

a. phrasing the question to illicit the correct response
b. typing your notes within two weeks of the interview
c. establishing expectation levels about the new system
d. seeking a variety of perspectives from the interviews

Answer: d   **Difficulty**: Med   **Reference**: p. 209

66. A representative sample can be achieved by:

a. using a stratified sample
b. selecting those convenient to sample
c. using a random sample
d. all of the above

Answer: d   **Difficulty**: Med   **Reference**: p. 210

67. Having several categories of people to include in a sample and choosing a random set from each category is an example of a:

a. stratified sample
b. convenient sample
c. purposeful sample
d. random sample

Answer: a   **Difficulty**: Med   **Reference**: p. 210

68. Selecting only people who satisfy a certain criteria, such as users of the system for more than four years, is an example of a:

     a. stratified sample
     b. convenient sample
     c. purposeful sample
     d. random sample

     Answer: c   **Difficulty**: Med   **Reference**: p. 210

69. A nonresponse bias refers to:

     a. less than 25 percent of the questionnaires not being returned
     b. a systematic bias in the results since those who responded are different from those who did not respond
     c. no questionnaires being returned
     d. ensuring that questions are worded correctly

     Answer: b   **Difficulty**: Med   **Reference**: p. 210

70. Compared to interviews, questionnaires:

     a. take less time to complete
     b. provide you with the chance to judge the accuracy of the responses
     c. are richer in information content than interviews
     d. are administered to fewer people

     Answer: a   **Difficulty**: Med   **Reference**: p. 212

71. Compared to questionnaires, interviews:

     a. take less time to complete
     b. are quite time-intensive and expensive
     c. are less rich in information content than questionnaires
     d. can be used to collect information from large numbers of people

     Answer: b   **Difficulty**: Med   **Reference**: p. 212

72. Comparing interviews to questionnaires, which of the following is correct?

     a. Using a questionnaire enables the interviewer to identify the interviewee.
     b. The involvement of the subject via the questionnaire is very active.
     c. The potential audience of an interview can be quite large.
     d. The time required to administer a questionnaire is low to moderate.

     Answer: d   **Difficulty**: Med   **Reference**: p. 212

73. If you know little about the system or the organization, a good strategy would be to:

a. identify key users and stakeholders and interview them, then use this information to create a questionnaire that can be distributed to a large number of users
b. interview only one or two key users or stakeholders
c. administer a questionnaire to key stakeholders, and then interview all end users
d. administer a questionnaire to all end users, and then select the best responses to interview

Answer: a   **Difficulty**: Hard   **Reference**: p. 212

74. Interviewing several key people at once refers to:

a. stakeholder interviewing
b. group interviewing
c. user interviewing
d. strategic interviewing

Answer: b   **Difficulty**: Med   **Reference**: p. 213

75. Which of the following is a disadvantage to group interviewing?

a. Group interviewing does not effectively utilize your time.
b. Interviewing several people together allows them to hear the opinions of other key people.
c. Group interviewing requires significantly more time than does the JAD process.
d. Scheduling group interviews can be a problem.

Answer: d   **Difficulty**: Med   **Reference**: p. 213

76. A facilitated process that supports idea generation by groups where at the beginning of the process, group members work alone to generate ideas, which are then pooled under the guidance of a trained facilitator best describes:

a. affinity clustering
b. requirements structuring
c. group interviews
d. nominal group technique

Answer: d   **Difficulty**: Hard   **Reference**: p. 213

77. Which of the following is a reason for directly observing end users?

a. The analyst gets a snap-shot image of the person or task being observed.
b. Observations are not very time consuming.
c. People often do not have a completely accurate appreciation of what they do or how they do it.
d. Employees will alter their performance if they know that they are being observed.

Answer: c   **Difficulty**: Med   **Reference**: p. 214

78. Which of the following documents are useful in understanding possible future system requirements?

    a. written work procedures
    b. documents that describe the current information system
    c. reports generated by current systems
    d. all of the above

    Answer: d   **Difficulty**: Easy   **Reference**: p. 216

79. The analysis of documents can help you identify:

    a. problems with existing systems
    b. special information processing circumstances that occur irregularly and may not be identified by any other requirements
    c. the reason why current systems are designed the way they are
    d. all of the above

    Answer: d   **Difficulty**: Med   **Reference**: p. 216

80. A written work procedure:

    a. indicates the job an analyst will need to perform on a given project
    b. describes how a particular job or task is performed, including data and information that are used and created in the process of performing the job
    c. indicates what data flow in or out of a system and which are necessary for the system to function
    d. enables you to work backwards from the information on a report to the necessary data

    Answer: b   **Difficulty**: Med   **Reference**: p. 216

81. If your analysis of several written procedures reveals a duplication of effort in two jobs, you should:

    a. indicate that one job be deleted from the new system
    b. call the duplication to the attention of management as an issue to be resolved before system design can proceed
    c. justify the duplication of effort
    d. restructure the tasks so that the duplication is removed

    Answer: b   **Difficulty**: Med   **Reference**: p. 216

82. The official way a system works as described in organizational documentation is referred to as a(n):

    a. formal system
    b. informal system
    c. official system
    d. desired system

    Answer: a   **Difficulty**: Med   **Reference**: p. 218

83. The way a system actually works is referred to as a(n):

    a. unofficial system
    b. informal system
    c. actual system
    d. formal system

    Answer: b   **Difficulty**: Med   **Reference**: p. 218

84. Forms are important for understanding a business because they:

    a. indicate the correct sequencing of tasks
    b. describe how particular tasks are performed
    c. indicate what data flow in or out of a system and which are necessary for the system to function
    d. enable you to work backwards from the information on a report to the necessary data

    Answer: c   **Difficulty**: Med   **Reference**: p. 219

85. Forms are most useful:

    a. when they do not contain any data
    b. during the initial planning stages
    c. when they contain actual organizational data
    d. during the design stage

    Answer: c   **Difficulty**: Easy   **Reference**: p. 219

86. A report:

    a. indicates the inputs required for the new system
    b. describes how a particular job or task is performed, including data and information that are used and created in the process of performing the job
    c. indicates what data flow in or out of a system and which are necessary for the system to function
    d. enables you to work backwards from the information on a report to the data that must have been necessary to generate them

    Answer: d   **Difficulty**: Med   **Reference**: p. 219

87. When comparing observations and document analysis:

    a. the time required to conduct observations compared to document analysis is low
    b. the observee is not known to the interviewer
    c. the potential audience of the observation method is limited
    d. with document analysis, a clear commitment is discernible

    Answer: c   **Difficulty**: Hard   **Reference**: p. 220

88. Which of the following is not a modern method for collecting system requirements?

    a. interviewing
    b. group support systems
    c. CASE tools
    d. Joint Application Design

    Answer: a   **Difficulty**: Med   **Reference**: p. 220

89.   Which of the following is a true statement regarding JAD?

a.   The primary purpose of using JAD in the analysis phase is to collect systems requirements simultaneously from the key people involved with the system.
b.   JAD follows a particular structure of roles and agenda that are similar to the group interview.
c.   JAD sessions are usually conducted in the organization's conference room.
d.   A JAD session is inexpensive to conduct.

Answer: a   **Difficulty**: Med   **Reference**: p. 221

90.   The typical participants in a JAD include:

a.   a session leader
b.   a scribe
c.   a sponsor
d.   all of the above

Answer: d   **Difficulty**: Easy   **Reference**: p. 221

91.   The trained individual who plans and leads Joint Application Design sessions is referred to as the:

a.   scribe
b.   JAD session leader
c.   JAD manager
d.   JAD contributor

Answer: b   **Difficulty**: Med   **Reference**: p. 221

92.   The person who makes detailed notes of the happenings at a Joint Application Design session is referred to as the:

a.   JAD analyst
b.   scribe
c.   JAD manager
d.   JAD session leader

Answer: b   **Difficulty**: Med   **Reference**: p. 222

93.   The CASE tools most useful to the analyst during JAD are:

a.   lower CASE
b.   cross life cycle CASE
c.   upper CASE
d.   code generators

Answer: c   **Difficulty**: Med   **Reference**: p. 223

94.   Which of the following is a way that JAD can benefit from GSS?

a.   GSS-supported JADs tend to be more time-efficient than traditional JADs.
b.   Comments are more likely to be obtained from everyone.
c.   Important ideas are less likely to be missed.
d.   All of the above are correct.

Answer: d   **Difficulty**: Med   **Reference**: p. 225

95. Drawbacks to prototyping include:

    a. a tendency to avoid creating formal documentation of systems requirements which can then make the system more difficult to develop into a fully working system
    b. prototypes becoming very idiosyncratic to the initial user and difficult to diffuse or adapt to other potential users
    c. prototypes being built as stand-alone systems
    d. all of the above

Answer: d   **Difficulty**: Med   **Reference**: p. 226

96. Prototyping is most useful for requirements determination when:

    a. user requirements are well understood
    b. communication problems have existed in the past between users and analysts
    c. possible designs are simple and require an abstract form to fully evaluate
    d. multiple stakeholders are involved with the system

Answer: b   **Difficulty**: Med   **Reference**: p. 226

97. The search for, and implementation of, radical change in business processes to achieve breakthrough improvements in products and services best defines:

    a. Joint Application Design
    b. Rapid Application Development
    c. structured programming
    d. business process reengineering

Answer: d   **Difficulty**: Med   **Reference**: p. 226

98. The structured, measured set of activities designed to produce a specific output for a particular customer or market best defines:

    a. formal systems
    b. key business processes
    c. secondary activities
    d. production systems

Answer: b   **Difficulty**: Med   **Reference**: p. 227

99. Technologies that enable the breaking of long-held business rules that inhibit organizations from making radical business changes best defines:

    a. technology barriers
    b. business process reengineering
    c. disruptive technologies
    d. business constraints

Answer: c   **Difficulty**: Med   **Reference**: p. 228

100.   Which of the following technologies disrupted the business rule that information can appear only in one place at a time?

    a.   high-performance computing
    b.   distributed databases
    c.   expert systems
    d.   advanced telecommunications networks

Answer: b   **Difficulty**: Hard   **Reference**: p. 228

Fill In the Blanks

101.   During requirements determination, the systems analyst characteristic that says you should question everything is ***impertinence***.

                                          Difficulty: Med   **Reference**: p. 204

102.   During requirements determination, the systems analyst characteristic that says your role is to find the best solution to a business problem is ***impartiality***.

                                          Difficulty: Med   **Reference**: p. 204

103.   During requirements determination when you assume anything is possible and eliminate the infeasible, this corresponds to the systems analyst characteristic of ***relaxing of constraints***.

                                          Difficulty: Hard   **Reference**: p. 204

104.   During requirements determination when every fact must fit with every other fact, this corresponds to the systems analyst characteristic of ***attention to details***.

                                          Difficulty: Hard   **Reference**: p. 204

105.   During requirements determination, challenging yourself to look at the organization in new ways corresponds to the systems analyst characteristic of ***reframing***.

                                          Difficulty: Hard   **Reference**: p. 204

106.   General types of deliverables associated with requirements determination are ***information collected from conversations with users or observations of users***, ***existing written information***, and ***computer-based information***.

                                          Difficulty: Med   **Reference**: p. 205

107.   ***Analysis paralysis*** describes a project that has bogged down in an abundance of analysis work.

                                          Difficulty: Med   **Reference**: p. 205

108.   ***JAD*** and ***prototyping*** techniques were developed to keep the analysis effort to a minimum yet still effective.

                                          Difficulty: Med   **Reference**: p. 205

109. Traditional methods of collecting system requirements include ***interviews***, ***questionnaires***, ***observations***, and ***business documents***.

    Difficulty: Med   **Reference**: p. 206

110. ***Open-ended questions*** are questions in interviews and on questionnaires that have no prespecified answers.

    Difficulty: Med   **Reference**: p. 208

111. ***Open-ended questions*** are usually used to probe for information when you cannot anticipate all possible responses or when you do not know the precise questions to ask.

    Difficulty: Med   **Reference**: p. 208

112. ***Closed-ended questions*** are questions in interviews and on questionnaires that ask those responding to choose from among a set of specified responses.

    Difficulty: Med   **Reference**: p. 208

113. Referencing questionnaire respondent selection, a ***convenience sample*** selects individuals willing to be surveyed, or those most motivated to respond.

    Difficulty: Med   **Reference**: p. 210

114. Referencing questionnaire respondent selection, the ***random group*** method chooses every *nth* person on the list.

    Difficulty: Med   **Reference**: p. 210

115. Referencing questionnaire respondent selection, the ***purposeful sample*** method selects only people who satisfy certain criteria.

    Difficulty: Med   **Reference**: p. 210

116. Referencing questionnaire respondent selection, the ***stratified sample*** method chooses a random set from each category of people that you definitely want to include.

    Difficulty: Hard   **Reference**: p. 210

117. The ***Nominal Group Technique*** is a facilitated process that supports idea generation by groups; at the beginning of the process, group members work alone to generate ideas, which are then pooled under the guidance of a trained facilitator.

    Difficulty: Hard   **Reference**: p. 213

118. A ***formal system*** is the official way a system works as described in organizational documentation.

    Difficulty: Med   **Reference**: p. 218

119. An ***informal system*** is the way a system actually works.

    Difficulty: Med   **Reference**: p. 218

120. A ***JAD session leader*** is the trained individual who plans and leads Joint Application Design sessions.

Difficulty: Med   **Reference**: p. 221

121. A **_scribe_** is the person who makes detailed notes of the happenings at a Joint Application Design session.

Difficulty: Hard   **Reference**: p. 222

122. ***Prototyping*** is a repetitive process in which analysts and users build a rudimentary version of an information system based on user feedback.

Difficulty: Med   **Reference**: p. 225

123. ***Business process reengineering*** is the search for, and implementation of, radical change in business processes to achieve breakthrough improvements in products and services.

Difficulty: Med   **Reference**: p. 226

124. ***Key business processes*** are the structured, measured set of activities designed to produce a specific output for a particular customer or market.

Difficulty: Med   **Reference**: p. 227

125. ***Disruptive technologies*** are technologies that enable the breaking of long-held business rules that inhibit organizations from making radical business changes.

Difficulty: Hard   **Reference**: p. 228

Matching Questions

Match each of the following terms with its corresponding definition.

   a. business process reengineering
   b. closed-ended questions
   c. disruptive technologies
   d. formal system
   e. informal system
   f. JAD session leader
   g. key business processes
   h. open-ended questions
   i. scribe

126. Technologies that enable the breaking of long-held business rules that inhibit organizations from making radical business changes.

           Answer: c   **Reference:** p. 228

127. The person who makes detailed notes of the happenings at a Joint Application Design session.

           Answer: i   **Reference:** p. 222

128. The structured, measured set of activities designed to produce a specific output for a particular customer or market.

           Answer: g   **Reference:** p. 227

129. Questions in interviews and on questionnaires that ask those responding to choose from among a set of specified responses.

           Answer: b   **Reference:** p. 208

130. The search for, and implementation of, radical change in business processes to achieve breakthrough improvements in products and services.

           Answer: a   **Reference:** p. 226

131. The trained individual who plans and leads Joint Application Design sessions.

           Answer: f   **Reference:** p. 221

132. The way a system actually works.

           Answer: e   **Reference:** p. 218

133. The official way a system works as described in organizational documentation.

           Answer: d   **Reference:** p. 218

134. Questions in interviews and on questionnaires that have no prespecified answers.

           Answer: h   **Reference:** p. 208

For each of the following statements, answer "a" if it is characteristic of an interview, or answer "b" if it is characteristic of a questionnaire.

135.   In terms of information richness, it is regarded as high.

Answer: a   **Reference**:   p. 212

136.   In terms of confidentiality, the respondent can be unknown.

Answer: b   **Reference**:   p. 212

137.   In terms of potential audience, it has limited numbers, but complete responses.

Answer: a   **Reference**:   p. 212

138.   In terms of subject involvement, the respondent is passive, no clear commitment.

Answer: b   **Reference**:   p. 212

139.   In terms of expense, it can be high.

Answer: a   **Reference**:   p. 212

For each of the following statements, answer "a" if it is characteristic of an observation, or answer "b" if it is characteristic of document analysis.

140.   In terms of information richness, it is judged low (passive) and old.

Answer: b   **Reference**:   p. 220

141.   In terms of expense, it can be high.

Answer: a   **Reference**:   p. 220

142.   In terms of confidentiality, the individual is known.

Answer: a   **Reference**:   p. 220

143.   In terms of subject involvement, there is no clear commitment.

Answer: b   **Reference**:   p. 220

144.   In terms of potential audience, there are limited numbers and limited time (snap shot) of each.

Answer: a   **Reference**:   p. 220

Match each of the following typical JAD participants with its description.

      a. scribe
      b. systems analyst
      c. sponsor
      d. user
      e. JAD session leader
      f. manager
      g. IS staff

145.   This individual takes notes; a personal computer or laptop is usually used to take the notes.

           Answer: a   **Reference:** p. 222

146.   A person who is relatively high level in the company and usually attends only at the very beginning or the end of the session.

           Answer: c   **Reference:** p. 222

147.   This person organizes and runs the JAD, and has been trained in group management and facilitation, as well as in systems analysis.

           Answer: e   **Reference:** p. 221

148.   This individual is the only one who has a clear understanding of what it means to use the system on a daily basis.

           Answer: d   **Reference:** p. 221

149.   This individual is part of the development team; she attends the JAD session to learn from the users and managers.

           Answer: b   **Reference:** p. 222

150.   This individual provides insight into new organizational directions, motivations for and organizational impacts of systems, and support for requirements determined during the JAD.

           Answer: f   **Reference:** p. 221

151.   This individual may attend JAD to learn from the discussion and possibly to contribute ideas on the technical feasibility of ideas or on technical limitations of current systems.

           Answer: g   **Reference:** p. 222

For each of the following situations, answer "a" if prototyping would be useful or answer "b" if prototyping would not be useful.

152. User requirements are well understood.

Answer: b   **Reference:**   p. 226

153. A significant number of users or stakeholders are involved with the system.

Answer: b   **Reference:**   p. 226

154. Possible designs are complex and require concrete form to fully evaluate.

Answer: a   **Reference:**   p. 226

155. Communication problems have existed in the past between users and analysts, and both parties want to be sure that system requirements are as specific as possible.

Answer: a   **Reference:**   p. 226

156. Tools and data are readily available to build working systems rapidly.

Answer: a   **Reference:**   p. 226

Essay Questions

157. *Briefly identify several characteristics for a good systems analyst to have during requirements determination.*

Five characteristics that will come in handy during the requirements determination stage are impertinence, impartiality, relax constraints, attention to details, and reframing. Impertinence questions everything. Impartiality describes your quest to find the best solution to a business problem or opportunity. Assuming anything is possible, and eliminating the infeasible defines the third characteristic, relax constraints. By making sure that every fact fits with every other fact, the analyst is paying attention to details. Since analysis is a creative process, the analyst should challenge himself to look at the organization in new ways. This characteristic is referred to as reframing.

158. *Briefly identify the traditional methods for determining requirements.*

The traditional methods for collecting system requirements are interviews, questionnaires, observations, Nominal Group Technique, and document analysis.

159. *Briefly identify and describe the modern methods for determining requirements.*

Prototyping and JAD are two methods mentioned in the textbook. Prototyping is a repetitive process in which analysts and users build a rudimentary version of an information system based on user feedback. Joint Application Design is a structured process in which users, managers, and analysts work together for several days to specify or review system requirements.

160. *Briefly identify and discuss four types of documents that would be helpful in determining future system requirements.*

While any written document can provide insight into the future system requirements, four documents were specifically mentioned in the chapter. They are the written work procedure, business form, report, and current system documentation. The written work procedure describes how a particular job or task is performed and includes data and information requirements needed by the job. Business forms are important because they can demonstrate what data flow in or out of a system and which are necessary for the system to function. Reports are beneficial because they provide information about system output. The fourth type of documentation, current system documentation, refers to documents that describe the current information system. This type of documentation can provide insight concerning how the systems were built and how they work.

161. *Briefly identify and describe the participants of a JAD session.*

A JAD session consists of a JAD session leader, users, managers, sponsors, systems analysts, a scribe, and information systems staff. The JAD session leader is responsible for running the session. The scribe is the individual who takes notes during the session. Users are important because they understand the current system. Managers are needed to provide insight into new organizational directions, motivations, organizational impacts of systems, and support for requirements determined during the JAD. Since new systems cost money, high-level management support is demonstrated through the appearance of system sponsors. Attendance by these individuals is usually at the beginning or ending of the session. Systems analysts are present so they can learn from the users and managers. Information systems staff can contribute ideas to the process as well as learn from it.

162. *Define disruptive technologies. Identify eight disruptive technologies and how they have eliminated long-held organizational rules.*

Disruptive technologies enable the breaking of long-held business rules that inhibit organizations from making radical business changes. Distributed databases, expert systems, advanced telecommunications networks, decision-support tools, wireless data communication and portable computers, interactive communication technologies, automatic identification and tracking technologies, and high-performance computing are eight disruptive technologies. Distributed databases allow the sharing of information, and expert systems can aid nonexperts. Advanced telecommunications networks can support dynamic organizational structures; decision-support tools can aid nonmanagers. Wireless data communication and portable computers provide a "virtual" office for workers. Interactive communication technologies allow complex messaging capabilities. Automatic identification and tracking technology know where things are, and high-performance computing can provide real-time updating.

163. *Identify four drawbacks to using prototyping as a requirements determination tool.*

The four drawbacks mentioned in the textbook are: (1) a tendency to avoid creating formal documentation of system requirements; (2) prototypes become very idiosyncratic to the initial user and difficult to diffuse or adapt to other potential users; (3) prototypes are often built as stand-alone systems, often ignoring issues of sharing data, interactions with other existing systems, and scaling up applications; and (4) checks in the SDLC are bypassed so that some more subtle system requirements might be forgotten.

164. *Assume you are analyzing a golf course scheduling system. Identify two open-ended questions and two closed-ended questions you might ask.*

Open-ended questions might include the following: What information is currently provided by the scheduling system? What information would you like to have that the current scheduling system does not provide? Closed-ended questions might ask the system users to rate a response to the following questions: Does the existing system provide tee-scheduling information in a timely manner? Is the existing system easy to use?

165. *What is the Nominal Group Technique? How is it beneficial to requirements determination?*

The Nominal Group Technique is a facilitated process that supports idea generation by groups. At the beginning of the process, group members work alone to generate ideas, which are then pooled under the guidance of a trained facilitator. During requirements determination, the group will identify and prioritize a list of problems associated with the existing system, or they may identify and prioritize a list of requirements for the new system.

166. *How can a GSS benefit JAD?*

GSS alleviates many of the problems associated with a JAD. With JAD, individuals have limited time to state a particular view; an individual may dominate the discussion; individuals may fear personal criticism, and individuals may fear contradicting their boss. GSS are more time efficient and encourage equal participation from all individuals. Idea contribution is anonymous, thus alleviating the fear of criticism directed at the individual and fear of retribution.

Chapter 8
Structuring System Requirements: Process Modeling

True-False Questions

1. A data flow diagram is a graphical tool that allows analysts to illustrate the flow of data in an information system.

    Answer: True   **Difficulty**: Med   **Reference**: p. 238

2. Logic modeling graphically represents the processes that capture, manipulate, store, and distribute data between a system and its environment and among components within a system.

    Answer: False   **Difficulty**: Med   **Reference**: p. 239

3. Data flow diagramming is one of several structured analysis techniques used to increase software development productivity.

    Answer: True   **Difficulty**: Easy   **Reference**: p. 239

4. A primitive level data flow diagram is the first deliverable produced during requirements structuring.

    Answer: False   **Difficulty**: Med   **Reference**: p. 240

5. Data flow diagrams evolve from the more general to the more detailed as current and replacement systems are better understood.

    Answer: True   **Difficulty**: Med   **Reference**: p. 241

6. A data flow represents data in motion, moving from one place in the system to another.

    Answer: True   **Difficulty**: Med   **Reference**: p. 241

7. On a data flow diagram, a check and payment coupon are represented as a data store.

    Answer: False   **Difficulty**: Med   **Reference**: p. 241

8. A course schedule request is represented on a data flow diagram as a data flow.

    Answer: True   **Difficulty**: Med   **Reference**: p. 241

9. Assume shipment data is entered into a logbook once shipments are received at the company's warehouse; the logbook is represented on a data flow diagram as a sink.

    Answer: False   **Difficulty**: Med   **Reference**: p. 241

10. Assume your local veterinarian records information about each of his patients on patient medical history forms; the collection of medial history forms is represented on a data flow diagram as a data store.

    Answer: True   **Difficulty**: Hard   **Reference**: p. 241

11.   The calculation of a student's grade is represented on a data flow diagram as a data flow.

      Answer: False   **Difficulty**: Med   **Reference**: p. 242

12.   The determination of which items are low in stock is represented on a data flow diagram as a process.

      Answer: True   **Difficulty**: Med   **Reference**: p. 242

13.   Sources and sinks are internal to the system.

      Answer: False   **Difficulty**: Med   **Reference**: p. 242

14.   When constructing data flow diagrams, you should show the interactions that occur between sources and sinks.

      Answer: False   **Difficulty**: Med   **Reference**: p. 242

15.   The data a sink receives and often what data a source provides are fixed.

      Answer: True   **Difficulty**: Hard   **Reference**: p. 242

16.   A Web site's customer is represented as a source on a data flow diagram.

      Answer: True   **Difficulty**: Med   **Reference**: p. 242

17.   On a data flow diagram, an arrow represents an action, such as calculating an employee's pay.

      Answer: False   **Difficulty**: Med   **Reference**: p. 242

18.   On a data flow diagram, a diamond represents a process.

      Answer: False   **Difficulty**: Med   **Reference**: p. 242

19.   On a data flow diagram in the DeMarco and Yourdon model, two parallel lines represent a data store.

      Answer: True   **Difficulty**: Med   **Reference**: p. 243

20.   A context diagram shows the scope of the organizational system, system boundaries, external entities that interact with the system, and major information flows between entities and the system.

      Answer: True   **Difficulty**: Med   **Reference**: p. 243

21.   Context diagrams have only one process labeled "P-1."

      Answer: False   **Difficulty**: Med   **Reference**: p. 243

22.   Because the system's data stores are conceptually inside one process, no data stores appear on a context diagram.

      Answer: True   **Difficulty**: Med   **Reference**: p. 243

23.   A level-0 diagram is a data flow diagram that represents a system's major processes, data flows, and data stores at a high level of detail.

      Answer: True   **Difficulty**: Med   **Reference**: p. 245

24. Assume Process 7.4 produces a data flow and that Process 7.2 must be ready to accept it; we would say that these processes are physically linked to each other.

   Answer: False   **Difficulty**: Hard   **Reference**: p. 246

25. Assume we have placed a data store between Process 5.1 and Process 5.5; we would say that these processes are decoupled.

   Answer: True   **Difficulty**: Hard   **Reference**: p. 246

26. A data flow can go directly back to the same process it leaves.

   Answer: False   **Difficulty**: Med   **Reference**: p. 247

27. A fork in a data flow means that exactly the same data go from a common location to two or more different processes, data stores, or sources/sinks.

   Answer: True   **Difficulty**: Med   **Reference**: p. 247

28. A data flow to a data store means update.

   Answer: True   **Difficulty**: Easy   **Reference**: p. 247

29. Data cannot move directly from a source to a sink.

   Answer: True   **Difficulty**: Easy   **Reference**: p. 247

30. More than one data flow noun phrase can appear on a single arrow as long as all of the flows on the same arrow move together as one package.

   Answer: True   **Difficulty**: Med   **Reference**: p. 247

31. A process has a verb phrase label.

   Answer: True   **Difficulty**: Easy   **Reference**: p. 247

32. To keep a data flow diagram uncluttered, you may repeat data stores, sinks/sources, and processes.

   Answer: False   **Difficulty**: Med   **Reference**: p. 247

33. Double-ended arrows are used to represent data flowing in both directions.

   Answer: False   **Difficulty**: Med   **Reference**: p. 247

34. Because data flow names represent a specific set of data, another data flow that has even one more or one less piece of data must be given a different, unique name.

   Answer: True   **Difficulty**: Med   **Reference**: p. 247

35. Functional decomposition is a repetitive process of breaking the description or perspective of a system down into finer and finer detail.

   Answer: True   **Difficulty**: Med   **Reference**: p. 247

36. The lowest-level data flow diagrams are called level-0 diagrams.

     Answer: False   **Difficulty**: Med   **Reference**: p. 249

37. The decomposition of Process 1.1 is shown on a level-1 diagram.

     Answer: False   **Difficulty**: Hard   **Reference**: pp. 249-250

38. The decomposition of Process 2.4.3.4 is shown on a level-4 diagram.

     Answer: True   **Difficulty**: Hard   **Reference**: pp. 249-250

39. As a rule of thumb, no data flow diagram should have more than about seven processes on it, because the diagram would be too crowded and difficult to understand.

     Answer: True   **Difficulty**: Med   **Reference**: p. 250

40. Coupling is the conservation of inputs and outputs to a data flow diagram process when that process is decomposed to a lower level.

     Answer: False   **Difficulty**: Med   **Reference**: p. 251

41. A composite data flow on one level can be split into component data flows at the next level, but no new data can be added and all data in the composite must be accounted for in one or more subflows.

     Answer: True   **Difficulty**: Hard   **Reference**: p. 252

42. DFD cohesion means your DFDs include all of the necessary components for the system you are modeling.

     Answer: False   **Difficulty**: Med   **Reference**: p. 258

43. A data flow repository entry would include the composition or list of data elements contained in the data flow.

     Answer: True   **Difficulty**: Med   **Reference**: p. 262

44. A gross violation of DFD consistency would be a level-1 diagram with no level-0 diagram.

     Answer: True   **Difficulty**: Med   **Reference**: p. 262

45. Completeness, consistency, timing, iterative development, and primitive DFDs are guidelines for drawing DFDs.

     Answer: True   **Difficulty**: Med   **Reference**: p. 258

46. One of the primary purposes of a DFD is to represent time, giving a good indication of whether data flows occur constantly in real time, once a day, or once a year.

     Answer: False   **Difficulty**: Hard   **Reference**: p. 262

47. Structured analysis is the process of discovering discrepancies between two or more sets of data flow diagrams or discrepancies within a single DFD.

     Answer: False   **Difficulty**: Med   **Reference**: p. 263

48. To date, data flow diagrams have not been useful tools for modeling processes in business process reengineering.

    Answer: False   **Difficulty**: Med   **Reference**: p. 264

49. A functional hierarchy diagram is a picture of the various tasks performed in a business and how they are related to each other.

    Answer: True   **Difficulty**: Med   **Reference**: p. 268

50. Process modeling for Internet applications is not as important as it is for more traditional systems.

    Answer: False   **Difficulty**: Med   **Reference**: p. 271

Multiple Choice Questions

51. Data flow diagrams that concentrate on the movement of data between processes are referred to as:

    a. process models
    b. data models
    c. flow models
    d. flow charts

    Answer: a   **Difficulty**: Med   **Reference**: p. 238

52. Which of the following is not one of the four types of data flow diagrams?

    a. current physical
    b. current logical
    c. updated physical
    d. new physical

    Answer: c   **Difficulty**: Med   **Reference**: p. 239

53. Graphically representing the functions, or processes, which capture, manipulate, store, and distribute data between a system and its environment and between components within a system refers to:

    a. data modeling
    b. flow charting
    c. process modeling
    d. transition modeling

    Answer: c   **Difficulty**: Med   **Reference**: p. 239

54. Data flow diagrams that specify what people and technologies are used in which processes to move and transform data, accepting inputs and producing outputs are referred to as:

    a. logical data flow diagrams
    b. reference data flow diagrams
    c. current physical data flow diagrams
    d. logistic data flow diagrams

    Answer: c   **Difficulty**: Hard   **Reference**: p. 240

55. The diagram that shows the scope of the system, indicating what elements are inside and which are outside the system, is called a:

    a. context diagram
    b. level-2 diagram
    c. referencing diagram
    d. representative diagram

    Answer: a   **Difficulty**: Med   **Reference**: p. 240

56. Which of the following is not one of the primary deliverables resulting from studying and documenting a system's processes?

    a. context data flow diagram
    b. thorough descriptions of each DFD component
    c. DFDs of the current logical system
    d. state-transition diagram

    Answer: d   **Difficulty**: Med   **Reference**: p. 240

57. The deliverables of process modeling state:

    a. how you should develop the system during physical design
    b. what you learned during requirements determination
    c. how you should implement the new system during implementation
    d. what you learned during project planning

    Answer: b   **Difficulty**: Med   **Reference**: p. 240

58. Student data contained on an enrollment form is represented on a data flow diagram as a:

    a. process
    b. data flow
    c. source
    d. data store

    Answer: b   **Difficulty**: Med   **Reference**: p. 241

59. Data in motion, moving from one place in a system to another, defines:

    a. data store
    b. process
    c. source
    d. data flow

    Answer: d　　　　　**Difficulty**: Med　　　　　**Reference**: p. 241

60. Data at rest, which may take the form of many different physical representations, defines:

    a. source
    b. data store
    c. data flow
    d. process

    Answer: b　　　　　**Difficulty**: Med　　　　　**Reference**: p. 241

61. A file folder containing orders is represented on a data flow diagram as a:

    a. process
    b. source
    c. data flow
    d. data store

    Answer: d　　　　　**Difficulty**: Med　　　　　**Reference**: p. 241

62. A computer-based file containing employee information is represented on a data flow diagram as a:

    a. data flow
    b. source
    c. data store
    d. process

    Answer: c　　　　　**Difficulty**: Med　　　　　**Reference**: p. 241

63. Calculating an employee's salary is represented on a data flow diagram as a:

    a. data flow
    b. source
    c. data store
    d. process

    Answer: d　　　　　**Difficulty**: Med　　　　　**Reference**: p. 242

64. Recording a customer's payment is represented on a data flow diagram as a:

    a. process
    b. source
    c. data flow
    d. data store

    Answer: a　　　　　**Difficulty**: Med　　　　　**Reference**: p. 242

65.   A supplier of auto parts to our company is represented on a data flow diagram as a:

    a.   process
    b.   source
    c.   data flow
    d.   data store

Answer: b   **Difficulty**: Med   **Reference**: p. 242

66.   Which of the following is considered when diagramming?

    a.   the interactions occurring between sources and sinks
    b.   how to provide sources and sinks direct access to stored data
    c.   how to control or redesign a source or sink
    d.   none of the above

Answer: d   **Difficulty**: Med   **Reference**: p. 242

67.   The work or actions performed on data so that they are transformed, stored, or distributed defines:

    a.   source/sink
    b.   data store
    c.   data flow
    d.   process

Answer: d   **Difficulty**: Med   **Reference**: p. 242

68.   The origin and/or destination of data, sometimes referred to as external entities defines:

    a.   source/sink
    b.   data store
    c.   data flow
    d.   process

Answer: a   **Difficulty**: Med   **Reference**: p. 242

69.   An arrow on a data flow diagram represents a:

    a.   data store
    b.   data flow
    c.   process
    d.   source/sink

Answer: b   **Difficulty**: Med   **Reference**: p. 242

70.   A square on a data flow diagram represents a:

    a.   data store
    b.   data flow
    c.   process
    d.   source/sink

Answer: d   **Difficulty**: Med   **Reference**: p. 242

71. In the Gane and Sarson model, a rectangle with rounded corners on a data flow diagram represents a:

a. data store
b. data flow
c. process
d. source/sink

Answer: c   **Difficulty**: Med   **Reference**: p. 242

72. In the Gane and Sarson model, a rectangle that is missing its right vertical sides on a data flow diagram represents a:

a. data store
b. data flow
c. process
d. source/sink

Answer: a   **Difficulty**: Med   **Reference**: p. 242

73. Which of the following is a true statement regarding sources/sinks?

a. Sources/sinks are always outside the information system and define the boundaries of the system.
b. Data must originate outside a system from one or more sources.
c. The system must produce information to one or more sinks.
d. All of the above are true statements.

Answer: d   **Difficulty**: Hard   **Reference**: p. 243

74. A data flow diagram that represents a system's major processes, data flows, and data stores at a high level of detail refers to:

a. context diagram
b. level-1 diagram
c. level-0 diagram
d. level-00 diagram

Answer: c   **Difficulty**: Med   **Reference**: p. 245

75. If two processes are connected by a data flow, they are said to:

a. share the same timing effects
b. share the same data
c. be coupled to each other
d. be strapped to each other

Answer: c   **Difficulty**: Med   **Reference**: p. 246

76. By placing a data store between two processes, this:

a. decouples the processes
b. enables store and forward capabilities
c. enhances the flow of data between the processes
d. structures the processes

Answer: a   **Difficulty**: Med   **Reference**: p. 246

77.   A miracle process is one that:

    a.   has only inputs
    b.   has only outputs
    c.   cannot be exploded further
    d.   has insufficient inputs to produce the associated processes

    Answer: b   **Difficulty**: Hard   **Reference**: p. 247

78.   A black hole is one that:

    a.   has only inputs
    b.   has only outputs
    c.   has not been exploded to show enough detail
    d.   has insufficient inputs to produce the associated processes

    Answer: a   **Difficulty**: Med   **Reference**: p. 247

79.   Which of the following is a true statement regarding a data store?

    a.   Data can move directly from one data store to another data store.
    b.   Data can move directly from a sink to a data store.
    c.   A data store has a noun phrase label.
    d.   Data can move from an outside source to a data store.

    Answer: c   **Difficulty**: Med   **Reference**: p. 247

80.   Which of the following is a true statement regarding data flows?

    a.   A data flow may have multiple directions between symbols.
    b.   A data flow to a data store means retrieve or use.
    c.   A data flow from a data store means update.
    d.   A join in a data flow means that exactly the same data comes from any of two or more different processes, data stores, or sources/sinks to a common location.

    Answer: d   **Difficulty**: Hard   **Reference**: p. 247

81.   Which of the following is not a true statement regarding data flows?

    a.   A fork in a data flow means that exactly the same data goes from a common location to two or more different processes, data stores, or sources/sinks.
    b.   A data flow can go directly back to the same process it leaves.
    c.   A data flow has a noun phrase label.
    d.   A data flow has only one direction of flow between symbols.

    Answer: b   **Difficulty**: Hard   **Reference**: p. 247

82.   On a data flow diagram, you may:

    a.   repeat data stores
    b.   repeat sources/sinks
    c.   repeat processes
    d.   both a and b

    Answer: d   **Difficulty**: Med   **Reference**: p. 247

83. The act of going from a single system to several component processes refers to:

   a.   structuring
   b.   balancing
   c.   functional decomposition
   d.   formatting

   Answer: c   **Difficulty**: Med   **Reference**: p. 247

84. The lowest level of DFDs is called:

   a.   level-0 diagrams
   b.   context diagrams
   c.   level-1 diagrams
   d.   primitive data flow diagrams

   Answer: d   **Difficulty**: Med   **Reference**: p. 249

85. A DFD that is a result of three nested decompositions of a series of sub-processes from a process on a level-0 diagram defines a:

   a.   level-3 diagram
   b.   level-1 diagram
   c.   level-2 diagram
   d.   primitive diagram

   Answer: a   **Difficulty**: Hard   **Reference**: p. 249

86. The conservation of inputs and outputs to a data flow diagram process when that process is decomposed to a lower level defines:

   a.   decomposition
   b.   balancing
   c.   conservation
   d.   data flow structuring

   Answer: b   **Difficulty**: Med   **Reference**: p. 251

87. If a data flow appears on the context diagram and is also represented at level-0, this would be referred to as:

   a.   leveling
   b.   flow conservation
   c.   balancing
   d.   matching

   Answer: c   **Difficulty**: Med   **Reference**: p. 251

88. If an input from a source appears at level-0, it must:

    a. appear on the context diagram
    b. be connected to a data flow
    c. be connected to a sink
    d. be connect to a data store

    Answer: a   **Difficulty**: Med   **Reference**: p. 252

89. Which of the following is not an advanced rule governing data flow diagramming?

    a. To avoid having data flow lines cross each other, data stores may be repeated on a DFD.
    b. At the lowest level of DFDs, new data flows may be added to represent data that are transmitted under exceptional conditions.
    c. Composite data flows on one level cannot be split into component data flows at the next level.
    d. The inputs to a process must be sufficient to produce the outputs from the process.

    Answer: c   **Difficulty**: Hard   **Reference**: p. 252

90. The new logical model will differ from the current logical model by:

    a. identifying which system functions will be automated and which will be manual
    b. having additional functions, removing obsolete functions, and reorganizing inefficient flows
    c. including an identification of the "technology" used to process the data
    d. representing the physical implementation of the new system

    Answer: b   **Difficulty**: Med   **Reference**: p. 253

91. If your DFD contains data flows that do not lead anywhere, it is not:

    a. gap proof
    b. a primitive diagram
    c. complete
    d. consistent

    Answer: c   **Difficulty**: Hard   **Reference**: p. 258

92. The extent to which all necessary components of a data flow diagram have been included and fully described refers to:

    a. DFD consistency
    b. DFD completeness
    c. DFD gap proofing
    d. DFD flexibility

    Answer: b   **Difficulty**: Med   **Reference**: p. 258

93. Having a level-1 diagram with no level-0 diagram is an example of a:

    a. violation of completeness
    b. violation of consistency
    c. gap
    d. structuring violation

    Answer: b   **Difficulty**: Hard   **Reference**: p. 262

94. The extent to which information contained on one level of a set of nested data flow diagrams is also included on other levels refers to:

    a. DFD consistency
    b. DFD completeness
    c. DFD gap proofing
    d. DFD flexibility

    Answer: a   **Difficulty:** Med   **Reference:** p. 262

95. When you believe that you have shown each business form or transaction, computer screen, and report as a single data flow, you have probably reached the:

    a. level-0 diagrams
    b. level-1 diagrams
    c. primitive data flow diagrams
    d. level-3 diagrams

    Answer: c   **Difficulty:** Med   **Reference:** p. 263

96. The lowest level of decomposition for a data flow diagram is called the:

    a. context diagram
    b. level-0 diagram
    c. level-1 diagram
    d. primitive diagram

    Answer: d   **Difficulty:** Med   **Reference:** p. 263

97. The process in analysis in which the analyst tries to discover discrepancies between two or more sets of data flow diagrams, representing two or more states of an information system, or discrepancies within a single DFD, is referred to as:

    a. double checking
    b. sequencing
    c. referencing
    d. gap analysis

    Answer: d   **Difficulty:** Hard   **Reference:** p. 263

98. Which of the following is best described as a picture of the various tasks performed in a business and how there are related to each other, breaking the tasks into their various parts, and all the parts are shown in the same representation?

    a. structure chart
    b. decision table
    c. data flow diagram
    d. functional hierarchy diagram

    Answer: d   **Difficulty:** Hard   **Reference:** p. 268

99. When comparing Oracle's process models with data flow diagrams, which of the following is a true statement?

a. Oracle's process models contain detailed information about data in flow or in store.
b. Data flow diagrams do not have a numerical process hierarchy.
c. Data flow diagrams include animation, time and external calls.
d. Oracle's process models can be animated with time parameters.

Answer: d   **Difficulty**: Hard   **Reference**: p. 268

100. Referencing functional hierarchy diagrams, which of the following indicates that a display can be expanded?

a. a red pound sign in a orange diamond
b. a black plus sign in a blue diamond
c. a black plus sign in a red circle
d. a minus sign in a red circle

Answer: c   **Difficulty**: Hard   **Reference**: p. 269

Fill In the Blanks

101. ***Process modeling*** graphically represents the processes that capture, manipulate, store, and distribute data between a system and its environment and among components within a system.

Difficulty: Med   **Reference**: p. 239

102. A ***data flow diagram*** is a graphic that illustrates the movement of data between external entities and the processes and data stores within a system.

Difficulty: Med   **Reference**: p. 239

103. A ***data store*** represents data at rest, which may take the form of many different physical representations.

Difficulty: Easy   **Reference**: p. 241

104. On a data flow diagram, supplier information kept in a notebook is represented as a ***data store***.

Difficulty: Med   **Reference**: p. 241

105. ***Processes*** are the works or actions performed on data so that they are transformed, stored, or distributed.

Difficulty: Med   **Reference**: p. 242

106. Determining an employee's schedule is an example of a ***process***.

Difficulty: Med   **Reference**: p. 242

107.　*Source/sink* is the origin and/or destination of data.

Difficulty: Med　　　　　　　　　**Reference**: p. 242

108.　An *arrow* represents a data flow.

Difficulty: Easy　　　　　　　　**Reference**: p. 242

109.　In the DeMarco and Yourdon model, the symbol for a process is a *circle*.

Difficulty: Easy　　　　　　　　**Reference**: p. 242

110.　In the DeMarco and Yourdon model, the symbol for a data store is *two parallel lines*.

Difficulty: Med　　　　　　　　　**Reference**: p. 242

111.　The symbol for sources/sinks is a *square*.

Difficulty: Med　　　　　　　　　**Reference**: p. 242

112.　A *context diagram* is a data flow diagram of the scope of an organizational system that shows the system boundaries, external entities that interact with a system, and the major information flows between entities and the system.

Difficulty: Hard　　　　　　　　**Reference**: p. 243

113.　A *level-0 diagram* is a data flow diagram that represents a system's major processes, data flows, and data stores at a high level of detail.

Difficulty: Hard　　　　　　　　**Reference**: p. 245

114.　*Functional decomposition* is a repetitive process of breaking the description or perspective of a system down into finer and finer detail.

Difficulty: Hard　　　　　　　　**Reference**: p. 247

115.　A *level-n diagram* is a DFD that is the result of *n* nested decomposition of a series of subprocesses from a process on a level-0 diagram.

Difficulty: Hard　　　　　　　　**Reference**: p. 249

116.　*Balancing* is the conservation of inputs and outputs to a data flow diagram process when that process is decomposed to a lower level.

Difficulty: Med　　　　　　　　　**Reference**: p. 251

117.　*DFD completeness* is the extent to which all necessary components of a data flow diagram have been included and fully described.

Difficulty: Hard　　　　　　　　**Reference**: p. 258

118.　If your DFD contains data flows that do not lead anywhere, then your DFD violates the *DFD completeness* guideline.

Difficulty: Med　　　　　　　　　**Reference**: p. 258

119.   The five guidelines for drawing DFDs include ***completeness***, ***consistency***, ***timing considerations***, the
        iterative nature of drawing DFDs, and ***drawing primitive DFDs***.

                              Difficulty: Hard   **Reference**: p. 258

120.   ***DFD consistency*** is the extent to which information contained on one level of a set of nested data flow
        diagrams is also included on other levels.

                              Difficulty: Hard   **Reference**: p. 262

121.   If a data flow appears on a higher level DFD but not on lower levels, this situation violates the ***DFD
        consistency*** guideline.

                              Difficulty: Med   **Reference**: p. 262

122.   A ***primitive DFD*** is the lowest level of decomposition for a data flow diagram.

                              Difficulty: Med   **Reference**: p. 263

123.   ***Gap analysis*** is the process of discovering discrepancies between two or more sets of data flow
        diagrams or discrepancies within a single DFD.

                              Difficulty: Hard   **Reference**: p. 263

124.   ***Data flow diagramming***, ***process modeler***, and ***functional hierarchy modeling*** are three types of
        process modeling.

                              Difficulty: Hard   **Reference**: p. 266

125.   A ***functional hierarchy diagram*** is a picture of the various tasks performed in a business and how
        they are related to each other; these tasks are broken down into their various parts, and all the parts are
        shown in the same representation.

                              Difficulty: Hard   **Reference**: p. 268

Matching Questions

Match each of the following terms with its description.

a. source/sink
b. level-0 diagram
c. data flow
d. data store
e. balancing
f. DFD completeness
g. DFD consistency
h. level-*n* diagram
i. primitive DFD
j. process
k. gap analysis

126. Data in motion, moving from one place in a system to another.

    Answer: c   **Reference**: p. 241

127. A data flow diagram that represents a system's major processes, data flows, and data stores at a high level of detail.

    Answer: b   **Reference**: p. 245

128. The conservation of inputs and outputs to a data flow diagram process when that process is decomposed to a lower level.

    Answer: e   **Reference**: p. 251

129. The origin and/or destination of data, sometimes referred to as external entities.

    Answer: a   **Reference**: p. 242

130. The extent to which all necessary components of a data flow diagram have been included and fully described.

    Answer: f   **Reference**: p. 258

131. The work or actions performed on data so that they are transformed, stored, or distributed.

    Answer: j   **Reference**: p. 242

132. The extent to which information contained on one level of a set of nested data flow diagrams is also included on other levels.

    Answer: g   **Reference**: p. 262

133. The process of discovering discrepancies between two or more sets of data flow diagrams or discrepancies within a single DFD.

    Answer: k   **Reference**: p. 263

134.   Data at rest, which may take the form of many different physical representations.

                            Answer: d   **Reference**: p. 241

135.   The lowest level of decomposition for a data flow diagram.

                            Answer: i   **Reference**: p. 263

136.   A DFD that is the result of *n* nested decompositions of a series of subprocesses from a process on a level-0 diagram.

                            Answer: h   **Reference**: p. 249

Match each of the data flow diagramming symbols with corresponding examples. (Answers may occur more than once.)

    a.   process
    b.   data flow
    c.   source/sink
    d.   data store

137.   Customer order form

                              Answer: b   **Reference**: p. 241

138.   Customer

                              Answer: c   **Reference**: p. 242

139.   Generate paycheck

                              Answer: a   **Reference**: p. 242

140.   Calculating overtime pay

                              Answer: a   **Reference**: p. 242

141.   Sales report

                              Answer: b   **Reference**: p. 241

142.   Computing a grade point average

                              Answer: a   **Reference**: p. 242

143.   Preparing a purchase order

                              Answer: a   **Reference**: p. 242

144.   Teller

                              Answer: c   **Reference**: p. 242

145.   Student enrollment file

Answer: d   **Reference:** p. 241

146.   Supplier

Answer: c   **Reference:** p. 242

For each of the following statements, answer "a" if the statement is a true data flow diagramming rule, and answer "b" if the rule is false.

147.   Data can move directly from one data store to another data store.

Answer: b   **Reference:** p. 247

148.   A process has a noun phrase label.

Answer: b   **Reference:** p. 247

149.   Objects on a DFD have unique names.

Answer: a   **Reference:** p. 247

150.   A data flow to a data store means update.

Answer: a   **Reference:** p. 247

151.   Data can move directly from an outside source to a data store.

Answer: b   **Reference:** p. 247

152.   A data store has a verb phrase label.

Answer: b   **Reference:** p. 247

153.   A data flow is bi-directional between symbols.

Answer: b   **Reference:** p. 247

154.   A join in a data flow means that exactly the same data comes from any of two or more different processes, data stores, or sources/sinks to a common location.

Answer: a   **Reference:** p. 247

155.   The inputs to a process are different from the outputs of that process.

Answer: a   **Reference:** p. 246

156.   A process can have only inputs.

Answer: b   **Reference:** p. 247

For each of the following statements, answer "a" if the statement is a true data flow diagramming rule, and answer "b" if the rule is false.

157.   Data cannot move directly to an outside sink from a data store.

Answer: a   Reference: p. 247

158.   A data flow has a verb phrase label.

Answer: b   Reference: p. 247

159.   A data flow cannot go directly back to the same process it leaves.

Answer: a   Reference: p. 247

160.   A source/sink has a noun phrase label.

Answer: a   Reference: p. 247

161.   A fork in a data flow means that exactly the same data goes from a common location to two or more different processes, data stores, or sources/sinks.

Answer: a   Reference: p. 247

162.   Data can move directly from a source to a sink.

Answer: b   Reference: p. 247

163.   A data flow from a data store means retrieve or use.

Answer: a   Reference: p. 247

164.   There must be at least one other process that handles the data flow, produces some other data flow, and returns the original data flow to the beginning process.

Answer: a   Reference: p. 247

165.   A process must have both inputs and outputs.

Answer: a   Reference: p. 247

Match each of the following terms with its description.

a. gap analysis
b. functional decomposition
c. process modeling
d. balancing
e. DFD completeness
f. functional hierarchy diagram

166. Graphically representing the functions that capture, manipulate, store, and distribute data between a system and its environment and between components within a system.

Answer: c   **Reference**: p. 239

167. Breaking a larger system into smaller subsystems or processes.

Answer: b   **Reference**: p. 247

168. A picture of the various tasks performed in a business and how they are related to each other; the tasks are broken down into their various parts, and all the parts are shown in the same representation.

Answer: f   **Reference**: p. 268

169. Using data flow diagrams to discover discrepancies between two or more sets of data flow diagrams, representing two or more states of an information system, or discrepancies within a single DFD.

Answer: a   **Reference**: p. 263

170. The extent to which all necessary components of a data flow diagram have been included and fully described.

Answer: e   **Reference**: p. 258

171. The conservation of inputs and outputs to a data flow diagram process when that process is decomposed to a lower level.

Answer: d   **Reference**: p. 251

Essay Questions

172. *Briefly describe the data flow diagramming symbols. Provide one example of each.*

A process is the work or action performed on data, and is represented by a circle. A data store represents data at rest, and is represented by two parallel lines. A data flow represents data in motion, and is represented by an arrow. A source/sink is the origin or destination of data. Sources and sinks are identified by square symbols. Computing a grade point average is an example of a process. A file folder containing orders is an example of a data store. An enrollment form being routed through the enrollment center is representative of a data flow. A student enrolling in school is representative of a source/sink.

173. *Discuss the guidelines for drawing a DFD.*

The guidelines for constructing DFDs are completeness, consistency, timing considerations, the iterative nature of drawing DFDs, and drawing primitive DFDs. Completeness refers to the extent to which all necessary components of a data flow diagram have been included and fully described. Consistency refers to the extent to which information contained on one level of a set of nested data flow diagrams is also included on other levels. Timing is not indicated on DFDs. Iterative development recognizes that requirements determination and requirements structuring are interacting analysis subphases. Primitive DFDs are the lowest level of decomposition for a data flow diagram. The analyst must make a determination of when he/she has reached the primitive level DFDs.

174. *Briefly discuss how DFDs can be used as analysis tools.*

Data flow diagrams are used to model both the physical and logical systems. Data models are analyzed to identify possible inconsistencies that exist between two sets of diagrams or within a single DFD. Redundant data flows, procedural redundancies, and inefficiencies are identified by studying data flow diagrams.

175. *What is meant by DFD completeness? What is meant by DFD consistency?*

DFD completeness is the extent to which all necessary components of a data flow diagram have been included and fully described. DFD consistency is the extent to which information contained on one level of a set of nested data flow diagrams is also included on other levels.

176. *What is gap analysis? Why is gap analysis useful?*

Gap analysis is the process of discovering discrepancies between two or more sets of data flow diagrams or discrepancies within a single DFD. Gap analysis is used to identify inconsistencies with DFDs, determine which processes should be added or revised, and compare alternative logical DFDs.

177. *What is process modeling? Identify three types of process models.*

Process modeling involves graphically representing the functions that capture, transform, store, and distribute data. Data flow diagramming, functional hierarchy modeling, and Oracle's process modeler are three types of process models.

178. *Identify seven features of Oracle's process models.*

Oracle's process models illustrate processes, flows, organizational units, but not external units; show unit ownership of processes, data flows, and data stores; do not provide detail of data in flow or store; do not show numerical hierarchy; show external triggers; can be animated with time parameters and run programs; are most useful in strategy and pre-analysis phases of the life cycle.

179. *Identify six concrete rules for stopping the decomposition process.*

The rules include: (1) when you have reduced each process to a single decision or calculation or to a single database operation; (2) when each data store represents data about a single entity; (3) when the system user does not care to see any more detail or when you and other analysts have documented sufficient detail to do subsequent systems development tasks; (4) when every data flow does not need to be split further to show that different data are handled in different ways; (5) when you believe that you have shown each business form or transaction, computer on-line display, and report as a single data flow; and (6) when you believe there is a separate process for each choice on all lowest-level menu options for the system.

180. *Identify the deliverables for process modeling.*

The deliverables include a context data flow diagram, DFDs for the current physical system, DFDs for the current logical system, DFDs for the proposed logical system, and thorough descriptions of each DFD component.

181. *For the following situation, draw a context-level diagram and a level-0 data flow diagram. Kellogg State Bank provides car and home loans to its banking customers. Initially, a potential loan customer meets with a Kellogg loan officer, requests a loan for a certain amount and time frame, and completes a loan application. Next, the loan officer determines the customer's credit standing, the type of loan required, and available interest rates. While the loan officer can authorize car loans for credit worthy customers, a loan committee must approve all home loans.*

A suggested context-level data flow diagram is provided below.

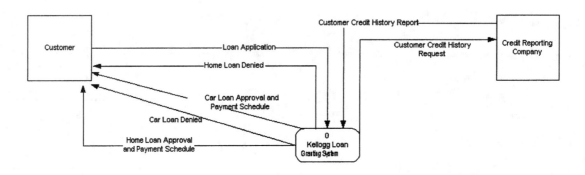

A suggested level-0 data flow diagram is provided below.

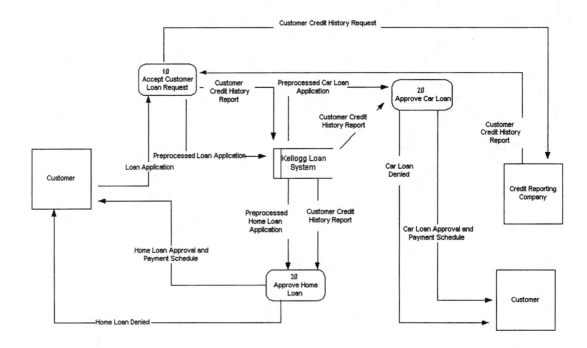

Chapter 9
Structuring System Requirements: Logic Modeling

True-False Questions

1. Data flow diagrams are designed to show the detailed logic of processes.

    Answer: False   **Difficulty**: Med   **Reference**: p. 282

2. Structured English is useful for representing the logic in information system processes.

    Answer: True   **Difficulty**: Easy   **Reference**: p. 282

3. Structured English represents the three fundamental structured programming statements: choice, repetition, and sequence.

    Answer: True   **Difficulty**: Med   **Reference**: p. 282

4. Reference, linking, and selection programming statements are represented in Structured English.

    Answer: False   **Difficulty**: Med   **Reference**: p. 282

5. Decision tables allow you to represent a set of conditions and the actions that follow from them in a tabular format.

    Answer: True   **Difficulty**: Med   **Reference**: p. 282

6. Data flow diagrams are adequate for modeling all of the complexity of an information system.

    Answer: False   **Difficulty**: Med   **Reference**: p. 283

7. Data flow diagrams are not adequate for modeling all of the complexity of an information system.

    Answer: True   **Difficulty**: Med   **Reference**: p. 283

8. Logic modeling represents the internal structure and functionality of the processes represented on data flow diagrams.

    Answer: True   **Difficulty**: Med   **Reference**: p. 283

9. In the analysis phase, logic modeling reflects the structure or syntax of a particular programming language.

    Answer: False   **Difficulty**: Hard   **Reference**: p. 283

10. Logic modeling is an activity associated with requirements structuring.

    Answer: True   **Difficulty**: Easy   **Reference**: p. 283

11. Although logic modeling represents a process's structure, it cannot represent the temporal dimensions of systems.

    Answer: False   **Difficulty**: Hard   **Reference**: p. 283

12. In structured analysis, the primary deliverables of logic modeling are structured descriptions and diagrams that outline the logic contained within each DFD process as well as diagrams that show the temporal dimensions of systems.

    Answer: True   **Difficulty**: Hard   **Reference**: p. 283

13. Logic modeling deliverables may take the form of new entries into the project dictionary.

    Answer: True   **Difficulty**: Med   **Reference**: p. 283

14. For each primitive process, the analyst should develop Structured English, decision table, and decision tree representations.

    Answer: False   **Difficulty**: Med   **Reference**: p. 283

15. State transition diagrams, sequence diagrams, and activity diagrams are types of logic models.

    Answer: True   **Difficulty**: Med   **Reference**: p. 285

16. Structured English is a process modeling technique.

    Answer: False   **Difficulty**: Easy   **Reference**: p. 285

17. Structured English is a modified form of the English language used to specify the logic of information system processes.

    Answer: True   **Difficulty**: Med   **Reference**: p. 285

18. The Unified Modeling Language is a modified form of the English language used to specify the logic of information system processes.

    Answer: False   **Difficulty**: Med   **Reference**: p. 285

19. Structured English relies heavily on adjectives and adverbs.

    Answer: False   **Difficulty**: Med   **Reference**: p. 285

20. The standard version of Structured English is called the Unified Modeling Language.

    Answer: False   **Difficulty**: Med   **Reference**: p. 285

21. If and case are two types of conditional statements.

    Answer: True   **Difficulty**: Easy   **Reference**: p. 285

22. Referencing Structured English, terms that specify logical comparisons are spelled out rather than represented by their arithmetic symbols.

    Answer: True   **Difficulty**: Med   **Reference**: p. 287

23. When preparing Structured English statements, the analyst includes statements to initialize variables, open and close files, and find related records in separate files.

    Answer: False   **Difficulty**: Hard   **Reference**: p. 288

24. Structured English resembles a programming language.

    Answer: False   **Difficulty**: Med   **Reference**: p. 288

25. Structured English is a communication technique used for analysts and programmers.

    Answer: False   **Difficulty**: Med   **Reference**: p. 288

26. Structured English becomes more difficult to understand and verify as logic becomes more complicated.

    Answer: True   **Difficulty**: Med   **Reference**: p. 288

27. A decision table is a matrix representation of the logic of a decision, which specifies the possible conditions for the decision and the resulting actions.

    Answer: True   **Difficulty**: Med   **Reference**: p. 288

28. Condition stubs are that part of a decision table that lists the actions that result for a given set of conditions.

    Answer: False   **Difficulty**: Med   **Reference**: p. 288

29. Action stubs are that part of a decision table that lists the conditions relevant to the decision.

    Answer: False   **Difficulty**: Med   **Reference**: p. 288

30. Referencing a decision table, specific combinations of conditions trigger specific actions.

    Answer: True   **Difficulty**: Med   **Reference**: p. 288

31. Assume condition one has three values, condition two has four values, and condition three has two values; the number of rules required for the decision table is nine.

    Answer: False   **Difficulty**: Med   **Reference**: pp. 288-289

32. Assume condition one has two values, condition two has five values, condition three has three values, and condition four has two values; the number of rules required for the decision table is sixty.

    Answer: True   **Difficulty**: Hard   **Reference**: pp. 288-289

33. Rules are that part of the decision table that specify which actions are to be followed for a given set of conditions.

    Answer: True   **Difficulty**: Med   **Reference**: p. 288

34. An insignificant condition is a condition in a decision table whose value does not affect which actions are taken for two or more rules.

    Answer: False   **Difficulty**: Med   **Reference**: p. 289

35. In a decision table, an indifferent condition is represented by an asterisk.

     Answer: False   **Difficulty**: Med   **Reference**: p. 289

36. If the different values for the employee type condition do not affect the action taken, then employee type is an indifferent condition.

     Answer: True   **Difficulty**: Hard   **Reference**: p. 289

37. Referencing a decision table, a limited entry occurs when a condition has only two possible values.

     Answer: True   **Difficulty**: Med   **Reference**: p. 289

38. Referencing a decision table, an employee condition that has only two possible values is considered a limited entry.

     Answer: True   **Difficulty**: Med   **Reference**: p. 289

39. If an inventory item is either perishable or nonperishable, its condition is classified as an extended entry.

     Answer: False   **Difficulty**: Med   **Reference**: p. 289

40. Referencing a decision table, every possible combination of conditions must be represented.

     Answer: True   **Difficulty**: Med   **Reference**: p. 289

41. Referencing a decision table, an action is provided for each rule.

     Answer: True   **Difficulty**: Med   **Reference**: p. 290

42. Decision tables support nested conditions.

     Answer: True   **Difficulty**: Med   **Reference**: p. 290

43. Decision tables are more useful than Structured English for complicated logic.

     Answer: True   **Difficulty**: Med   **Reference**: p. 291

44. An analyst can check a decision table to determine the extent to which the logic is complete, consistent, and not redundant.

     Answer: True   **Difficulty**: Med   **Reference**: p. 291

45. On a decision tree, ovals represent decision points.

     Answer: False   **Difficulty**: Med   **Reference**: p. 292

46. On a decision tree, a credit granting decision is represented by an oval.

     Answer: False   **Difficulty**: Med   **Reference**: p. 292

47. On a decision tree, the root node is placed on the far right.

     Answer: False   **Difficulty**: Med   **Reference**: p. 292

48. From each node on a decision tree, there are at least two paths that lead to the next step.

    Answer: True   **Difficulty**: Med   **Reference**: p. 292

49. On a decision tree, a rule is represented by tracing a series of paths from the root node, down a path to the next node until an action oval is reached.

    Answer: True   **Difficulty**: Med   **Reference**: p. 292

50. When comparing decision tables with decision trees, decision trees are better for portraying complex logic.

    Answer: False   **Difficulty**: Med   **Reference**: p. 294

Multiple Choice Questions

51. Which of the following is not a logic model?

    a. Structured English
    b. decision tables
    c. decision trees
    d. data flow diagrams

    Answer: d   **Difficulty**: Med   **Reference**: p. 284

52. Which of the following is a modified version of the English language that is useful for representing the logic in information system processes?

    a. Structured English
    b. COBOL
    c. Unified Modeling Language
    d. pseudocode

    Answer: a   **Difficulty**: Med   **Reference**: p. 282

53. A modeling technique that allows you to represent a set of conditions and the actions that follow from them in a tabular format best describes:

    a. data flow diagram
    b. decision table
    c. decision tree
    d. Structured English

    Answer: b   **Difficulty**: Med   **Reference**: p. 282

54. Techniques used for modeling process decision logic include:

    a. decision trees
    b. decision tables
    c. Structured English
    d. all of the above

    Answer: d   **Difficulty**: Med   **Reference**: p. 284

55. In the analysis phase, logic modeling:

    a. will be complete and reasonably detailed, but it will also be generic in that it will not reflect the structure or syntax of a particular programming language
    b. should not be complete and detailed; it will be generic in that it will not reflect the structure or syntax of a particular programming language
    c. should be complete and detailed, reflecting the structure and syntax of a particular programming language
    d. should be complete and reflect the physical aspects of the system

    Answer: a   **Difficulty**: Hard   **Reference**: p. 283

56. Modeling a system's logic is part of:

    a. requirements determination
    b. requirements structuring
    c. alternative generation and selection
    d. logical design

    Answer: b   **Difficulty**: Med   **Reference**: p. 283

57. The deliverables for logic modeling include:

    a. a Structured English representation of process logic
    b. state-transition diagrams
    c. decision tree representations
    d. all of the above

    Answer: d   **Difficulty**: Med   **Reference**: p. 284

58. The deliverables for logic modeling would not include:

    a. decision table representations
    b. structure charts
    c. Structured English representations of process logic
    d. decision tree representations

    Answer: b   **Difficulty**: Med   **Reference**: p. 284

59.   A modified form of the English language used to specify the logic of information system processes defines:

a.   Structured English
b.   shorthand
c.   decision logic
d.   state-transition diagram

Answer: a   **Difficulty**: Med   **Reference**: p. 285

60.   The modeling technique that relies on action verbs and noun phrases, and contains no adjectives or adverbs is called:

a.   decision logic
b.   Unified Modeling Language
c.   Structured English
d.   English pseudocode

Answer: c   **Difficulty**: Med   **Reference**: p. 285

61.   Action verbs are used in Structured English to name:

a.   data structures
b.   sources
c.   processes
d.   entities

Answer: c   **Difficulty**: Med   **Reference**: p. 285

62.   Which of the following is a true statement regarding Structured English?

a.   Adjectives and adverbs are used to enhance process descriptions.
b.   Noun phrases describe processes.
c.   Each analyst should use the standard version of Structured English.
d.   Structured English uses a subset of the English vocabulary to express information system process procedures.

Answer: d   **Difficulty**: Med   **Reference**: p. 285

63.   Which of the following processes can Structured English represent?

a.   sequence
b.   repetition
c.   conditional statements
d.   all of the above

Answer: d   **Difficulty**: Med   **Reference**: p. 285

64. Which of the following is a difference between Structured English and pseudocode?

    a. Structured English is a communication technique between programmers and systems analysts.
    b. Pseudocode is a communication technique between analysts and users.
    c. Structured English resembles spoken English; pseudocode resembles a programming language.
    d. Actually, Structured English and pseudocode are synonymous terms.

    Answer: c   **Difficulty**: Med   **Reference**: p. 288

65. Structured English requires the analyst to:

    a. note the opening and closing of files
    b. use adverbs and adjectives when describing data structures
    c. initialize variables
    d. do none of the above

    Answer: d   **Difficulty**: Med   **Reference**: p. 288

66. If several different conditions are involved, and combinations of these conditions dictate which of several actions should be taken, then:

    a. Structured English is preferred over a state-transition diagram
    b. a decision table is much clearer than a Structured English statement
    c. Structured English provides a better representation than a decision tree
    d. decision tables are less effective in presenting the process logic

    Answer: b   **Difficulty**: Med   **Reference**: p. 288

67. A decision table does not include:

    a. statements
    b. condition stubs
    c. action stubs
    d. rules

    Answer: a   **Difficulty**: Med   **Reference**: p. 288

68. The part of a decision table that links conditions to actions is the section that contains the:

    a. action statements
    b. rules
    c. condition statements
    d. decision stubs

    Answer: b   **Difficulty**: Med   **Reference**: p. 288

69. A matrix representation of the logic of a decision, which specifies the possible conditions for the decision and the resulting actions, defines a:

    a. structure chart
    b. state transition diagram
    c. decision table
    d. sequence diagram

    Answer: c   **Difficulty**: Med   **Reference**: p. 288

70. The part of a decision table that lists the actions that result for a given set of conditions is called:

    a. action stubs
    b. condition stubs
    c. rule section
    d. condition execution

    Answer: a　　　　　　**Difficulty**: Easy　　　　　　**Reference**: p. 288

71. The part of a decision table that lists the conditions relevant to the decision is called:

    a. action stubs
    b. condition stubs
    c. condition list
    d. condition execution

    Answer: b　　　　　　**Difficulty**: Easy　　　　　　**Reference**: p. 288

72. The part of a decision table that specifies which actions are to be followed for a given set of conditions refers to:

    a. action stubs
    b. condition list
    c. rules
    d. decision list

    Answer: c　　　　　　**Difficulty**: Med　　　　　　**Reference**: p. 288

73. In a decision table, a condition whose value does not affect which actions are taken for two or more rules is referred to as a(n):

    a. indifferent condition
    b. static condition
    c. fixed condition
    d. flexible condition

    Answer: a　　　　　　**Difficulty**: Med　　　　　　**Reference**: p. 289

74. If Rules 2, 4, and 6 are indifferent conditions, then:

    a. Rules 2, 4, and 6 are eliminated from the matrix
    b. the number of rules is reduced by condensing Rules 2, 4, and 6 into one rule
    c. Rules 2, 4, and 6 will result in at least two additional rules being included in the matrix
    d. Rules 2, 4, and 6 have no impact on the interpretation of the matrix

    Answer: b　　　　　　**Difficulty**: Med　　　　　　**Reference**: p. 289

75. An indifferent condition is represented by a(n):

    a. dash (-)
    b. asterisk (*)
    c. exclamation point (!)
    d. pound sign (#)

    Answer: a　　　　　　**Difficulty**: Med　　　　　　**Reference**: p. 289

76. Basic procedures for constructing a decision table do not include:

 a. listing all possible rules
 b. naming the conditions and the values each condition can assume
 c. identifying selection criteria
 d. simplifying the decision table

 Answer: c   **Difficulty**: Hard   **Reference**: pp. 289-290

77. When condition values are either "yes" or "no", these values are called a(n):

 a. extended entry
 b. simple entry
 c. complex entry
 d. limited entry

 Answer: d   **Difficulty**: Med   **Reference**: p. 289

78. A condition that has more than two values is a(n):

 a. extended entry
 b. simple entry
 c. complex entry
 d. limited entry

 Answer: a   **Difficulty**: Med   **Reference**: p. 289

79. To determine the number of rules required for the decision table, you would:

 a. add the number of values for each condition to the number of values for every other condition
 b. multiply the number of conditions by two
 c. add the number of values for each condition to the number of values for every other condition, then subtract 1
 d. multiply the number of values for each condition by the number of values for every other condition

 Answer: d   **Difficulty**: Hard   **Reference**: p. 289

80. Assume we have three conditions. Condition one has two values; condition two has three values; condition three has three values. How many rules are needed?

 a. 8
 b. 6
 c. 5
 d. 18

 Answer: d   **Difficulty**: Med   **Reference**: p. 289

81. Assume the first condition has two values; the second condition has two values; the third condition has three values. How many rules will there be?

    a. 7
    b. 12
    c. 6
    d. 11

    Answer: b   **Difficulty**: Med   **Reference**: p.289

82. Assume the first condition has four values; the second condition has two values; the third condition has two values. How many rules will there be?

    a. 8
    b. 7
    c. 16
    d. 24

    Answer: c   **Difficulty**: Med   **Reference**: p. 289

83. A decision table is simplified by:

    a. removing extended entries
    b. removing any rules with impossible actions
    c. removing simple entries
    d. removing any rules with static actions

    Answer: b   **Difficulty**: Med   **Reference**: p. 290

84. Which of the following is true regarding decision tables?

    a. Decision tables can model the relatively complicated logic of a process.
    b. Decision tables are more useful than Structured English for complicated logic.
    c. Decision tables convey information in a tabular format.
    d. All of the above are true.

    Answer: d   **Difficulty**: Med   **Reference**: p. 291

85. Which of the following is not true regarding decision tables?

    a. Structured English is more useful than decision tables when modeling the complicated logic of a process.
    b. Decision tables are compact.
    c. Decision tables allow you to check for the extent to which your logic is complete, consistent, and not redundant.
    d. Decision tables can model the relatively complicated logic of a process.

    Answer: a   **Difficulty**: Med   **Reference**: p. 291

86. A graphical technique that depicts a decision or choice situation as a connected series of nodes and branches is a:

a. decision tree
b. decision table
c. structure chart
d. hierarchical chart

Answer: a   **Difficulty**: Med   **Reference**: p. 292

87. A graphical representation of a decision situation in which decision points are connected together by arcs and terminate in ovals is a:

a. state-transition diagram
b. decision tree
c. decision table
d. sequence diagram

Answer: b   **Difficulty**: Med   **Reference**: p. 292

88. Components of a decision tree include:

a. states
b. rules
c. decision points
d. stubs

Answer: c   **Difficulty**: Med   **Reference**: p. 292

89. On a decision tree, decision points are represented by:

a. arrows
b. ovals
c. squares
d. nodes

Answer: d   **Difficulty**: Med   **Reference**: p. 292

90. To read a decision tree, you begin at the:

a. top root node
b. far-left root node
c. far-right root node
d. bottom root node

Answer: b   **Difficulty**: Med   **Reference**: p. 292

91. Which of the following is not true regarding a decision tree?

a. To read a decision tree, you begin at the top root node.
b. Each path leaving a node corresponds to one of the options for that choice.
c. All possible actions are listed on the far right of the diagram in leaf nodes.
d. Decision points are represented by nodes.

Answer: a   **Difficulty**: Med   **Reference**: p. 292

92. Based on the criteria of determining conditions and actions, decision trees:

    a. are considered to be not as effective as Structured English and decision tables
    b. support the process better than Structured English, but not as well as decision tables
    c. are considered to be the best technique to support the process
    d. support the process better than decision tables, but not as well as Structured English

    Answer: c   **Difficulty**: Hard   **Reference**: p. 294

93. When converting conditions and actions to sequential statements, Structured English:

    a. is superior to decision tables and decision trees
    b. and decision trees are viewed as being the best techniques
    c. is rated the third best
    d. is rated second best

    Answer: b   **Difficulty**: Med   **Reference**: p. 294

94. For checking consistency and completeness, Structured English was rated as:

    a. the best technique
    b. the second best technique
    c. the third best technique
    d. not very useful

    Answer: c   **Difficulty**: Med   **Reference**: p. 294

95. For checking consistency and completeness, decision tables:

    a. were rated as second best when compared with Structured English and decision trees
    b. were rated best when compared with Structured English and decision trees
    c. were rated third best when compared with Structured English and decision trees
    d. tied with decision trees as the best technique

    Answer: d   **Difficulty**: Hard   **Reference**: p. 294

96. For which of the following criteria are decision tables rated best when compared to decision trees?

    a. portraying complex logic
    b. making decisions
    c. portraying simple problems
    d. none of the above

    Answer: a   **Difficulty**: Med   **Reference**: p. 294

97. For which of the following criteria are decision trees rated best when compared to decision tables?

    a. portraying complex logic
    b. more compact
    c. easier to manipulate
    d. making decisions

    Answer: d   **Difficulty**: Med   **Reference**: p. 294

98.   For which of the following criteria were decision tables rated worst when compared to decision trees?

a.   more compact
b.   easier to manipulate
c.   portraying complex logic
d.   portraying simple problems

Answer: d   **Difficulty**: Med   **Reference**: p. 294

99.   For which of the following criteria were decision trees rated worst when compared to decision tables?

a.   being harder to graph
b.   portraying complex logic
c.   making decisions
d.   portraying simple problems

Answer: b   **Difficulty**: Med   **Reference**: p. 294

100.   Which of the following is a true statement?

a.   Both decision tables and trees can be checked for completeness, consistency, and degree of redundancy.
b.   The pioneers of structured analysis and design thought decision tables were best for portraying complex logic.
c.   The pioneers of structured analysis and design thought decision trees were better for simpler problems.
d.   All of the above are true statements.

Answer: d   **Difficulty**: Med   **Reference**: p. 294

Fill In the Blanks

101.   **_Logic modeling_** represents the internal structure and functionality of the processes represented on data flow diagrams.

Difficulty: Med   **Reference**: p. 283

102.   **_Structured English_**, **_decision tables_**, and **_decision trees_** are three types of logic models.

Difficulty: Med   **Reference**: p. 282

103.   Modeling a system's logic is performed during the analysis subphase of **_requirements structuring_**.

Difficulty: Med   **Reference**: p. 283

104.   Logic modeling deliverables include **_Structured English representations of process logic_**, **_decision table representations_**, **_decision tree representations_**, **_state-transition diagrams or tables_**, **_sequence diagrams_**, and **_activity diagrams_**.

Difficulty: Hard   **Reference**: p. 284

105. **_Structured English_** is a modified form of the English language used to specify the logic of information system processes.

    Difficulty: Med   **Reference**: p. 285

106. Structured English represents three processes typical to structured programming: **_sequence_**, **_conditional statements_**, and **_repetition_**.

    Difficulty: Hard   **Reference**: p. 285

107. A **_case statement_** is a type of conditional statement where there are many different actions a program can follow, but only one is chosen.

    Difficulty: Med   **Reference**: p. 285

108. **_If_** and **_case_** are two types of conditional statements.

    Difficulty: Med   **Reference**: p. 285

109. **_Do-Until loops_** and **_Do-While loops_** are types of repetition statements.

    Difficulty: Hard   **Reference**: p. 286

110. A **_decision table_** is a matrix representation of the logic of a decision, which specifies the possible conditions for the decision and the resulting actions.

    Difficulty: Med   **Reference**: p. 288

111. **_Condition stubs_** are the part of a decision table that lists the conditions relevant to the decision.

    Difficulty: Med   **Reference**: p. 288

112. **_Action stubs_** are the part of a decision table that lists the actions that result for a given set of conditions.

    Difficulty: Med   **Reference**: p. 288

113. **_Rules_** are the part of a decision table that specifies which actions are to be followed for a given set of conditions.

    Difficulty: Med   **Reference**: p. 288

114. The three parts of a decision table are **_condition stubs_**, **_action stubs_**, and **_rules_**.

    Difficulty: Med   **Reference**: p. 288

115. The **_rules_** section is the part of the decision table that link the conditions to actions.

    Difficulty: Med   **Reference**: p. 288

116. An **_indifferent condition_** is a condition in a decision table whose value does not affect which actions are taken for two or more rules.

    Difficulty: Med   **Reference**: p. 289

117. In a decision table, an indifferent condition is represented with a ***dash***.

> **Difficulty**: Med   **Reference**: p. 289

118. If condition one has four values, condition two has five values, condition three has two values, and condition four has three values, then the number of rules required for the decision table is ***120***.

> **Difficulty**: Hard   **Reference**: p. 289

119. A ***decision tree*** is a graphical representation of a decision situation in which decision situation points are connected together by arcs and terminate in ovals.

> **Difficulty**: Med   **Reference**: p. 292

120. The two main components on a decision tree are ***decision points*** and ***actions***.

> **Difficulty**: Med   **Reference**: p. 292

121. On a decision tree, decision points are represented by ***nodes***.

> **Difficulty**: Med   **Reference**: p. 292

122. On a decision tree, actions are represented by ***ovals***.

> **Difficulty**: Med   **Reference**: p. 292

123. When compared to Structured English and decision tables, decision trees are rated as ***best*** for determining conditions and actions.

> **Difficulty**: Hard   **Reference**: p. 294

124. When compared to decision tables and decision trees, Structured English is rated as ***third best*** when checking for consistency and completeness.

> **Difficulty**: Hard   **Reference**: p. 294

125. When compared to Structured English and decision trees, decision tables are rated as ***third best*** for transforming conditions and actions into sequence.

> **Difficulty**: Hard   **Reference**: p. 294

Matching Questions

Match each of the following terms with its corresponding definition.

     a.   rules
     b.   decision tree
     c.   Structured English
     d.   action stubs
     e.   decision table
     f.   indifferent condition
     g.   condition stubs

126.   The part of a decision table that lists the actions that result for a given set of conditions.

     Answer: d   **Reference**: p. 288

127.   Modified form of the English language used to specify the logic of information system processes.

     Answer: c   **Reference**: p. 285

128.   The part of a decision table that specifies which actions are to be followed for a given set of conditions.

     Answer: a   **Reference**: p. 288

129.   The part of a decision table that lists the conditions relevant to the decision.

     Answer: g   **Reference**: p. 288

130.   A matrix representation of the logic of a decision, which specifies the possible conditions for the decision and the resulting actions.

     Answer: e   **Reference**: p. 288

131.   A graphical representation of a decision situation in which decision points are connected together by arcs and terminate in ovals.

     Answer: b   **Reference**: p. 292

132.   In a decision table, a condition whose value does not affect which actions are taken for two or more rules.

     Answer: f   **Reference**: p. 289

Match each of the following terms with its corresponding definition.

     a. Structured English
     b. decision table
     c. decision tree
     d. indifferent condition

133.   Modified form of the English language used to specify the logic of information system processes.

Answer: a   **Reference**: p. 285

134.   A graphical representation of a decision situation in which decision points are connected together by arcs and terminate in ovals.

Answer: c   **Reference**: p. 292

135.   A matrix representation of the logic of a decision, which specifies the possible conditions for the decision and the resulting actions.

Answer: b   **Reference**: p. 288

136.   Refers to a condition whose value does not affect which actions are taken for two or more rules.

Answer: d   **Reference**: p. 289

Match each of the following terms with its corresponding description.

      a.   decision table
      b.   rules
      c.   condition stubs
      d.   decision tree
      e.   indifferent condition
      f.   action stubs
      g.   structured English

137.   A matrix representation of the logic of a decision, which specifies the possible conditions for the decision and the resulting actions.

         Answer: a   **Reference**: p. 288

138.   A graphical representation of a decision situation in which decision points are connected together by arcs and terminate in ovals.

         Answer: d   **Reference**: p. 292

139.   A condition whose value does not affect which actions are taken for two or more rules.

         Answer: e   **Reference**: p. 289

140.   The part of a decision table that lists the conditions relevant to the decision.

         Answer: c   **Reference**: p. 288

141.   The part of a decision table that specifies which actions are to be followed for a given set of conditions.

         Answer: b   **Reference**: p. 288

142.   Modified form of the English language used to specify the logic of information system processes.

         Answer: g   **Reference**: p. 285

143.   The part of a decision table that lists the actions that result for a given sets of conditions.

         Answer: f   **Reference**: p. 288

Match each of the following logic modeling techniques with the statements that most closely describe the technique. (Answers may occur more than once.)

     a. Structured English
     b. decision table
     c. decision tree

144.   This technique can represent all three of the fundamental statements necessary for structured programming.

          Answer: a   **Reference:** p. 285

145.   Each analyst will have his or her own particular dialect of this technique because there is no standard version.

          Answer: a   **Reference:** p. 285

146.   This technique enables you to represent a set of conditions and the actions that follow from them in a tabular format.

          Answer: b   **Reference:** p. 288

147.   This technique is a modified version of the English language that is useful for representing the logic in information system processes.

          Answer: a   **Reference:** p. 285

148.   This technique was first devised as a management science technique to simplify a choice where some of the needed information is not known for certain.

          Answer: c   **Reference:** p. 292

149.   This technique models the same elements as a decision table but in a more graphical manner.

          Answer: c   **Reference:** p. 292

150.   This technique divides a matrix into three parts: condition stubs, action stubs, and rules.

          Answer: b   **Reference:** p. 288

151.   Each rule is represented by tracing a series of paths from the root node, down a path to the next node, and so on, until an action oval is reached.

          Answer: c   **Reference:** p. 292

Match each of the following terms with its corresponding description.

    a.   limited entry
    b.   extended entry
    c.   action stubs
    d.   condition stubs
    e.   decision table
    f.   decision tree
    g.   indifferent condition
    h.   rules
    i.   Structured English

152.   A matrix representation of the logic of a decision, which specifies the possible conditions for the decision and the resulting actions.

        Answer: e   **Reference:** p. 288

153.   The part of the decision table that lists the actions that result for a given set of conditions.

        Answer: c   **Reference:** p. 288

154.   Occurs when the condition values are simply "yes" or "no."

        Answer: a   **Reference:** p. 289

155.   The part of the decision table that specifies which actions are to be followed for a given set of conditions.

        Answer: h   **Reference:** p. 288

156.   The part of a decision table that lists the conditions relevant to the decision.

        Answer: d   **Reference:** p. 288

157.   Occurs when the condition values are more than two.

        Answer: b   **Reference:** p. 289

158.   Modified form of the English language used to specify the logic of information system processes.

        Answer: i   **Reference:** p. 285

159.   This occurs when a value does not affect which actions are taken for two or more rules.

        Answer: g   **Reference:** p. 289

160.   A graphical representation of a decision situation in which decision points are connected together by arcs and terminate in ovals.

        Answer: f   **Reference:** p. 292

Essay Questions

161. *Briefly identify the deliverables from logic modeling.*

The deliverables for logic modeling (discussed in this chapter) include a Structured English representation of process logic, decision table representation, and decision tree representation. Structured English is a modified form of the English language used to specify the logic of information system processes. A decision table is a matrix representation of the logic of a decision, which specifies the possible conditions for the decision and the resulting actions. A decision tree is a graphical representation of a decision situation in which decision points (nodes) are connected together by arcs and terminate in ovals.

162. *Briefly discuss how to select among Structured English, decision tables, and decision trees.*

The selection of the appropriate technique depends on the task you are performing and the purpose of the technique. Decision trees are considered the best technique for determining conditions and actions, transforming conditions and actions into sequence, and checking consistency and completeness. Structured English is the best choice for transforming conditions and actions into sequence. For determining conditions and actions, Structured English is rated second best. For checking consistency and completeness, Structured English is rated third best. Decision tables are rated best for checking consistency and completeness. Decision tables are rated third best for both determining conditions and actions and transforming conditions and actions into sequence. Table 9-2 in the text can be referenced to support this answer. Decision tables and trees are easily checked for completeness, consistency, and degree of redundancy. Decision tables are more compact and easier to manipulate than decision trees. While decision trees are better for representing simpler problems, decision tables are best for portraying complex logic.

163. *Briefly discuss modeling logic with Structured English.*

Structured English uses a subset of the English vocabulary to record information system process procedures. Processes are named with action verbs; data structures are named with noun phrases. Adjectives and adverbs are not used. Sequence, conditional statements, and repetition processes are represented by utilizing Structured English. The structured part of Structured English mimics the indentation format utilized in programming languages. Initializing variables, opening and closing files, and finding related records in separate files do not require notation. While Structured English is used as a communication technique for analysts and users, pseudocode is the communication technique utilized by programmers and analysts.

164. *Briefly discuss modeling logic with decision tables.*

A decision table is a matrix representation of the logic of a decision and specifies the possible conditions for the decision and the resulting actions. Decision tables facilitate the diagramming of process logic when the logic is reasonably complicated. Decision tables consist of three parts: condition stubs, action stubs, and rules. Condition stubs list the conditions relevant to the decision. Action stubs list the actions that result for a given set of conditions. Rules specify which actions are to be followed for a given set of conditions.

165. *Identify the five basic procedures to follow when constructing a decision table.*

The five basic procedures are (1) name the conditions and the values each condition can assume, (2) name all possible actions that can occur, (3) list all possible rules, (4) define the actions for each rule, and (5) simplify the decision table.

166.   *What is logic modeling? How does it differ from process modeling?*

Process modeling graphically represents the functions that capture, store, manipulate, and distribute data between a system and its environment. In contrast, logic modeling represents the internal structure and functionality of the processes found on data flow diagrams. Logic modeling explains how these processes are performed.

167.   *An individual wishes to withdraw cash from an ATM machine. Prepare a structured English representation for this situation. Please note any assumptions that you make.*

A suggested answer is provided below. For simplicity, this representation assumes that the individual performs only one transaction.

Accept Personal-identification-number
PEFORM Validate Personal Identification Number Process
BEGIN IF
    IF Personal-identification-number IS CORRECT
    THEN PERFORM Withdrawal Process
    ELSE PERFORM Unsuccessful Log-in Process
END IF
PERFORM Transaction Completion Process
RETURN

(Validate Personal Identification Number Process)
DO
    BEGIN IF
        IF Personal-identification-number IS NOT CORRECT
        THEN NOTIFY user that Personal-identification-number IS NOT CORRECT AND
            REQUEST Personal-identification-number
        ELSE RETURN
    END IF
UNTIL log-in-attempt is greater than 3
RETURN

(Withdrawal Process)
    ACCEPT Requested-withdrawal-amount
    BEGIN IF
        IF Requested-withdrawal-amount is less than OR equal to Checking-balance
            THEN GIVE Requested-withdrawal-amount in cash AND SUBTRACT Requested-
                withdrawal-amount from Checking-balance AND RECORD new Checking-balance
        ELSE NOTIFY user that Requested-withdrawal-amount is greater than Checking-balance
RETURN

(Transaction Completion Process)
BEGIN IF
    IF Cash IS GIVEN
        THEN GENERATE receipt
        ELSE GENERATE unsuccessful withdrawal message
ENDIF
END Transaction

(Unsuccessful Log-in Process)
Keep bank card
NOTIFY user that log-in failed
END Transaction

168.   *An individual wishes to withdraw cash from an ATM machine. Prepare a decision table to represent this situation. Please note any assumptions that you make.*

A suggested answer is provided below.

Conditions/ Courses of Actions	Rules		
	1	**2**	**3**
Correct User ID	Y	N	Y
Withdrawal Amount	< or = Balance	--	>Balance
Give Cash	X		
Generate Receipt	X		
Update Checking Balance	X		
End Transaction		X	X

169.   *An individual wishes to withdraw cash from an ATM machine. Prepare a decision tree to represent this situation. Please note any assumptions that you make.*

A suggested answer is provided below.

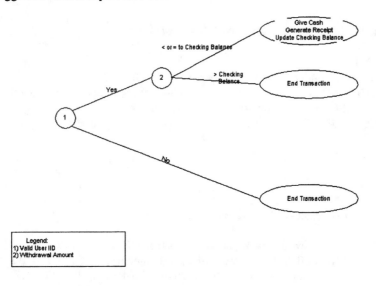

170.   *Construct a decision tree for the following situation. A student can only enroll in an MIS class if the class is not full and if he has completed the necessary prerequisite course.*

A suggested answer is provided below.

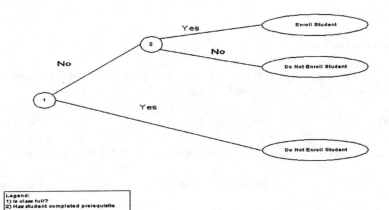

Legend:
1) Is class full?
2) Has student completed prerequisite course?

Chapter 10
Structuring System Requirements:
Conceptual Data Modeling

True-False Questions

1. The characteristics of data captured during data modeling are crucial in the design of databases, programs, computer screens, and printed reports.

    Answer: True   **Difficulty**: Easy   **Reference**: p. 305

2. Processes, rather than data, are the most complex aspects of many modern information systems.

    Answer: False   **Difficulty**: Med   **Reference**: p. 305

3. The purpose of the conceptual data model is to show as many rules about the meaning and interrelationships among data as possible.

    Answer: True   **Difficulty**: Med   **Reference**: p. 306

4. The names of data stores on primitive-level data flow diagrams often correspond to the names of data entities in entity-relationship diagrams.

    Answer: True   **Difficulty**: Med   **Reference**: p. 306

5. During systems design, an entity-relationship diagram with attributes is prepared.

    Answer: False   **Difficulty**: Med   **Reference**: p. 307

6. An enterprise-wide data model is prepared during systems implementation.

    Answer: False   **Difficulty**: Med   **Reference**: p. 307

7. A logical data model is prepared during systems analysis.

    Answer: False   **Difficulty**: Med   **Reference**: p. 307

8. The primary deliverable for the conceptual data modeling step within the analysis phase is an entity-relationship diagram.

    Answer: True   **Difficulty**: Med   **Reference**: p. 308

9. A deliverable from conceptual data modeling is a set of entries about data objects to be stored in the project dictionary or repository

    Answer: True   **Difficulty**: Easy   **Reference**: p. 309

10. When constructing a data model, the analyst needs to know how or when data is processed.

    Answer: False   **Difficulty**: Med   **Reference**: p. 309

11. The top-down approach to data modeling derives the business rules for a data model from an intimate understanding of the nature of the business.

   Answer: True　　　　　　**Difficulty**: Med　　　　　　**Reference**: p. 309

12. The bottom-up approach to data modeling derives a data model by reviewing specific business documents.

   Answer: True　　　　　　**Difficulty**: Med　　　　　　**Reference**: p. 310

13. An analyst would ask "What must we know about each object in order to run a business?" in order to determine relationships, their cardinality, and degrees.

   Answer: False　　　　　　**Difficulty**: Hard　　　　　　**Reference**: p. 310

14. In order to determine attributes and secondary keys, an analyst might ask, "What characteristics describe each object?"

   Answer: True　　　　　　**Difficulty**: Hard　　　　　　**Reference**: p. 310

15. In order to determine security controls and understand who really knows the meaning of data, an analyst might ask, "What natural activities or transactions of the business involve handling data about several objects of the same or different type?"

   Answer: False　　　　　　**Difficulty**: Hard　　　　　　**Reference**: p. 310

16. In order to determine the integrity rules, minimum and maximum cardinality, and time dimensions of data, an analyst might ask, "Are values for data characteristics limited in any way?"

   Answer: True　　　　　　**Difficulty**: Hard　　　　　　**Reference**: p. 310

17. An entity is a person, place, object, event, or concept in the user environment about which the organization wishes to maintain data.

   Answer: True　　　　　　**Difficulty**: Med　　　　　　**Reference**: p. 311

18. Social security number, last name, and first name are entity types.

   Answer: False　　　　　　**Difficulty**: Med　　　　　　**Reference**: p. 311

19. Book, supplier, and state are entity types.

   Answer: True　　　　　　**Difficulty**: Med　　　　　　**Reference**: p. 311

20. Since a name represents a set of entities, it is plural on an entity-relationship diagram.

   Answer: False　　　　　　**Difficulty**: Med　　　　　　**Reference**: p. 311

21. A circle represents a relationship on an entity-relationship diagram.

   Answer: False　　　　　　**Difficulty**: Med　　　　　　**Reference**: p. 312

22. An ellipse represents an entity on an entity-relationship diagram.

   Answer: False　　　　　　**Difficulty**: Med　　　　　　**Reference**: p. 312

23. Use a verb or verb phrase to name an entity.

    Answer: False   **Difficulty**: Easy   **Reference**: p. 313

24. A true data entity will have many possible instances, each with a distinguishing characteristic, as well as one or more other descriptive pieces of data.

    Answer: True   **Difficulty**: Med   **Reference**: p. 312

25. An entity instance is a single occurrence of an entity type.

    Answer: True   **Difficulty**: Med   **Reference**: p. 312

26. Employee identification number, name, address, and skill are attributes.

    Answer: True   **Difficulty**: Med   **Reference**: p. 314

27. An order number is a good example of a candidate key.

    Answer: True   **Difficulty**: Med   **Reference**: p. 315

28. A faculty identification number can serve as an identifier.

    Answer: True   **Difficulty**: Easy   **Reference**: p. 315

29. A primary key should be null.

    Answer: False   **Difficulty**: Med   **Reference**: p. 315

30. An identifier is a candidate key that has been selected as the unique, identifying characteristic for an entity type.

    Answer: True   **Difficulty**: Med   **Reference**: p. 315

31. When selecting an identifier, one should choose a candidate key that will not change its value over the life of each instance of the entity type.

    Answer: True   **Difficulty**: Med   **Reference**: p. 315

32. Analysts should use intelligent keys as identifiers.

    Answer: False   **Difficulty**: Med   **Reference**: p. 315

33. Analysts should substitute single-attribute surrogate keys for large composite keys.

    Answer: True   **Difficulty**: Med   **Reference**: p. 316

34. Referencing an employee entity, an employee's skills are a multivalued attribute.

    Answer: True   **Difficulty**: Med   **Reference**: p. 316

35. One way to handle repeating data within an entity is to separate the repeating data into another entity, called a weak entity.

    Answer: True   **Difficulty**: Med   **Reference**: p. 316

36. A multivalued attribute is an attribute that may take on more than one value for each entity instance.

    Answer: True   **Difficulty**: Med   **Reference**: p. 316

37. A repeating group is a set of two or more multivalued attributes that are logically related.

    Answer: True   **Difficulty**: Med   **Reference**: p. 316

38. A join is an association between the instances of one or more entity types that is of interest to the organization.

    Answer: False   **Difficulty**: Med   **Reference**: p. 317

39. Relationships are labeled with verb phrases.

    Answer: True   **Difficulty**: Easy   **Reference**: p. 317

40. The goal of conceptual data modeling is to capture as much of the meaning of data as possible.

    Answer: True   **Difficulty**: Med   **Reference**: p. 318

41. A ternary relationship is a relationship between the instances of one entity type.

    Answer: False   **Difficulty**: Med   **Reference**: p. 318

42. A unary relationship is the most common type of relationship encountered in data modeling.

    Answer: False   **Difficulty**: Med   **Reference**: p. 319

43. A ternary relationship is the equivalent of three binary relationships.

    Answer: False   **Difficulty**: Med   **Reference**: p. 320

44. Cardinality is the number of instances of entity B that can (or must) be associated with each instance of entity A.

    Answer: True   **Difficulty**: Med   **Reference**: p. 320

45. The minimum cardinality of a relationship is the minimum number of instances of entity B that may be associated with each instance of entity A.

    Answer: True   **Difficulty**: Med   **Reference**: p. 321

46. A plural relationship is a relationship that the data modeler chooses to model as entity type.

    Answer: False   **Difficulty**: Med   **Reference**: p. 324

47. A relationship must be turned into an associative entity when the associative entity has other relationships with entities besides the relationship that caused its creation.

    Answer: True   **Difficulty**: Hard   **Reference**: pp. 324-325

48. On an entity relationship diagram, the U-shaped symbol indicates that the subtype is a subset of the supertype.

    Answer: True   **Difficulty**: Med   **Reference**: p. 326

49. On an entity relationship diagram, total specialization is shown by a single line from the supertype to the subtype.

    Answer: False   **Difficulty**: Hard   **Reference**: p. 327

50. Conceptual data modeling for an Internet-based electronic commerce application differs significantly from the process followed when analyzing the data needs for other types of applications.

    Answer: False   **Difficulty**: Med   **Reference**: p. 335

Multiple Choice Questions

51. Some systems developers believe that a data model is the most important part of the statement of information system requirements because:

    a. the characteristics of data captured during data modeling are crucial in the design of databases, programs, computer screens, and printed reports
    b. data rather than processes are the most complex aspects of many modern information systems and thus require a central role in structuring system requirements
    c. the characteristics about data are reasonably permanent
    d. all of the above

    Answer: d   **Difficulty**: Med   **Reference**: p. 305

52. Each of the following are the focus of current systems development except:

    a. transaction processing systems
    b. management information systems
    c. decision support systems
    d. executive support systems

    Answer: a   **Difficulty**: Med   **Reference**: p. 305

53. Which of the following is a true statement?

    a. Data characteristics are dynamic.
    b. A data model explains the transient form of an organization.
    c. An information system design based on a data orientation, rather than a process or logic orientation, should have a longer useful life.
    d. Data flow paths are permanent.

    Answer: c   **Difficulty**: Med   **Reference**: p. 305

54. The most common format used for data modeling is:

    a. state-transition diagramming
    b. entity-relationship diagramming
    c. process modeling
    d. decision table diagramming

    Answer: b   **Difficulty**: Med   **Reference**: p. 305

55. During requirements structuring:

    a. an E-R model represents conceptual data requirements for a particular system
    b. the conceptual E-R data model is refined before it is translated into a logical format from which database definition and physical database design are done
    c. an enterprise-wide data model with very broad categories of data and little detail is prepared
    d. a specific E-R model is built to help explain the scope of a particular systems analysis and design effort

    Answer: a   **Difficulty**: Med   **Reference**: p. 305

56. Conceptual data modeling is typically done in parallel with other requirements analysis and structuring steps during:

    a. logical design
    b. physical design
    c. analysis
    d. implementation

    Answer: c   **Difficulty**: Med   **Reference**: p. 306

57. Process, logic, and data model descriptions of a system must be consistent and complete since:

    a. they each describe different but complementary views of the same information system
    b. they are prepared during the analysis phase
    c. they are constructed in parallel by separate analyst teams
    d. programming tasks require the integration of the information contained in the diagrams

    Answer: a   **Difficulty**: Med   **Reference**: p. 306

58. An E-R model with attributes is prepared during:

    a. design
    b. project identification and selection
    c. analysis
    d. project initiation and planning

    Answer: c   **Difficulty**: Med   **Reference**: p. 307

59. The primary deliverable from the conceptual modeling step within the analysis phase is a(n):

  a. state-transition diagram
  b. E-R diagram
  c. context data flow diagram
  d. decision tree

  Answer: b   **Difficulty**: Med   **Reference**: p. 308

60. The data modeling perspective that derives the business rules for a data model from an intimate understanding of the nature of the business, rather than from any specific information requirements in screens, reports, or business forms, is referred to as the:

  a. top-down approach
  b. bottom-up approach
  c. overview approach
  d. business approach

  Answer: a   **Difficulty**: Med   **Reference**: p. 309

61. Gathering the information you need for data modeling by reviewing specific business documents handled within the system describes the:

  a. top-down approach
  b. bottom-up approach
  c. investigative approach
  d. business approach

  Answer: b   **Difficulty**: Med   **Reference**: p. 310

62. The three main constructs of the entity-relationship modeling notation include each of the following except:

  a. data entities
  b. data flows
  c. relationships
  d. attributes

  Answer: b   **Difficulty**: Med   **Reference**: p. 311

63. A detailed, logical representation of the entities, associations, and data elements for an organization or business area defines:

  a. entity-relationship diagram
  b. conceptual model
  c. entity-relationship model
  d. data flow diagram

  Answer: c   **Difficulty**: Med   **Reference**: p. 311

64.   A graphical representation of an E-R model is a(n):

   a.   entity-relationship diagram
   b.   relationship diagram
   c.   data flow diagram
   d.   entity-relationship model

   Answer: a   **Difficulty:** Med   **Reference:** p. 311

65.   A person, place, object, event, or concept in the user environment about which the organization wishes to maintain data refers to a(n):

   a.   attribute
   b.   data element
   c.   relationship
   d.   entity

   Answer: d   **Difficulty:** Med   **Reference:** p. 311

66.   A product is an example of a(n):

   a.   data element
   b.   attribute
   c.   entity
   d.   relationship

   Answer: c   **Difficulty:** Med   **Reference:** p. 311

67.   A collection of entities that share common properties or characteristics defines:

   a.   entity type
   b.   entity instance
   c.   entity occurrence
   d.   entity collection

   Answer: a   **Difficulty:** Med   **Reference:** p. 311

68.   A single occurrence of an entity type defines:

   a.   entity instance
   b.   entity appearance
   c.   attribute
   d.   data element

   Answer: a   **Difficulty:** Med   **Reference:** p. 312

69.   Which of the following is a true statement?

   a.   Data entities correspond to sources/sinks on a data flow diagram.
   b.   Relationships correspond to data flows on a data flow diagram.
   c.   A data entity will have many possible instances.
   d.   Verbs are used to name entity types.

   Answer: c   **Difficulty:** Med   **Reference:** p. 312

70.   A named property or characteristic of an entity that is of interest to the organization defines:

a.   attribute
b.   relationship
c.   instance
d.   gerund

Answer: a   **Difficulty**: Med   **Reference**: p. 314

71.   An attribute (or combination of attributes) that uniquely identifies each instance of an entity type defines:

a.   data element occurrence
b.   trigger
c.   candidate key
d.   gerund

Answer: c   **Difficulty**: Med   **Reference**: p. 315

72.   When selecting an identifier, one should:

a.   use intelligent keys
b.   use large composite keys instead of single-attribute surrogate keys
c.   choose a candidate key that will not change its value over the life of each instance of the entity type
d.   choose a candidate key such that for each instance of the entity, the attribute is guaranteed to have valid values or is null

Answer: c   **Difficulty**: Med   **Reference**: p. 315

73.   A candidate key that has been selected as the identifier for an entity type is called a(n):

a.   attribute
b.   identifier
c.   secondary key
d.   gerund

Answer: b   **Difficulty**: Med   **Reference**: p. 315

74.   For each entity, the name of the identifier is:

a.   identified by using a double-lined ellipse
b.   underlined on an E-R diagram
c.   bold on an E-R diagram
d.   written in all capital letters on an E-R diagram

Answer: b   **Difficulty**: Med   **Reference**: p. 316

75. An attribute that can have more than one value for each entity instance is referred to as a:

    a. gerund
    b. multivalued attribute
    c. nonexclusive attribute
    d. supertype

    Answer: b   **Difficulty**: Med   **Reference**: p. 316

76. If each employee can have more than one skill, then SKILL is referred to as a:

    a. gerund
    b. multivalued attribute
    c. nonexclusive attribute
    d. repeating attribute

    Answer: b   **Difficulty**: Med   **Reference**: p. 316

77. A set of two or more multivalued attributes that are logically related defines:

    a. relationship
    b. gerund
    c. repeating group
    d. class

    Answer: c   **Difficulty**: Med   **Reference**: p. 316

78. An association between the instances of one or more entity types that is of interest to the organization best defines:

    a. occurrence
    b. relationship
    c. coupling
    d. cardinality

    Answer: b   **Difficulty**: Med   **Reference**: p. 317

79. If STUDENT and COURSE participate in a relationship, their relationship is a(n):

    a. unary relationship
    b. binary relationship
    c. ternary relationship
    d. extraordinary relationship

    Answer: b   **Difficulty**: Med   **Reference**: p. 319

80. A relationship between the instances of one entity type is a:

    a. unary relationship
    b. binary relationship
    c. ternary relationship
    d. singular occurrence

    Answer: a   **Difficulty**: Med   **Reference**: p. 318

81. A simultaneous relationship among instances of three entity types is a:

    a. unary relationship
    b. binary relationship
    c. ternary relationship
    d. multiple occurrence

    Answer: c   **Difficulty**: Med   **Reference**: p. 320

82. The number of instances of entity B that can (or must) be associated with each instance of entity A refers to:

    a. cardinality
    b. domain
    c. ternary occurrence
    d. participation level

    Answer: a   **Difficulty**: Med   **Reference**: p. 320

83. The minimum number of instances of entity B that may be associated with each instance of entity A defines the:

    a. degree of the relationship
    b. minimum cardinality of the relationship
    c. maximum cardinality of the relationship
    d. domain of the relationship

    Answer: b   **Difficulty**: Hard   **Reference**: p. 321

84. If entity B is a mandatory participant, then:

    a. the minimum cardinality of the relationship is two
    b. the minimum cardinality of the relationship cannot be defined
    c. the minimum cardinality of the relationship is one
    d. the minimum cardinality of the relationship is optional

    Answer: c   **Difficulty**: Med   **Reference**: p. 321

85. A relationship that the data modeler chooses to model as an entity type best defines:

    a. recursive relationship
    b. associative entity
    c. domain
    d. complex relationship

    Answer: b   **Difficulty**: Med   **Reference**: p. 324

86. Which of the following is not a true statement?

    a. An associative entity is represented on an E-R diagram as an ellipse.
    b. A relationship must be turned into an associative entity when the associative entity has other relationships with entities besides the relationship which caused the creation of the associative entity.
    c. A double-lined ellipse indicates a multivalued attribute on an E-R diagram.
    d. A diamond represents a relationship on an E-R diagram.

    Answer: a   **Difficulty:** Med   **Reference:** p. 324

87. A subgrouping of the entities in an entity type that is meaningful to the organization and that shares common attributes or relationships distinct from other subgroupings best defines:

    a. child node
    b. disjoined entity
    c. subtype
    d. supertype

    Answer: c   **Difficulty:** Med   **Reference:** p. 326

88. Which of the following specifies that each entity instance of the supertype must be a member of some subtype in the relationship?

    a. total specialization rule
    b. partial specialization rule
    c. disjoint rule
    d. overlap rule

    Answer: a   **Difficulty:** Hard   **Reference:** p. 327

89. Which of the following specifies that an entity instance can simultaneously be a member of two (or more) subtypes?

    a. total specialization rule
    b. partial specialization rule
    c. disjoint rule
    d. overlap rule

    Answer: d   **Difficulty:** Med   **Reference:** p. 327

90. Which of the following specifies that an entity instance of the supertype is allowed not to belong to any subtype?

    a. total specialization rule
    b. partial specialization rule
    c. disjoint rule
    d. overlap rule

    Answer: b   **Difficulty:** Hard   **Reference:** p. 327

91. Which of the following specifies that if an entity instance of the supertype is a member of one subtype it cannot simultaneously be a member of any other subtype?

    a. total specialization rule
    b. partial specialization rule
    c. disjoint rule
    d. overlap rule

    Answer: c   **Difficulty**: Hard   **Reference**: p. 327

92. Specifications that preserve the integrity of the logical data model are:

    a. requirements specifications
    b. integrity restrictions
    c. business limitations
    d. business rules

    Answer: d   **Difficulty**: Med   **Reference**: p. 328

93. Which of the following addresses the rules concerning the relationships between entity types?

    a. referential integrity constraints
    b. triggering operations
    c. entity integrity
    d. domains

    Answer: a   **Difficulty**: Med   **Reference**: p. 328

94. Which of the following specifies that each instance of an entity type must have a unique identifier that is not null?

    a. referential integrity constraints
    b. triggering operations
    c. entity integrity
    d. domains

    Answer: c   **Difficulty**: Hard   **Reference**: p. 328

95. Which of the following are constraints on valid values for attributes?

    a. referential integrity constraints
    b. triggering operations
    c. entity integrity
    d. domains

    Answer: d   **Difficulty**: Med   **Reference**: p. 328

96. Which of the following protects the validity of attribute values?

    a. referential integrity constraints
    b. triggering operations
    c. entity integrity
    d. domains

    Answer: b   **Difficulty**: Hard   **Reference**: p. 328

97. The set of all data types and ranges of values that an attribute can assume defines:

a. cardinality
b. constraint set
c. domain
d. reference set

Answer: c   **Difficulty**: Med   **Reference**: p. 329

98. An assertion or rule that governs the validity of data manipulation operations such as insert, update, and delete is:

a. triggering operation
b. entity integrity
c. referential integrity constraints
d. domains

Answer: a   **Difficulty**: Med   **Reference**: p. 329

99. The data manipulation operation (insert, delete, or update) that initiates the operation is called a(n):

a. condition
b. action
c. user rule
d. event

Answer: d   **Difficulty**: Hard   **Reference**: p. 329

100. A concise statement of the business rule to be enforced by the triggering operation refers to:

a. user rule
b. condition
c. action
d. event

Answer: a   **Difficulty**: Hard   **Reference**: p. 329

Fill In the Blanks

101. A ***conceptual data model*** is a detailed model that shows the overall structure of organizational data while being independent of any database management system or other implementation considerations.

Difficulty: Med   **Reference**: p. 306

102. An ***entity-relationship diagram*** is a detailed, logical, and graphical representation of the entities, associations, and data elements for an organization or business area.

Difficulty: Med   **Reference**: p. 311

103. An ***entity-relationship data model*** is a detailed, logical representation of the entities, associations, and data elements for an organization or business area.

      Difficulty: Med   **Reference**: p. 311

104. An ***entity type*** is a collection of entities that share common properties or characteristics.

      Difficulty: Med   **Reference**: p. 311

105. An ***entity instance*** is a single occurrence of an entity type.

      Difficulty: Med   **Reference**: p. 312

106. An ***attribute*** is a named property or characteristic of an entity that is of interest to the organization.

      Difficulty: Med   **Reference**: p. 314

107. A ***candidate key*** is an attribute or combination of attributes that uniquely identifies each instance of an entity type.

      Difficulty: Med   **Reference**: p. 315

108. An ***identifier*** is a candidate key that has been selected as the unique, identifying characteristic for an entity type.

      Difficulty: Med   **Reference**: p. 315

109. A ***multivalued attribute*** is an attribute that may take on more than one value for each entity instance.

      Difficulty: Med   **Reference**: p. 316

110. A ***repeating group*** is a set of two or more multivalued attributes that are logically related.

      Difficulty: Med   **Reference**: p. 316

111. A ***relationship*** is an association between the instances of one or more entity types that is of interest to the organization.

      Difficulty: Med   **Reference**: p. 317

112. ***Degree*** refers to the number of entity types that participate in a relationship.

      Difficulty: Med   **Reference**: p. 318

113. A ***unary relationship*** is a relationship between the instances of one entity type.

      Difficulty: Hard   **Reference**: p. 318

114. A ***binary relationship*** is a relationship between instances of two entity types.

      Difficulty: Med   **Reference**: p. 319

115. A ***ternary relationship*** is a simultaneous relationship among instances of three entity types.

      Difficulty: Hard   **Reference**: p. 320

116. ***Cardinality*** refers to the number of instances of entity B that can (or must) be associated with each instance of entity A.

Difficulty: Med   **Reference**: p. 320

117. An ***associative entity*** is an entity type that associates the instances of one or more entity types and contains attributes that are peculiar to the relationship between those entity instances.

Difficulty: Med   **Reference**: p. 324

118. A ***subtype*** is a subgrouping of the entities in an entity type that is meaningful to the organization and that shares common attributes or relationships distinct from other subgroupings.

Difficulty: Med   **Reference**: p. 326

119. A ***supertype*** is a generic entity type that has a relationship with one or more subtypes.

Difficulty: Med   **Reference**: p. 326

120. The ***disjoint rule*** specifies that if an entity instance of the supertype is a member of one subtype, it cannot simultaneously be a member of any other subtype.

Difficulty: Hard   **Reference**: p. 327

121. The ***overlap rule*** specifies that an entity instance can simultaneously be a member of two (or more) subtypes.

Difficulty: Hard   **Reference**: p. 327

122. The ***partial specialization rule*** specifies that an entity instance of the supertype is allowed not to belong to any subtype.

Difficulty: Hard   **Reference**: p. 327

123. ***Business rules*** are specifications that preserve the integrity of a conceptual or logical data model.

Difficulty: Med   **Reference**: p. 328

124. A ***domain*** is the set of all data types and values that an attribute can assume.

Difficulty: Med   **Reference**: p. 329

125. A ***triggering operation*** is an assertion or rule that governs the validity of data manipulation operations such as insert, update, and delete.

Difficulty: Hard   **Reference**: p. 330

Matching Questions

Match each of the following terms with its corresponding definition.

a. entity
b. entity type
c. attribute
d. multivalued attribute
e. entity instance
f. supertype
g. subtype

126. A person, place, object, event, or concept in the user environment about which the organization wishes to maintain data.

   Answer: a   **Reference**: p. 311

127. A single occurrence of an entity type.

   Answer: e   **Reference**: p. 312

128. A subgrouping of the entities in an entity type that is meaningful to the organization and that shares common attributes or relationships distinct from other subgroupings.

   Answer: g   **Reference**: p. 326

129. A generic entity type that has a relationship with one or more subtypes.

   Answer: f   **Reference**: p. 326

130. A named property or characteristic of an entity that is of interest to the organization.

   Answer: c   **Reference**: p. 314

131. A collection of entities that share common properties or characteristics.

   Answer: b   **Reference**: p. 311

132. An attribute that can have more than one value for each entity instance.

   Answer: d   **Reference**: p. 316

Match each of the following terms with its corresponding definition.

    a.   unary relationship
    b.   ternary relationship
    c.   binary relationship
    d.   relationship
    e.   repeating group
    f.   associative entity
    g.   disjoint rule
    h.   overlap rule
    i.   partial specialization rule
    j.   total specialization rule

133.   Specifies that if an entity instance of the supertype is a member of one subtype, it cannot simultaneously be a member of any other subtype.

          Answer: g   **Reference**: p. 327

134.   Specifies that an entity instance can simultaneously be a member of two (or more) subtypes.

          Answer: h   **Reference**: p. 327

135.   Specifies that an entity instance of the supertype is allowed not to belong to any subtype.

          Answer: i   **Reference**: p. 327

136.   Specifies that each entity instance of the supertype must be a member of some subtype in the relationship.

          Answer: j   **Reference**: p. 327

137.   A many-to-many (or one-to-one) relationship that the data modeler chooses to model as an entity type with several associated one-to-many relationships with other entity types.

          Answer: f   **Reference**: p. 324

138.   A set of two or more multivalued attributes that are logically related.

          Answer: e   **Reference**: p. 316

139.   An association between the instances of one or more entity types that is of interest to the organization.

          Answer: d   **Reference**: p. 317

140.   A relationship between instances of two entity types.

          Answer: c   **Reference**: p. 319

141.   A simultaneous relationship among instances of three entity types.

          Answer: b   **Reference**: p. 320

142.   A relationship between the instances of one entity type.

          Answer: a   **Reference**: p. 318

For each of the following statements, answer "a" if it is a true statement, or answer "b" if the statement is false.

143.   The name of the identifier of each entity is underlined on an E-R diagram.

                          Answer: a   **Reference**: p. 316

144.   To illustrate a multivalued attribute, use a double-lined ellipse.

                          Answer: a   **Reference**: p. 316

145.   On E-R diagrams, relationships are labeled with verb phrases.

                          Answer: a   **Reference**: p. 317

146.   The goal of conceptual data modeling is to identify as much of the processing activity as possible.

                          Answer: b   **Reference**: p. 318

147.   To illustrate a multivalued attribute, separate the repeating data into another entity, then using a relationship, link the weak entity to its associated regular entity.

                          Answer: a   **Reference**: p. 316

148.   A recursive relationship is a relationship between the instances of two entity types.

                          Answer: b   **Reference**: pp. 318-319

For each of the following statements, answer "a" if it is a true statement, or answer "b" if the statement is false.

149.   A singular noun is used to name an entity type.

Answer: a   **Reference:** pp. 311-312

150.   Upper- and lowercase letters are used in naming an entity type.

Answer: b   **Reference:** p. 312

151.   A diamond represents an entity.

Answer: b   **Reference:** p. 312

152.   An entity instance is a single occurrence of an entity type.

Answer: a   **Reference:** p. 312

153.   Many instances of an entity type are represented by data stored in the database.

Answer: a   **Reference:** p. 312

Match each of the following terms with its corresponding definition.

    a.   business rule
    b.   disjoint rule
    c.   overlap rule
    d.   partial specialization rule
    e.   total specialization rule

154.   Specifies that if an entity instance of the supertype is a member of one subtype, it cannot simultaneously be a member of any other subtype.

Answer: b   **Reference:** p. 327

155.   Specifies that an entity instance can simultaneously be a member of two (or more) subtypes.

Answer: c   **Reference:** p. 327

156.   Specifies that an entity instance of the supertype is allowed not to belong to any subtype.

Answer: d   **Reference:** p. 327

157.   Specifies that each entity instance of the supertype must be a member of some subtype in the relationship.

Answer: e   **Reference:** p. 327

158.   Specifications that preserve the integrity of a conceptual or logical data model.

Answer: a   **Reference:** p. 328

Essay Questions

159. *Define the following key data modeling terms: entity, attribute, relationship, degree, cardinality, and associative entity.*

An entity is a person, place, object, event, or concept in the user environment about which the organization wishes to collect and maintain data. An attribute is a named property or characteristic of an entity that is of interest to the organization. A relationship is an association between the instances of one or more entity types that is of interest to the organization. Degree defines the number of entity types that participate in a relationship. Cardinality specifies the number of instances of entity B that can (or must) be associated with each instance of entity A. An associative entity is a many-to-many (or one-to-one) relationship that the data modeler chooses to model as an entity type with several associated one-to-many relationships with other entity types.

160. *Discuss unary, binary, and ternary relationships. Provide an example of each.*

The number of entity types participating in a relationship defines the degree of the relationship. The most common relationships are unary, binary, and ternary. A unary relationship is a relationship between the instances of one entity type. An example of this type of relationship is of the "person" entity. One person (or instance) can be married to another person (or instance). The binary relationship is a relationship between instances of two entity types. An example of this relationship is of a supplier and part. The binary relationship is the most common type of relationship encountered in data modeling. The ternary relationship is a simultaneous relationship among instances of three entity types. An example is a supplier shipping a part to a warehouse.

161. *Contrast data modeling to process modeling and logic modeling.*

Data modeling, process modeling, and logic modeling provide complimentary views of the system. Data modeling focuses on the data that must be stored by the system. Process modeling graphically represents the processes that capture, distribute, and store data between a system and its environment. Logic modeling represents the internal structure and functionality of the system.

162. *Briefly identify the four entity-relationship diagrams that are produced and analyzed during conceptual data modeling.*

The four entity-relationship diagrams are: (1) an entity-relationship diagram that illustrates the data needed in the project's application; (2) an entity-relationship diagram for the system being replaced; (3) an entity-relationship diagram that illustrates the entire database from which the new application's data are extracted; and (4) an entity-relationship diagram for the entire database for the existing application system.

163. *What are multivalued attributes and repeating groups? Provide an example of each.*

A multivalued attribute is an attribute that may assume more than one value for each entity instance. A repeating group is a related set of multivalued attributes. Using a student and the courses she takes as an example, the course number, name, and grade are multivalued attributes and repeat for each course that the student takes.

164. *What is the role of CASE in conceptual modeling? What information is placed in the CASE repository during conceptual modeling?*

During conceptual modeling, CASE tools maintain E-R diagrams as a visual depiction of structured data requirements and link objects on E-R diagrams to corresponding descriptions in the CASE repository. Although the actual list of data elements varies, information about entities, attributes, and relationships is maintained in the CASE repository.

165. *What is a triggering operation? What components are included? Provide an example.*

A triggering operation is an assertion or rule that governs the validity of data manipulation operations such as insert, update, and delete. A triggering operation includes a user rule, event, entity name, condition, and action. An example is an attempt to order an item that is not currently in stock.

User rule: ORDER Quantity may not exceed PRODUCT In-Stock-Quantity
Event: Insert
Entity Name: ORDER
Condition: ORDER Quantity > PRODUCT In-Stock-Quantity
Action: Reject the insert transaction

166. *Define domains for the following attributes: GPA, rank, and age.*

A student's GPA is numeric with two decimal places, ranges and allows values from 0 to 4.00, is not unique, and allows null values. (An entering freshman would not have a GPA until after her first semester.) Student rank is a numeric field, does not allow null values, and is not unique. Assuming all students are undergraduate students, the field contains values, ranging from 1 to 4.

167. *Assume you work for Technology Central, an organization that provides on-site technology seminars for various companies. Identify at least four entities that your company would track. Build a conceptual model.*

Technology Central tracks information about its courses, staff, locations, and students. The organization needs to identify which courses are offered at certain locations and which instructors are teaching these classes. The company also needs to associate students with a particular course offered at a particular location.

168. *Briefly identify four important business rules for supertype/subtype relationships.*

Total specialization, partial specialization, disjoint, and overlap are four business rules for supertype/subtype relationships. The total specialization rule specifies that each entity instance of the supertype must be a member of some subtype in the relationship. The partial specialization rule specifies that an entity instance of the supertype is allowed not to belong to any subtype. The disjoint rule specifies that if an entity instance of the supertype is a member of one subtype, it cannot simultaneously be a member of any other subtype. The overlap rule specifies that an entity instance can simultaneously be a member of two (or more) subtypes.

Chapter 11
Selecting the Best Alternative
Design Strategy

True-False Questions

1. To bring analysis to conclusion, your job is to take the structured requirements and transform them into several alternative design strategies.

    Answer: True   **Difficulty**: Med   **Reference**: p. 349

2. Selecting the best alternative system involves generating a comprehensive set of alternative design strategies and selecting the one that is most likely to result in the desired information system.

    Answer: True   **Difficulty**: Med   **Reference**: p. 349

3. A system design strategy represents a particular approach to developing a system.

    Answer: True   **Difficulty**: Easy   **Reference**: p. 349

4. In theory, if there are four sets of requirements, three implementation environments, and four sources of application software, then there would be thirty-six possible design strategies.

    Answer: False   **Difficulty**: Med   **Reference**: p. 351

5. During alternative generation and selection, management may decide to end the project for a variety of reasons, including the fact that the needs of the organization have changed.

    Answer: True   **Difficulty**: Med   **Reference**: p. 351

6. The primary deliverables for alternative generation and selection are process, data, and logic models.

    Answer: False   **Difficulty**: Med   **Reference**: p. 351

7. The primary deliverable for alternative generation and selection is an updated Baseline Project Plan.

    Answer: True   **Difficulty**: Med   **Reference**: p. 351

8. A good number of alternatives to generate is five.

    Answer: False   **Difficulty**: Med   **Reference**: p. 351

9. Midrange alternatives are the most conservative in terms of the effort, cost, and technology involved in developing a new system.

    Answer: False   **Difficulty**: Med   **Reference**: p. 352

10. High-end alternatives not only solve the problem in question but include many extra features as well.

    Answer: True   **Difficulty**: Med   **Reference**: p. 352

11. Cost is the primary focus of high-end alternatives.

     Answer: False   **Difficulty**: Med   **Reference**: p. 352

12. The minimum requirements for a new system are also its mandatory features.

     Answer: True   **Difficulty**: Med   **Reference**: p. 352

13. Essential features are those that everyone agrees are necessary to solve the problem or meet the opportunity.

     Answer: False   **Difficulty**: Med   **Reference**: p. 352

14. The identification of a system's mandatory features is performed during systems planning and selection.

     Answer: False   **Difficulty**: Hard   **Reference**: p. 352

15. While essential features help screen out possible solutions, desirable features help compare alternative design strategies.

     Answer: False   **Difficulty**: Hard   **Reference**: p. 352

16. Desired features are those that users could live without but that are used to select between design strategies that are of almost equal value in terms of essential features.

     Answer: True   **Difficulty**: Med   **Reference**: p. 352

17. During systems development, essential features to consider include data, output, and analyses.

     Answer: True   **Difficulty**: Med   **Reference**: p. 352

18. Constraints on systems development include time, finances, and legal.

     Answer: True   **Difficulty**: Med   **Reference**: p. 352

19. When identifying alternative design strategies, the date when the replacement system is needed is a possible constraint.

     Answer: True   **Difficulty**: Med   **Reference**: p. 352

20. Low-end alternatives will meet every requirement.

     Answer: False   **Difficulty**: Med   **Reference**: p. 353

21. High-end alternatives meet every constraint.

     Answer: False   **Difficulty**: Med   **Reference**: p. 353

22. Most of the substantive debate about alternative design strategies hinges on the relative importance of system features.

     Answer: True   **Difficulty**: Med   **Reference**: p. 353

23. Issues of functionality help determine whether the system should be developed and run in-house, software and hardware selection, implementation, and organizational limitations.

     Answer: True   **Difficulty**: Med   **Reference**: p. 353

24. System consignment is the practice of turning over responsibility of some to all of an organization's information systems applications and operations to an outside firm.

     Answer: False   **Difficulty**: Med   **Reference**: p. 353

25. Hiring a company to run your applications on your own computers is an example of outsourcing.

     Answer: True   **Difficulty**: Med   **Reference**: p. 353

26. A company may consider outsourcing if it feels that its core mission does not involve managing an information systems unit and that it might achieve more effective computing by turning over all of its operations to a more experienced, computer-oriented company.

     Answer: True   **Difficulty**: Med   **Reference**: p. 354

27. Hardware manufacturers, packaged software producers, custom software producers, enterprise-wide solutions, and in-house developers are sources of software.

     Answer: True   **Difficulty**: Med   **Reference**: p. 354

28. Sun and Hitachi are well known for their enterprise-wide solutions.

     Answer: False   **Difficulty**: Med   **Reference**: p. 356

29. SAP, PeopleSoft, and Baan specialize in enterprise-wide solutions.

     Answer: True   **Difficulty**: Med   **Reference**: p. 357

30. Software companies will test their systems in actual organizations to determine whether there are any problems or if any improvements can be made, and until this testing is complete, the system is not offered for sale to the general public.

     Answer: True   **Difficulty**: Hard   **Reference**: p. 355

31. A tiered system cannot be modified to meet the specific, individual needs of a particular organization.

     Answer: False   **Difficulty**: Med   **Reference**: p. 356

32. Properly designed turnkey systems will perfectly match the way an organization does business.

     Answer: False   **Difficulty**: Med   **Reference**: p. 356

33. A reasonable estimate is that off-the-shelf software can at best meet 70 percent of an organization's needs.

     Answer: True   **Difficulty**: Med   **Reference**: p. 356

34. A turnkey system is a system that integrates individual, traditional business functions into a series of modules so that a single transaction occurs seamlessly within a single information system rather than several separate systems.

    Answer: False   **Difficulty**: Med   **Reference**: p. 356

35. Referencing enterprise solutions, the difference between the modules and traditional approaches is that the modules are integrated to focus on the business functional areas, rather than on business processes.

    Answer: False   **Difficulty**: Hard   **Reference**: p. 356

36. Using enterprise software solutions, a firm can integrate all parts of a business process in a unified information system.

    Answer: True   **Difficulty**: Med   **Reference**: p. 357

37. One of the primary benefits of using an enterprise software solution is the short time period required for implementation.

    Answer: False   **Difficulty**: Med   **Reference**: p. 357

38. Lack of in-house expertise is a disadvantage associated with enterprise solutions software.

    Answer: True   **Difficulty**: Med   **Reference**: p. 357

39. One of the primary advantages of using an enterprise software solution is that the organization does not have to change how it does business.

    Answer: False   **Difficulty**: Hard   **Reference**: p. 357

40. The choice to acquire software from outside sources is made at the end of the systems design phase.

    Answer: False   **Difficulty**: Med   **Reference**: p. 358

41. When choosing off-the-shelf software, cost, functionality, response time, and ease of installation are several of the common criteria that should be considered.

    Answer: True   **Difficulty**: Med   **Reference**: p. 359

42. When choosing off-the-shelf software, the two most important criteria are functionality and ease of installation.

    Answer: False   **Difficulty**: Med   **Reference**: p. 359

43. Functionality refers to the tasks the software can perform and the mandatory, essential, and desired system features.

    Answer: True   **Difficulty**: Med   **Reference**: p. 360

44. When a task requires custom support and the system cannot be built internally, a company should consider obtaining its software from a packaged software producer.

    Answer: False   **Difficulty**: Hard   **Reference**: p. 359

45. When a company needs complete systems that cross functional boundaries, it should use in-house development.

Answer: False   **Difficulty**: Hard   **Reference**: p. 359

46. When a company needs system software and utilities, hardware manufacturers are a good source.

Answer: True   **Difficulty**: Hard   **Reference**: p. 359

47. If a company purchases application software, it does not necessarily need to conduct systems analysis.

Answer: False   **Difficulty**: Med   **Reference**: p. 360

48. Selecting the best design strategy for an Internet-based electronic commerce application differs significantly from the process used for other types of applications.

Answer: False   **Difficulty**: Med   **Reference**: p. 373

49. Scalable refers to the ability to seamlessly upgrade the capabilities of the system through hardware upgrades, software upgrades, or both.

Answer: True   **Difficulty**: Med   **Reference**: p. 374

50. A Web server is a "middle tier" software and hardware combination that lies between the host computer and the corporate network and systems.

Answer: False   **Difficulty**: Hard   **Reference**: p. 374

Multiple Choice Questions

51. The point in the analysis phase where the analyst is ready to transform all of the information he or she has gathered and structured into some concrete ideas about the nature of the design for the new or replacement information system is referred to as:

     a. the design strategy
     b. requirements determination
     c. requirements structuring
     d. logic modeling

     Answer: a   **Difficulty**: Med   **Reference**: p. 348

52. As a result of this sub-phase, the analyst knows what the current system does and knows what the users would like the replacement system to do.

     a. requirements structuring
     b. requirements determination
     c. alternative generation and selection
     d. project initiation and planning

     Answer: b   **Difficulty**: Med   **Reference**: p. 348

53. As a result of this sub-phase, the analyst understands what forms the replacement system's process flow, process logic, and data should take, at a logical level independent of any physical implementation.

    a.   requirements structuring
    b.   requirements determination
    c.   alternative generation and selection
    d.   project initiation and planning

    Answer: a   **Difficulty**: Hard   **Reference**: p. 348

54. To bring analysis to a conclusion, the analyst should:

    a.   determine what forms the replacement system's process flow, process logic, and data should take, at a logical level independent of any physical implementation
    b.   define what the current system does and identify what the users would like the replacement system to do
    c.   take the structured requirements and transform them into several competing design strategies
    d.   state the general functions within the system to be analyzed

    Answer: c   **Difficulty**: Hard   **Reference**: p. 349

55. Part of generating a design strategy is:

    a.   specifying in general terms what types of information and information processing are needed
    b.   stating in general terms what functions within the system or department will be analyzed
    c.   programming the system, building all data files, and testing the new system
    d.   determining how the replacement system can be acquired by using a combination of sources inside and outside the organization

    Answer: d   **Difficulty**: Hard   **Reference**: p. 349

56. Selecting the best alternative system involves:

    a.   generating a comprehensive set of alternative design strategies
    b.   selecting the alternative design strategy that is most likely to result in the desired information system, given all of the organizational, economic, and technical constraints that limit what can be done
    c.   developing all technology and organizational specifications necessary to implement the new information system
    d.   both a and b

    Answer: d   **Difficulty**: Med   **Reference**: p. 349

57. A high-level statement about the approach to developing an information system refers to:

    a.   design strategy
    b.   problem statement
    c.   requirements statement
    d.   scope

    Answer: a   **Difficulty**: Med   **Reference**: p. 349

58. This statement includes statements on the system's functionality, hardware and system software platform, and method for acquisition.

    a. problem statement
    b. requirements statement
    c. design strategy
    d. systems service request

    Answer: c   **Difficulty**: Med   **Reference**: p. 349

59. All of the following are systems analysis subphases except:

    a. alternative generation and selection
    b. requirements structuring
    c. logical design of user dialogue and interfaces
    d. requirements determination

    Answer: c   **Difficulty**: Med   **Reference**: p. 350

60. Shaping alternative system design strategies involves:

    a. enumerating different potential implementation environments
    b. proposing different ways to source or acquire the various sets of capabilities for the different implementation environments
    c. dividing requirements into different sets of capabilities
    d. all of the above

    Answer: d   **Difficulty**: Med   **Reference**: p. 350

61. In theory, if there are four sources of application software, two implementation environments, and three sets of requirements, how many design strategies are possible?

    a. 4
    b. 24
    c. 9
    d. 2

    Answer: b   **Difficulty**: Med   **Reference**: p. 351

62. Who is responsible for making the ultimate decision about which systems design strategy to follow?

    a. systems analysts
    b. management
    c. consultants
    d. programmers

    Answer: b   **Difficulty**: Med   **Reference**: p. 351

63. The primary deliverable from generating alternative design strategies and selecting the best one that is carried forward into design is:

    a. an updated Baseline Project Plan
    b. business case
    c. request for proposal
    d. requirements statement

    Answer: a   **Difficulty**: Med   **Reference**: p. 351

64. Which of the following are deliverables for the subphase that involves generating alternatives and selecting the best one?

    a. identifying at least three substantively different system design strategies for building the replacement information system
    b. identifying a design strategy judged most likely to lead to the most desirable information system
    c. updating the Baseline Project Plan to detail the work necessary to turn the selected design strategy into the desired replacement system
    d. all of the above

    Answer: d   **Difficulty**: Med   **Reference**: p. 351

65. A good number of alternatives to generate is:

    a. 3
    b. 2
    c. 4
    d. 5

    Answer: a   **Difficulty**: Med   **Reference**: p. 351

66. The most conservative solutions in terms of the effort, cost, and technology involved in developing a new system are the:

    a. low-end solutions
    b. high-end solutions
    c. midrange solutions
    d. recommended solutions

    Answer: a   **Difficulty**: Med   **Reference**: p. 352

67. The alternative that goes beyond simply solving the problem in question and focuses instead on systems that contain many extra features users may desire is referred to as a:

    a. low-end alternative
    b. high-end alternative
    c. quality-focused alternative
    d. high-gloss alternative

    Answer: b   **Difficulty**: Med   **Reference**: p. 352

68. Which of the following types of alternatives represent compromise solutions?

    a. low-end alternatives
    b. high-end alternatives
    c. midrange alternatives
    d. leveled alternatives

    Answer: c   **Difficulty**: Med   **Reference**: p. 352

69. The minimum requirements for the new system are called:

    a. essential features
    b. desired features
    c. minimum features
    d. mandatory features

    Answer: d   **Difficulty**: Med   **Reference**: p. 352

70. Features that everyone agrees are necessary to solve the problem or meet the opportunity are called:

    a. desired features
    b. essential features
    c. mandatory features
    d. minimum features

    Answer: c   **Difficulty**: Med   **Reference**: p. 352

71. Identifying mandatory features by surveying users and other stakeholders who have been involved in requirements determination would occur:

    a. near the end of the analysis phase, after all requirements have been structured and analyzed
    b. near the end of the project identification and selection phase, after a formal request to conduct a project to design and develop an information systems solution has been approved
    c. during the logical design phase, while detailed function specifications of all data, forms, reports, screens, and processing rules for all aspects of the system are prepared
    d. during project initiation and planning

    Answer: a   **Difficulty**: Med   **Reference**: p. 352

72. The difference between mandatory features and essential features is that:

    a. mandatory features screen out possible solutions; essential features are the important capabilities of a system that will serve as the primary basis for comparison of different design strategies
    b. essential features screen out possible solutions; mandatory features are the important capabilities of a system that will serve as the primary basis for comparison of different design strategies
    c. mandatory features screen out possible solutions; essential features are those that users could live without
    d. essential features screen out possible solutions; mandatory features are those that users could live without

    Answer: a   **Difficulty**: Med   **Reference**: p. 352

73. Constraints on systems development may include such factors as:

    a. available financial and human resources
    b. elements of the current system that cannot change
    c. legal and contractual restrictions
    d. all of the above

    Answer: d   **Difficulty**: Med   **Reference**: p. 352

74. Which of the following is a true statement?

    a. Low-end alternatives will meet every constraint.
    b. High-end alternatives will meet every constraint.
    c. Low-end alternatives fulfill every wish end users have for the new system.
    d. Midrange alternatives include all desired features.

    Answer: a   **Difficulty**: Med   **Reference**: p. 353

75. The practice of turning over responsibility of some to all of an organization's information systems applications and operations to an outside firm is referred to as:

    a. realignment
    b. downsizing
    c. outsourcing
    d. time sharing

    Answer: c   **Difficulty**: Med   **Reference**: p. 353

76. Hiring a company to run your applications at your site on your computers is an example of:

    a. a turnkey system
    b. outsourcing
    c. downsizing
    d. realignment

    Answer: b   **Difficulty**: Med   **Reference**: p. 353

77. Which of the following are major categories of organizations that produce software?

    a. hardware manufacturers
    b. packaged software producers
    c. custom software producers
    d. all of the above

    Answer: d   **Difficulty**: Easy   **Reference**: p. 354

78. Based on 1999 revenues, which of the following companies had the highest revenues?

    a. Price Waterhouse Coopers
    b. IBM
    c. Microsoft
    d. SAP

    Answer: b   **Difficulty**: Med   **Reference**: p. 355

79. Based on software license revenues, which of the following companies ranks fourth?

    a. Microsoft
    b. IBM
    c. Novell
    d. Oracle

    Answer: d   **Difficulty**: Hard   **Reference**: p. 355

80. Off-the-shelf software systems that cannot be modified to meet the specific needs of a particular organization are sometimes called:

    a. custom software systems
    b. in-house developed systems
    c. turnkey systems
    d. standard systems

    Answer: c   **Difficulty**: Med   **Reference**: p. 356

81. Based on service revenue, the top ranked software company is:

    a. Andersen Consulting
    b. IBM
    c. SAP AG
    d. Compaq

    Answer: b   **Difficulty**: Med   **Reference**: p. 356

82. SAP AG, J. D. Edwards, and The Baan Company can best be classified as:

    a. hardware manufacturers
    b. application service providers
    c. enterprise solution software providers
    d. custom software producers

    Answer: c   **Difficulty**: Med   **Reference**: p. 357

83. Organizations that host and run computer applications for other companies, typically on a per use or license basis best describe:

    a. hardware manufacturers
    b. application service providers
    c. enterprise solution software providers
    d. Internet service providers

    Answer: b   **Difficulty**: Med   **Reference**: p. 357

84. An organization should acquire software from hardware manufacturers when:

    a. the supported task is generic
    b. system software and utilities are needed
    c. the task requires custom support, and the system cannot be built internally
    d. the resources and staff are available, and the system must be built from scratch

    Answer: b   **Difficulty**: Med   **Reference**: p. 359

85. An organization should acquire software from in-house developers when:

a. the supported task is generic
b. system software and utilities are needed
c. the task requires custom support and the system cannot be built internally
d. the resources and staff are available and the system must be built from scratch

Answer: d   **Difficulty**: Med   **Reference**: p. 359

86. An organization should acquire software from packaged software producers when:

a. the supported task is generic
b. system software and utilities are needed
c. the task requires custom support and the system cannot be built internally
d. the resources and staff are available and the system must be built from scratch

Answer: a   **Difficulty**: Med   **Reference**: p. 359

87. The choice to acquire software from outside sources should be made:

a. at the beginning of the analysis phase
b. at the middle of the analysis phase
c. at the end of the analysis phase
d. at the end of the design phase

Answer: c   **Difficulty**: Med   **Reference**: p. 358

88. When purchasing off-the-shelf software, you should consider:

a. flexibility
b. response time
c. vendor viability
d. all of the above

Answer: d   **Difficulty**: Med   **Reference**: p. 359

89. Which of the following are ways of validating purchased software information?

a. reviewing software documentation and technical marketing literature
b. sending prospective vendors a questionnaire asking specific questions about their packages
c. using the software yourself and running it through a series of tests based on the criteria for selecting software
d. all of the above

Answer: d   **Difficulty**: Med   **Reference**: p. 361

90. Advantages to running your new system on the existing platform include each of the following except:

a. some software components of your new system will only run on particular platforms with particular operating systems
b. the information systems staff is familiar with the existing platform
c. the odds of integrating your new application system with existing applications are enhanced
d. costs are lower

Answer: a   **Difficulty**: Med   **Reference**: pp. 361-362

91. Reasons for acquiring new hardware or system software include each of the following except:

   a. some software components of your new system will only run on particular platforms with particular operating systems
   b. costs are lower
   c. new platform requirements may allow your organization to radically change its computing operations
   d. developing your system for a new platform gives your organization the opportunity to upgrade or expand its current technology holdings

   Answer: b   **Difficulty**: Med   **Reference**: p. 362

92. The document sent to vendors asking them to propose hardware and software that will meet the requirements of your new system is called a:

   a. requirements statement
   b. request for proposal
   c. baseline project plan
   d. business case

   Answer: b   **Difficulty**: Med   **Reference**: p. 361

93. Each of the following is a true statement except:

   a. implementing a new information system is just as much an organizational change process as it is a technical process
   b. new systems often entail new ways of performing the same work, new working relationships, and new skills
   c. implementing a new information system is primarily a technical process
   d. systems implementation involves training users

   Answer: c   **Difficulty**: Hard   **Reference**: p. 362

94. Which of the following are organizational issues?

   a. overall costs and the availability of funding
   b. management support of alternatives
   c. the extent to which users will accept the new system and use it as designed
   d. all of the above

   Answer: d   **Difficulty**: Med   **Reference**: pp. 362-363

95. The system requirement assigned the highest priority for Hoosier Burger's new inventory control system was:

   a. management must be able to easily enter shipments into the system as soon as they are received
   b. the new system must be operational in no more than six months from the start of the contract
   c. the system must automatically determine whether and when a new order should be placed
   d. management should be able to determine at any time approximately what inventory levels are for any given item in stock

   Answer: a   **Difficulty**: Hard   **Reference**: p. 364

96. The weighted approach for alternative selection includes:

    a. identifying the criteria and the weights
    b. rating each requirement and constraint for each alternative
    c. determining a weighted score for each alternative
    d. all of the above

    Answer: d   **Difficulty**: Med   **Reference**: p. 366

97. Which of the following is a true statement concerning the updating of the Baseline Project Plan?

    a. Every section of the Baseline Project Plan report is updated.
    b. The feasibility assessment section will include in one of its subsections a detailed schedule for the activities in the design phases and any more details that can be anticipated for later phases.
    c. As part of the management issues section, a subsection will outline issues for management that have been discovered during analysis.
    d. All of the above are correct.

    Answer: d   **Difficulty**: Med   **Reference**: p. 367

98. The ability to seamlessly upgrade the capabilities of the system through either hardware upgrades, software upgrades, or both best describes:

    a. system maintenance
    b. system enhancement
    c. value-added improvements
    d. scalable

    Answer: d   **Difficulty**: Med   **Reference**: p. 374

99. A computer that is connected to the Internet and stores files written in HTML, which are publicly available through an Internet application best describes:

    a. application server
    b. thin client
    c. peer
    d. Web server

    Answer: d   **Difficulty**: Med   **Reference**: p. 374

100. A "middle tier" software and hardware combination that lies between the Web server and the corporate network and systems best describes:

    a. application server
    b. thin client
    c. peer
    d. Web server

    Answer: a   **Difficulty**: Med   **Reference**: p. 374

Fill In the Blanks

101. A **_design strategy_** is a particular approach to developing an information system.

       Difficulty: Easy   **Reference**: p. 349

102. **_Mandatory features_** are those that everyone agrees are necessary to solve the problem or meet the opportunity.

       Difficulty: Med   **Reference**: p. 352

103. Essential features to consider during systems development include **_data_**, **_output_**, and **_analyses_**.

       Difficulty: Med   **Reference**: p. 352

104. Systems development constraints include **_time_**, **_financial_**, and **_legal_**.

       Difficulty: Med   **Reference**: p. 352

105. **_Outsourcing_** is the practice of turning over responsibility of some to all of an organization's information systems applications and operations to an outside firm.

       Difficulty: Med   **Reference**: p. 353

106. **_Turnkey systems_** are off-the-shelf software systems that cannot be modified to meet the specific, individual needs of a particular organization.

       Difficulty: Hard   **Reference**: p. 356

107. **_Enterprise resource planning systems_** integrate individual traditional business functions into a series of modules so that a single transaction occurs seamlessly within a single information system rather than several separate systems.

       Difficulty: Med   **Reference**: p. 356

108. **_Enterprise software solutions_** enable a firm to integrate all parts of a business process into a unified information system.

       Difficulty: Med   **Reference**: p. 357

109. An **_application service provider_** is an organization that hosts and runs computer applications for other companies, typically on a per use or license basis.

       Difficulty: Med   **Reference**: p. 357

110. When choosing off-the-shelf software, the eight most common criteria are **_cost_**, **_functionality_**, **_vendor support_**, **_vendor viability_**, **_flexibility_**, **_documentation_**, **_response time_**, and **_ease of installation_**.

       Difficulty: Hard   **Reference**: p. 359

111. When considering off-the-shelf software, the two most important criteria are **_vendor support_** and **_vendor viability_**.

       Difficulty: Hard   **Reference**: p. 359

112. When resources and staff are available and the system must be built from scratch, a company should consider ***in-house developers***.

                                  Difficulty: Med   **Reference**: p. 359

113. For complete systems that cross functional boundaries, a company should consider an ***enterprise-wide solution***.

                                  Difficulty: Med   **Reference**: p. 359

114. When a task requires custom support and the system cannot be built internally, then a company should consider acquiring its software from a ***custom software producer***.

                                  Difficulty: Med   **Reference**: p. 359

115. When a supported task is generic, a company should consider acquiring its software from a ***packaged software producer***.

                                  Difficulty: Med   **Reference**: p. 359

116. When a company needs to acquire system software and utilities, it should consider going to a ***hardware manufacturer*** for this software.

                                  Difficulty: Med   **Reference**: p. 359

117. ***Functionality*** refers to the tasks the software can perform and the mandatory, essential, and desired system features.

                                  Difficulty: Med   **Reference**: p. 360

118. ***Support*** includes assistance to install the software, train user and systems staff on the software, and provide help as problems arise after installation.

                                  Difficulty: Easy   **Reference**: p. 360

119. ***Flexibility*** refers to how easy it is for you, or the vendor, to customize the software.

                                  Difficulty: Med   **Reference**: p. 360

120. ***Response time*** refers to how long it takes the software package to respond to the user's request in an interactive session.

                                  Difficulty: Med   **Reference**: p. 360

121. ***Ease of installation*** is a measure of the difficulty of loading the software and making it operational.

                                  Difficulty: Med   **Reference**: p. 360

122. ***Independent software testing services*** periodically evaluate software and collect user opinions, thus providing a range of opinions about possible software packages.

                                  Difficulty: Hard   **Reference**: p. 361

123. **_Scalable_** is the ability to seamlessly upgrade the capabilities of the system through hardware upgrades, software upgrades, or both.

    Difficulty: Med   **Reference**: p. 374

124. A **_Web server_** is a computer that is connected to the Internet and stores files written in HTML, which are publicly available through an Internet connection.

    Difficulty: Med   **Reference**: p. 374

125. An **_application server_** is a "middle tier" software and hardware combination that lies between the Web server and the corporate network and systems.

    Difficulty: Med   **Reference**: p. 374

Matching Questions

Match each of the following terms with its corresponding definition.

    a.   application server
    b.   design strategy
    c.   enterprise resource planning systems
    d.   outsourcing
    e.   request for proposal
    f.   scalable
    g.   Web server

126.   A "middle tier" software and hardware combination that lies between the Web server and the corporate network and systems.

        Answer: a   **Reference:** p. 374

127.   A document provided to vendors to ask them to propose hardware and system software that will meet the requirements of your new system.

        Answer: e   **Reference:** p. 361

128.   The ability to seamlessly upgrade the capabilities of the system through hardware upgrades, software upgrades, or both.

        Answer: f   **Reference:** p. 374

129.   The practice of turning over responsibility of some to all of an organization's information systems applications and operations to an outside firm.

        Answer: d   **Reference:** p. 353

130.   A system that integrates individual traditional business functions into a series of modules so that a single transaction occurs seamlessly within a single information system rather than several separate systems.

        Answer: c   **Reference:** p. 356

131.   A computer that is connected to the Internet and stores files written in HTML, which are publicly available through an Internet connection.

        Answer: g   **Reference:** p. 374

132.   A particular approach to developing an information system.

        Answer: b   **Reference:** p. 349

Match each of the following terms with its corresponding definition.

a. off-the-shelf systems
b. Baseline Project Plan
c. custom software producer
d. design strategy
e. vendor support
f. outsourcing
g. turnkey systems

133. Off-the-shelf software systems that cannot be modified to meet the specific, individual needs of a particular organization.

Answer: g   **Reference**: p. 356

134. The primary deliverable from alternative generation and selection; it details the work necessary to turn the selected design strategy into the desired replacement information system.

Answer: b   **Reference**: p. 367

135. A high-level statement about the approach to developing an information system.

Answer: d   **Reference**: p. 349

136. The practice of turning over responsibility of some to all of an organization's information systems applications and operations to an outside firm.

Answer: f   **Reference**: p. 353

137. Software packages that are ready-to-use.

Answer: a   **Reference**: p. 359

138. A consulting firm hired to help your company develop custom information systems for internal use.

Answer: c   **Reference**: p. 356

139. This occurs in the form of assistance to install the software, to train user and systems staff on the software, and provide help as problems arise after installation.

Answer: e   **Reference**: p. 360

Match each of the following alternatives with its corresponding definition. (Answers may occur more than once.)

    a.   high-end alternatives
    b.   mid-range alternatives
    c.   low-end alternatives

140.   These alternatives go beyond simply solving the problem in question and focus instead on systems that contain many extra features users may desire.

              Answer: a   **Reference:** p. 352

141.   These alternatives represent compromise solutions.

              Answer: b   **Reference:** p. 352

142.   Functionality, not cost, is the primary focus of these alternatives.

              Answer: a   **Reference:** p. 352

143.   These alternatives are the most conservative in terms of the effort, cost, and technology involved in developing a new system.

              Answer: c   **Reference:** p. 352

144.   These alternatives provide all the required functionality users demand with a system that is minimally different from the current system.

              Answer: c   **Reference:** p. 352

Indicate when software should be acquired from each of the following types of software producers.

    a.   packaged software producers
    b.   custom software producers
    c.   in-house developers
    d.   hardware manufacturers
    e.   enterprise-wide solutions

145.   When resources and staff are available and the system must be built from scratch.

        Answer: c   **Reference:** p. 359

146.   When the task requires custom support and the system cannot be built internally.

        Answer: b   **Reference:** p. 359

147.   For system software and utilities.

        Answer: d   **Reference:** p. 359

148.   When the supported task is generic.

        Answer: a   **Reference:** p. 359

149.   For complete systems that cross functional boundaries.

        Answer: e   **Reference:** p. 359

Match the internal staffing requirements to the recommended software producers.

     a.   packaged software producers
     b.   custom software producers
     c.   in-house developers
     d.   hardware manufacturers
     e.   enterprise-wide solutions

150.   Internal staff may be needed, depending on application.

              Answer: b   **Reference**: p. 359

151.   Internal staffing requirements vary.

              Answer: d   **Reference**: p. 359

152.   Some internal staff are necessary but mostly need consultants.

              Answer: e   **Reference**: p. 359

153.   Internal staff is necessary though staff size may vary.

              Answer: c   **Reference**: p. 359

154.   Some IS and user staff are needed to define requirements and evaluate packages.

              Answer: a   **Reference**: p. 359

Essay Questions

155.   *Briefly identify six sources of software.*

Software sources can be categorized as hardware manufacturers, packaged software producers, custom software producers, enterprise-wide solution providers, application service providers, and in-house developers. Hardware manufacturers are among the largest producers of software. While generally not a source of application software, hardware manufacturers are good choices for system software and utilities. Packaged software producers are potential sources of application software. These companies develop software to run on different computer platforms. Custom software producers help firms develop custom information systems for internal use. Custom software producers are often selected when the task requires custom support and the system cannot be built internally. Enterprise-wide solutions integrate individual traditional business functions into a series of modules so that a single transaction occurs seamlessly within a single information system rather than several separate systems. Enterprise-wide solutions are recommended for complete systems that cross functional boundaries. Application service providers are organizations that host and run computer applications for other companies, typically on a per use or license basis. ASPs are recommended when the supported task is generic, buying and installing the system locally would be too expensive, or for instance access to an application. In-house developers develop the system internally. This method is chosen when resources and staff are available and the system must be built from scratch.

156. *Briefly identify three deliverables from alternative generation and selection.*

Alternative generation and selection produces three deliverables: (1) at least three substantively different system design strategies for building the replacement information system; (2) a design strategy judged most likely to lead to the most desirable information system; and (3) a Baseline Project Plan for turning the most likely design strategy into a working information system. The primary deliverable carried forward into design is an updated Baseline Project Plan.

157. *Identify the most common criteria for choosing off-the-shelf software. Which two criteria would be among the most important?*

The most common criteria are cost, functionality, vendor support, vendor viability, flexibility, documentation, response time, and ease of installation. Cost involves comparing the cost of developing the same system in-house to the cost of purchasing or licensing the software package. Functionality refers to the tasks the software can perform and the mandatory, essential, and desired system features. While vendor support identifies the amount of support the vendor can be expected to provide, vendor viability examines the vendor's marketplace strength. Flexibility refers to the flexibility of customizing the software. The documentation criterion examines issues relating to the user's manual, technical documentation, and cost of acquiring additional copies of the documentation. Response time questions the length of time it takes the software package to respond to the user's requests in an interactive session and how long it takes the software to complete running a job. The ease of installation criterion examines the difficulty of loading the software and making it operational. Vendor support and viability will be among the most important.

158. *Briefly discuss generating alternative design strategies.*

The generation of at least three alternative solutions is recommended in the text. The three alternatives represent both ends and the middle of the alternative solution spectrum. A low-end solution, high-end solution, and midrange solution should be identified. Low-end solutions are conservative in terms of the effort, cost, and technology involved in developing a new system. This strategy provides all the required functionality users demand with a system and will meet every constraint. High-end solutions are potential solutions that contain many extra features users may desire. High-end solutions focus on functionality, not cost. High-end solutions will ignore most, if not all, system constraints. Midrange solutions are compromise solutions.

159. *Identify several issues to consider in generating alternatives.*

Issues to consider when generating alternatives include such areas as whether the system should be developed and run in-house, software and hardware selection, implementation, and organizational limitations. Each of these issues must be considered and will impact alternative generation and selection. Decisions addressing outsourcing or in-house development must be made. Software can be obtained from hardware manufacturers, packaged software producers, custom software producers, enterprise-wide solution providers, application service providers, and in-house developers. The advantages and disadvantages of utilizing current hardware and systems software should be studied. Technical concerns, new skills, new working relationships, user training, and changes in work practices are implementation issues. Cost, management support, and user acceptance are organizational issues.

160. *When shaping alternative design strategies, what processes are involved?*

Three primary processes are involved, including dividing requirements into different sets of capabilities, enumerating different potential implementation environments, and proposing different ways to source or acquire the various sets of capabilities for the different implementation environments.

161. *What are enterprise resource planning systems? How do they differ from traditional approaches?*
Identify three enterprise resource planning system vendors.

Enterprise resource planning systems integrate individual traditional business functions into a series of
modules so that a single transaction occurs seamlessly within a single information system rather than
several separate systems. ERP modules focus on business processes rather than on business functional
areas. SAP AG, The Baan Company, and PeopleSoft, Inc. are three vendors.

162. *What is an application service provider? What are the advantages and disadvantages of using an*
ASP?

An application service provider hosts and runs computer applications for other companies.
Advantages include less need for internal information technology staff, cost savings on internal
infrastructure and initial capital outlay, and access to big and complex systems. Disadvantages include
less control over the application and generic solutions.

163. *What is outsourcing? Identify two outsourcing arrangements. Identify two reasons for outsourcing.*

Outsourcing is the practice of turning over responsibility of some to all of an organization's
information systems applications and operations to an outside firm. A company may hire a third party
to develop and run its applications on the third party's computers. Another alternative is for the third
party to run the applications on-site and on your computers. Reasons for outsourcing include cost-
effectiveness and the company's core mission does not involve managing a management information
systems unit.

164. *Using the weighted approach, complete the following table. Which alternative do you recommend?*

Criteria	Weight	Alternative A		Alternative B		Alternative C	
		Rating	Score	Rating	Score	Rating	Score
Requirements							
Integrates with existing platform	15	3		4		2	
User friendly	10	4		5		3	
Real-time account balance retrieval	25	5		3		5	
Constraints							
Training	18	3		2		5	
Hardware Costs	15	2		4		5	
Site-Preparation	9	4		5		2	
Operating Costs	8	5		3		1	

A suggested answer is provided below. Based on the information in the table, Alternative C is recommended.

Criteria	Weight	Alternative A		Alternative B		Alternative C	
		Rating	Score	Rating	Score	Rating	Score
Requirements							
Integrates with existing platform	15	3	45	4	60	2	30
User friendly	10	4	40	5	50	3	30
Real-time account balance retrieval	25	5	125	3	75	5	125
	50		210		185		185
Constraints							
Training	18	3	54	2	36	5	90
Hardware Costs	15	2	30	4	60	5	75
Site-Preparation	9	4	36	5	45	2	18
Operating Costs	8	5	40	3	24	1	8
	50		160		165		191
Total			370		350		376

Chapter 12
Designing Databases

True-False Questions

1. One of the purposes of database design is to choose data storage technologies that will efficiently, accurately, and securely process database activities.

    Answer: True   **Difficulty**: Med   **Reference**: p. 387

2. The selection of data storage technologies is made during the systems implementation and operation phase.

    Answer: False   **Difficulty**: Med   **Reference**: p. 387

3. The network model is the most common style for a logical database model.

    Answer: False   **Difficulty**: Med   **Reference**: p. 387

4. Conceptual modeling is performed during systems design.

    Answer: False   **Difficulty**: Med   **Reference**: p. 388

5. Generally speaking, logical and physical database design is performed in parallel with other systems design steps.

    Answer: True   **Difficulty**: Easy   **Reference**: p. 388

6. Normalization helps build a data model that is simple, not redundant, and requires minimum maintenance.

    Answer: True   **Difficulty**: Med   **Reference**: p. 388

7. During logic modeling, the data requirements from all user interfaces are combined into one consolidated logical database model.

    Answer: False   **Difficulty**: Med   **Reference**: p. 389

8. The selection of the appropriate storage format for each attribute from the logical database model is made during physical database design.

    Answer: True   **Difficulty**: Med   **Reference**: p. 389

9. In general, data structure refers to grouping attributes from the logical database model into physical records.

    Answer: True   **Difficulty**: Med   **Reference**: p. 389

10. A file organization is an arrangement of related records in secondary memory so that individual and groups of records can be stored, retrieved, and updated rapidly.

    Answer: True   **Difficulty**: Med   **Reference**: p. 389

11. When using the relational notation, the primary key attribute is indicated by a dashed underline.

     Answer: False   **Difficulty**: Med   **Reference**: p. 392

12. The primary deliverable from logical database design is a conceptual model.

     Answer: False   **Difficulty**: Med   **Reference**: p. 392

13. A relation corresponds to a computer file.

     Answer: False   **Difficulty**: Med   **Reference**: p. 392

14. During physical database design, relations from logical database design are translated into computer file specifications.

     Answer: True   **Difficulty**: Med   **Reference**: p. 392

15. The network database model is a popular database technology for new information systems.

     Answer: False   **Difficulty**: Med   **Reference**: p. 393

16. Object-oriented database models are the most frequently used database technologies for new information systems development.

     Answer: False   **Difficulty**: Med   **Reference**: p. 393

17. Each column in a relation corresponds to an entity type.

     Answer: False   **Difficulty**: Med   **Reference**: p. 393

18. Each row of a relation corresponds to a record that contains data values for an entity.

     Answer: True   **Difficulty**: Med   **Reference**: p. 393

19. One property of a relation is that entries in a given column are from the same set of values.

     Answer: True   **Difficulty**: Med   **Reference**: p. 394

20. Referencing a relation, the sequence of columns cannot be interchanged without changing the meaning or use of the relation.

     Answer: False   **Difficulty**: Med   **Reference**: p. 394

21. A well-structured relation contains data about two or more entities.

     Answer: False   **Difficulty**: Med   **Reference**: p. 394

22. A relation is said to be in second normal form when its nonprimary key attributes do not depend on each other.

     Answer: False   **Difficulty**: Med   **Reference**: p. 395

23. The result of normalization is that every nonprimary key attribute depends upon the whole primary key and nothing but the primary key.

    Answer: True   **Difficulty**: Med   **Reference**: p. 395

24. Normalization is based on an analysis of weak entities.

    Answer: False   **Difficulty**: Easy   **Reference**: p. 395

25. If for every valid value of A the value of B is determined by the value of A, then B is functionally dependent on A.

    Answer: True   **Difficulty**: Hard   **Reference**: p. 395

26. An attribute can be functionally dependent on more than attribute.

    Answer: True   **Difficulty**: Med   **Reference**: p. 396

27. A relation is in second normal form if every nonprimary key attribute is functionally dependent on the whole primary key.

    Answer: True   **Difficulty**: Med   **Reference**: p. 396

28. A relation is said to be in second normal form if the primary key consists of only one attribute.

    Answer: True   **Difficulty**: Med   **Reference**: p. 396

29. Transitive attributes are attributes that determine other attributes.

    Answer: False   **Difficulty**: Med   **Reference**: p. 396

30. A relation is said to be in second normal form when there are no transitive dependencies.

    Answer: False   **Difficulty**: Hard   **Reference**: p. 397

31. A transitive dependency is an integrity constraint specifying that the value of an attribute in one relation depends on the value of the same attribute in another relation.

    Answer: False   **Difficulty**: Med   **Reference**: p. 398

32. The creation of a separate relation is sometimes required to represent a relationship.

    Answer: True   **Difficulty**: Med   **Reference**: p. 398

33. A default value is a value a field will assume unless an explicit value is entered for that field.

    Answer: True   **Difficulty**: Easy   **Reference**: p. 411

34. A null value is used to represent the zero digit in a relation.

    Answer: False   **Difficulty**: Med   **Reference**: p. 412

35. Efficient use of secondary storage and data processing speed are the two goals of physical table design.

     Answer: True   **Difficulty**: Med   **Reference**: p. 412

36. Generally speaking, a physical table corresponds to a relation.

     Answer: False   **Difficulty**: Med   **Reference**: p. 412

37. Denormalization is the process of splitting or combining normalized relations into physical tables based on affinity of use of rows and fields.

     Answer: True   **Difficulty**: Med   **Reference**: p. 413

38. Denormalization reduces the chance of errors introduced by normalizing relations.

     Answer: False   **Difficulty**: Med   **Reference**: p. 414

39. A data marker is a field of data that can be used to locate a related field or row of data.

     Answer: False   **Difficulty**: Med   **Reference**: p. 416

40. A physical file is a named set of table rows stored in a contiguous section of secondary memory.

     Answer: True   **Difficulty**: Med   **Reference**: p. 416

41. Sequential files are practical for random row retrievals.

     Answer: False   **Difficulty**: Easy   **Reference**: p. 416

42. When using the sequential file organization, the addition of rows requires rewriting the file.

     Answer: True   **Difficulty**: Med   **Reference**: p. 416

43. Indexes should be used generously for databases intended primarily to support data retrievals.

     Answer: True   **Difficulty**: Med   **Reference**: p. 418

44. Indexes should be used judiciously for databases that support transaction processing and other applications with heavy updating requirements.

     Answer: True   **Difficulty**: Med   **Reference**: p. 418

45. Sequential retrieval on the primary key is very fast with the hashed file organization.

     Answer: False   **Difficulty**: Med   **Reference**: p. 419

46. Random key retrieval on the primary key is comparatively slow with the hashed file organization.

     Answer: False   **Difficulty**: Med   **Reference**: p. 419

47. Multiple key retrieval is possible with the hashed file organization.

     Answer: False   **Difficulty**: Med   **Reference**: p. 419

48. File restoration can be achieved through backup copies of a file, audit trails, and row image files.

    Answer: True   **Difficulty**: Med   **Reference**: pp. 419-420

49. Data security can be built into a file through encryption, passwords, or prohibiting users from directly manipulating a file.

    Answer: True   **Difficulty**: Med   **Reference**: p. 420

50. Designing the database for an Internet-based electronic commerce application differs significantly from the process followed when designing the database for other types of applications.

    Answer: False   **Difficulty**: Med   **Reference**: p. 421

Multiple Choice Questions

51. Which of the following is not associated with database design?

    a. Structure the data in stable structures that are not likely to change over time and that have minimal redundancy.
    b. The preparation of a final conceptual model and the implementation of the database.
    c. Develop a logical database design from which we can do physical database design.
    d. Develop a logical database design that reflects the actual data requirements that exist in the forms and reports of an information system.

    Answer: b   **Difficulty**: Hard   **Reference**: p. 386

52. The most common style for a logical database model is the:

    a. relational database model
    b. hierarchical database model
    c. network database model
    d. object-oriented database model

    Answer: a   **Difficulty**: Med   **Reference**: p. 387

53. During logical database design, the work of all systems development team members is coordinated and shared through:

    a. the project dictionary
    b. scheduled weekly meetings
    c. the project leader
    d. JAD sessions

    Answer: a   **Difficulty**: Easy   **Reference**: p. 388

54. Which of the following is not a key step in logical database modeling and design?

    a. Combine normalized data requirements from all user interfaces into one consolidated logical database model.
    b. Compare the consolidated logical database design with the translated E-R model and produce, through view integration, one final logical database design for the application.
    c. Model how data flow through an information system, the relationships among the data flows, and how data come to be stored at specific locations.
    d. Translate the conceptual E-R data model for the application into normalized data requirements.

    Answer: c   **Difficulty**: Hard   **Reference**: p. 389

55. Combining all normalized user views into one consolidated logical database model refers to:

    a. requirements structuring
    b. view integration
    c. normalization
    d. file integration

    Answer: b   **Difficulty**: Med   **Reference**: p. 389

56. During physical design, you consider:

    a. the definitions of each attribute
    b. the descriptions of where and when data are entered, retrieved, deleted, and updated
    c. the expectations for response time and data integrity
    d. all of the above

    Answer: d   **Difficulty**: Med   **Reference**: p. 389

57. Key physical database design decisions include:

    a. choosing the storage format for each attribute from the logical database model
    b. grouping attributes from the logical database model into physical records
    c. arranging related records in secondary memory so that individual and groups of records can be stored, retrieved, and updated rapidly
    d. all of the above

    Answer: d   **Difficulty**: Med   **Reference**: p. 389

58. Using relational notation, an attribute of a relation that is the primary key of another relation is indicated by:

    a. an underline
    b. a circle
    c. a dashed underline
    d. italics

    Answer: c   **Difficulty**: Med   **Reference**: p. 392

59. The primary deliverable from logical database design is:

     a. normalized relations
     b. design specifications
     c. an updated baseline project plan
     d. a list of alternatives design strategies

     Answer: a   **Difficulty**: Med   **Reference**: p. 392

60. A data model that represents data in the form of tables or relations is called a:

     a. hierarchical database model
     b. network database model
     c. relational database model
     d. hybrid database model

     Answer: c   **Difficulty**: Med   **Reference**: p. 393

61. A named two-dimensional table of data is a:

     a. network
     b. tree structure
     c. relation
     d. tuple

     Answer: c   **Difficulty**: Med   **Reference**: p. 393

62. Which of the following is not a true statement regarding a relation?

     a. Each relation consists of a set of named columns and an arbitrary number of unnamed rows.
     b. Each column in a relation corresponds to an attribute of that relation.
     c. An entry at the intersection of each row and column has a single value.
     d. Each row in a relation corresponds to an attribute of that relation.

     Answer: d   **Difficulty**: Med   **Reference**: pp. 393-394

63. Assume the structure of a relation is EMPLOYEE (Empid, Name, Dept, Salary). The number of attributes for this relation would be:

     a. three
     b. four
     c. five
     d. six

     Answer: b   **Difficulty**: Easy   **Reference**: p. 393

64. Which of the following properties of a relation states that an entry at the intersection of each row and column is single-valued?

     a. Entries in cells are simple.
     b. Entries in columns are from the same set of values.
     c. Each row is unique.
     d. The sequence of rows is insignificant.

     Answer: a   **Difficulty**: Easy   **Reference**: p. 394

65. A relation that contains a minimum amount of redundancy and allows users to insert, modify, and delete the rows in a table without errors or inconsistencies is a(n):

    a. independent relation
    b. simple relation
    c. unnormalized relation
    d. well-structured relation

    Answer: d   **Difficulty**: Med   **Reference**: p. 394

66. The process of converting complex data structures into simple, stable data structures is referred to as:

    a. normalization
    b. simplification
    c. structuring
    d. process modeling

    Answer: a   **Difficulty**: Med   **Reference**: p. 394

67. When each nonprimary key attribute is identified by the whole key, the relation is said to be in at least:

    a. second normal form
    b. third normal form
    c. fourth normal form
    d. fifth normal form

    Answer: a   **Difficulty**: Hard   **Reference**: p. 395

68. A particular relationship between two attributes best defines:

    a. context
    b. functional dependency
    c. normal form
    d. structure

    Answer: b   **Difficulty**: Med   **Reference**: p. 395

69. For any relation R, if, for every valid instance of A, that value of A uniquely determines the value of B:

    a. then a primary dependency exists in the relation
    b. then A is said to be functionally dependent on B
    c. then B is said to be functionally dependent on A
    d. then A and B are candidate keys for the relation

    Answer: c   **Difficulty**: Hard   **Reference**: p. 395

70. The relation state specifying that nonprimary key attributes do not depend on other nonprimary key attributes is:

    a. first normal form
    b. second normal form
    c. Boyce-Codd normal form
    d. third normal form

    Answer: d   **Difficulty**: Hard   **Reference**: p. 395

71. A functional dependency between two (or more) nonprimary key attributes in a relation defines a:

    a. weak dependency
    b. partial dependency
    c. simple dependency
    d. transitive dependency

    Answer: d   **Difficulty**: Hard   **Reference**: p. 397

72. An attribute that appears as a nonprimary key attribute in one relation and as a primary key attribute (or part of a primary key) in another relation is a:

    a. foreign key
    b. candidate key
    c. pointer
    d. relationship key

    Answer: a   **Difficulty**: Med   **Reference**: p. 398

73. If order number serves as the primary key in the ORDER relation and also appears as a nonprimary key attribute in the INVOICE relation, then order number is said to be a:

    a. foreign key
    b. candidate key
    c. pointer
    d. relationship key

    Answer: a   **Difficulty**: Med   **Reference**: p. 398

74. Which of the following statements is true regarding normalization?

    a. Normalization is a top-down process.
    b. Normalization produces a set of well-structured relations that contain all of the data mentioned in system inputs and outputs.
    c. Through the use of anomalies, stable structures are produced.
    d. Normalization is an integrity constraint specifying that the value of an attribute in one relation depends on the value of the same attribute in another relation.

    Answer: b   **Difficulty**: Med   **Reference**: p. 398

75. Each regular entity type in an E-R diagram is transformed into a:

    a. row in a relation
    b. column in a relation
    c. relation
    d. tuple in a relation

    Answer: c   **Difficulty**: Easy   **Reference**: p. 399

76. When transforming an E-R diagram into normalized relations, the identifier of the entity type becomes:

    a. the primary key of the corresponding relation
    b. the foreign key in the corresponding relation
    c. a nonkey attribute in the corresponding relation
    d. a secondary key in the corresponding relation

    Answer: a   **Difficulty**: Med   **Reference**: p. 399

77. Which of the following properties should be satisfied when the identifier of the entity type becomes the primary key of the corresponding relation?

    a. The value of the key must uniquely identify every row in the relation.
    b. The key should serve as a foreign key in at least two other relations.
    c. The key must be a composite of a primary key and a secondary key.
    d. The key should be an intelligent key.

    Answer: a   **Difficulty**: Med   **Reference**: p. 399

78. An entity whose primary key depends on the primary key of another entity is called a:

    a. referential entity
    b. candidate entity
    c. transitive entity
    d. weak entity

    Answer: d   **Difficulty**: Med   **Reference**: p. 399

79. A binary one-to-many relationship in an E-R diagram is best represented by:

    a. the creation of a separate relation; the primary key of this new relation is a composite key consisting of the primary key for each of the two entities in the relationship
    b. adding the primary key attribute (or attributes) of the entity on the one side of the relationship as a foreign key in the relation that is on the many side of the relationship
    c. adding the primary key attribute (or attributes) of the entity on the many side of the relationship as a foreign key in the relation that is on the one side of the relationship
    d. creating a relation with a composite primary key and nonkey attributes

    Answer: b   **Difficulty**: Hard   **Reference**: p. 404

80. For a binary one-to-one relationship between two entities A and B, the relationship is represented by:

    a. adding the primary key of A as a foreign key of B
    b. adding the primary key of B as a foreign key of A
    c. combining the two entities into one relation
    d. either a or b

    Answer: d   **Difficulty**: Hard   **Reference**: p. 404

81. For a unary one-to-one relationship between two entities A and B, the relationship is represented by:

    a. adding the primary key of A as a foreign key of B
    b. adding the primary key of B as a foreign key of A
    c. combining the two entities into one relation
    d. either a or b

    Answer: d   **Difficulty**: Hard   **Reference**: p. 404

82. For a binary many-to-many relationship existing between entity types A and B:

    a. a separate relation C is created; the primary key of relation C is a composite key consisting of the primary key for each of the two entities in the relationship
    b. the primary keys of relation A and relation B are designated as functionally dependent attributes
    c. secondary keys are used to establish the relationship
    d. place the primary key of either entity in the relation for the other entity or do this for both entities

    Answer: a   **Difficulty**: Hard   **Reference**: p. 404

83. If an associative entity exists, then:

    a. a separate relation C is created; the primary key of relation C is a composite key consisting of the primary key for each of the two entities in the relationship
    b. the primary keys of relation A and relation B are designated as functionally dependent attributes
    c. secondary keys are used to establish the relationship
    d. place the primary key of either entity in the relation for the other entity or do this for both entities

    Answer: a   **Difficulty**: Hard   **Reference**: p. 404

84. If a relationship exists among three or more entities, then:

    a. recursive relationships must be established through the use of recursive foreign keys
    b. a separate relation with a primary key that is the composite of the primary keys of each of the participating entities is created
    c. separate relations are established for each class and for each of the subclasses
    d. use the primary key of relation A as a foreign key in relations B and C

    Answer: b   **Difficulty**: Hard   **Reference**: p. 402

85. Relationships between instances of a single entity type are referred to as:

a. binary relationships
b. transitive relationships
c. recursive relationships
d. dependent relationships

Answer: c   **Difficulty**: Med   **Reference**: p. 402

86. A many-to-many relationship that associates certain items with their component items is called a:

a. binary structure
b. bill-of-materials structure
c. binary relationship
d. ternary relationship

Answer: b   **Difficulty**: Med   **Reference**: p. 402

87. A foreign key in a relation that references the primary key values of that same relation is referred to as a:

a. secondary key
b. recursive foreign key
c. composite key
d. complex key

Answer: b   **Difficulty**: Med   **Reference**: p. 402

88. For a unary M:N relationship:

a. the entity type is modeled as one relation; using as its primary key a composite key, a separate relation is created to represent the M:N relationship
b. the entity type and the M:N relationship are modeled as one relation; a composite key is used
c. separate relations for the class and for each subclass are created; primary and foreign keys are established for each class
d. the primary key of the entity on the one side of the relationship serves as a foreign key in the relation on the many side of the relationship

Answer: a   **Difficulty**: Hard   **Reference**: p. 404

89. "Create a relation with primary key and nonkey attributes" is the relational representation for which E-R structure?

a. weak entity
b. regular entity
c. gerund
d. IS-A relationship

Answer: b   **Difficulty**: Med   **Reference**: p. 404

90. Merging relations is also referred to as:

    a. view integration
    b. view consolidation
    c. encompassing
    d. normalizing

    Answer: a   **Difficulty**: Med   **Reference**: p. 404

91. Two different names that refer to the same data item best defines:

    a. homonym
    b. synonym
    c. transitive dependency
    d. alias

    Answer: b   **Difficulty**: Med   **Reference**: p. 405

92. A single name that is used for two or more different attributes best defines:

    a. homonym
    b. synonym
    c. transitive dependency
    d. alias

    Answer: a   **Difficulty**: Med   **Reference**: p. 405

93. When two 3NF relations are merged to form a single relation:

    a. weak entities are created
    b. recursive relationships may result
    c. transitive dependencies may result
    d. IS-A relationships are formed

    Answer: c   **Difficulty**: Med   **Reference**: p. 406

94. A named set of rows and columns that specifies the fields in each row of the table best describes:

    a. relation
    b. data structure
    c. entity type
    d. physical table

    Answer: d   **Difficulty**: Med   **Reference**: p. 412

95. A special field value, distinct from 0, blank, or any other value, that indicates that the value for the field is missing or otherwise unknown best defines:

    a. transitive value
    b. primary key
    c. null value
    d. pointer

    Answer: c   **Difficulty**: Med   **Reference**: p. 412

96.   The process of splitting or combining normalized relations into physical tables based on affinity of use of rows and fields best describes:

   a.   normalization
   b.   simplification
   c.   denormalization
   d.   data structure

   Answer: c   **Difficulty**: Med   **Reference**: p. 413

97.   Which of the following combines range and hash partitioning by first segregating data by ranges on the designated attribute and then within each of these partitions it further partitions by hashing on the designated attribute?

   a.   composite partitioning
   b.   combined partitioning
   c.   transitive partitioning
   d.   functional partitioning

   Answer: a   **Difficulty**: Hard   **Reference**: p. 414

98.   A field of data that can be used to locate a related field or row of data best describes:

   a.   pointer
   b.   marker
   c.   field locator
   d.   reference locator

   Answer: a   **Difficulty**: Med   **Reference**: p. 416

99.   A table used to determine the location of rows in a file that satisfy some condition best describes:

   a.   relation
   b.   structure chart
   c.   index
   d.   domain table

   Answer: c   **Difficulty**: Med   **Reference**: p. 416

100.   The index file organization:

   a.   provides very fast random retrieval on the primary key
   b.   provides slow random retrieval on the primary key
   c.   provides moderately fast random retrieval on the primary key
   d.   does not provide random retrieval on the primary key

   Answer: c   **Difficulty**: Med   **Reference**: p. 419

Fill In the Blanks

101. A *primary key* is an attribute whose value is unique across all occurrences of a relation.

    Difficulty: Med   **Reference**: p. 392

102. A *relational database model* represents data as a set of related tables or relations.

    Difficulty: Easy   **Reference**: p. 393

103. A *relation* is a named, two-dimensional table of data.

    Difficulty: Easy   **Reference**: p. 393

104. A *well-structured relation* is a relation that contains a minimum amount of redundancy and allows users to insert, modify, and delete the rows without errors or inconsistencies.

    Difficulty: Med   **Reference**: p. 394

105. *Normalization* is the process of converting complex data structures into simple, stable data structures.

    Difficulty: Med   **Reference**: p. 394

106. *Functional dependency* refers to a particular relationship between two attributes.

    Difficulty: Med   **Reference**: p. 395

107. A relation is in *second normal form* if every nonprimary key attribute is functionally dependent on the whole primary key.

    Difficulty: Hard   **Reference**: p. 396

108. A relation is in *third normal form* if it is in second normal form and there are no functional dependencies between two (or more) nonprimary key attributes.

    Difficulty: Hard   **Reference**: p. 397

109. A *foreign key* is an attribute that appears as a nonprimary key attribute in one relation and as a primary key attribute (or part of a primary key) in another relation.

    Difficulty: Med   **Reference**: p. 398

110. *Referential integrity* is an integrity constraint specifying that the value (or existence) of an attribute in one relation depends on the value (or existence) of the same attribute in another relation.

    Difficulty: Med   **Reference**: p. 398

111. A *recursive foreign key* is a foreign key in a relation that references the primary key values of that same relation.

    Difficulty: Hard   **Reference**: p. 402

112. **Synonym** refers to two different names that are used for the same attribute.

                    Difficulty: Med   **Reference**: p. 405

113. **Homonym** is a single attribute name that is used for two or more different attributes.

                    Difficulty: Med   **Reference**: p. 405

114. A **field** is the smallest unit of named application data recognized by system software.

                    Difficulty: Easy   **Reference**: p. 409

115. A **data type** is a coding scheme recognized by system software for representing organizational data.

                    Difficulty: Med   **Reference**: p. 410

116. A **calculated field** is a field that can be derived from other database fields.

                    Difficulty: Med   **Reference**: p. 411

117. A **default value** is a value a field will assume unless an explicit value is entered for that field.

                    Difficulty: Easy   **Reference**: p. 411

118. **Null value** is a special field value, distinct from 0, blank, or any other value, that indicates that the value for the field is missing or otherwise unknown.

                    Difficulty: Med   **Reference**: p. 412

119. A **physical table** is a named set of rows and columns that specifies the fields in each row of the table.

                    Difficulty: Med   **Reference**: p. 412

120. **Denormalization** is the process of splitting or combining normalized relations into physical tables based on affinity of use of rows and fields.

                    Difficulty: Hard   **Reference**: p. 413

121. **File organization** is a technique for physically arranging the records of a file.

                    Difficulty: Med   **Reference**: p. 416

122. A **pointer** is a field of data that can be used to locate a related field or row of data.

                    Difficulty: Med   **Reference**: p. 416

123. An **index** is a table used to determine the location of rows in a file that satisfy some condition.

                    Difficulty: Easy   **Reference**: p. 416

124. A **secondary key** is one or a combination of fields for which more than one row may have the same combination of values.

                    Difficulty: Med   **Reference**: p. 417

125. The ***hashed file organization*** uses an algorithm to determine the address for each row.

Difficulty: Hard   **Reference**: p. 419

Matching Questions

Match each of the following terms with its corresponding definition.

a. foreign key
b. functional dependency
c. homonym
d. normalization
e. recursive foreign key
f. referential integrity
g. relation
h. relational database model
i. second normal form (2NF)
j. synonym
k. third normal form (3NF)
l. well-structured relation

126. A relation that contains a minimum amount of redundancy and allows users to insert, modify, and delete the rows in a table without errors or inconsistencies.

Answer: l   **Reference**: p. 394

127. A relation is in this form if every nonprimary key attribute is functionally dependent on the whole primary key.

Answer: i   **Reference**: p. 396

128. A particular relationship between two attributes. For every valid instance of A, that value of A uniquely determines the value of B.

Answer: b   **Reference**: p. 395

129. An attribute that appears as a nonkey attribute in one relation and as a primary key attribute (or part of a primary key) in another relation.

Answer: a   **Reference**: p. 398

130. A data model that represents data as a set of related tables or relations.

Answer: h   **Reference**: p. 393

131. A foreign key in a relation that references the primary key values of that same relation.

Answer: e   **Reference**: p. 402

132. Two different names that are used to refer to the same data item.

Answer: j   **Reference**: p. 405

133. A named two-dimensional table of data.

Answer: g   **Reference**: p. 393

134. An integrity constraint that specifies that the value (or existence) of an attribute in one relation depends on the value (or existence) of the same attribute in another relation.

Answer: f   **Reference**: p. 398

135. A single name that is used for two or more different attributes.

Answer: c   **Reference**: p. 405

136. A relation is in this form if it is in second normal form and no transitive dependencies exist.

Answer: k   **Reference**: p. 397

137. The process of converting complex data structures into simple, stable data structures.

Answer: d   **Reference**: p. 394

Match each of the following terms with its corresponding definition.

    a. calculated field
    b. data type
    c. default value
    d. denormalization
    e. field
    f. hashed file organization
    g. index
    h. indexed file organization
    i. pointer
    j. sequential file organization

138.   The smallest unit of named application data recognized by system software.

        Answer: e   **Reference:** p. 409

139.   A value a field will assume unless an explicit value is entered for that field.

        Answer: c   **Reference:** p. 411

140.   A field that can be derived from other database fields.

        Answer: a   **Reference:** p. 411

141.   The process of splitting or combining normalized relations into physical tables based on affinity of use of rows and fields.

        Answer: d   **Reference:** p. 413

142.   A coding scheme recognized by system software for representing organizational data.

        Answer: b   **Reference:** p. 410

143.   A table used to determine the location of rows in a file that satisfy some condition.

        Answer: g   **Reference:** p. 416

144.   The address for each row is determined using an algorithm.

        Answer: f   **Reference:** p. 419

145.   The rows are stored either sequentially or nonsequentially, and a table is created that allows software to locate individual rows.

        Answer: h   **Reference:** p. 416

146.   The rows in the file are stored in sequence according to a primary key value.

        Answer: j   **Reference:** p. 416

147.   A field of data that can be used to locate a related field or row of data.

        Answer: i   **Reference:** p. 416

Match each of the following terms with its corresponding definition.

    a.   foreign key
    b.   functional dependency
    c.   homonym
    d.   recursive foreign key
    e.   referential integrity
    f.   relation
    g.   relational database model
    h.   synonym
    i.   well-structured relation

148.   A foreign key in a relation that references the primary key values of that same relation.

                  Answer: d   **Reference:** p. 402

149.   A particular relationship between two attributes. For every valid instance of A, the value of A uniquely determines the value of B.

                  Answer: b   **Reference:** p. 395

150.   A relation that contains a minimum amount of redundancy and allows users to insert, modify, and delete the rows in a table without errors or inconsistencies.

                  Answer: i   **Reference:** p. 394

151.   An attribute that appears as a nonkey attribute in one relation and as a primary key attribute (or part of a primary key) in another relation.

                  Answer: a   **Reference:** p. 398

152.   A named two-dimensional table of data.

                  Answer: f   **Reference:** p. 393

153.   A single name that is used for two or more different attributes.

                  Answer: c   **Reference:** p. 405

154.   An integrity constraint that specifies that the value (or existence) of an attribute in one relation depends on the value (or existence) of the same attribute in another relation.

                  Answer: e   **Reference:** p. 398

155.   Two different names that are used to refer to the same data item.

                  Answer: h   **Reference:** p. 405

156.   A data model that represents data in the form of tables or relations.

                  Answer: g   **Reference:** p. 393

Match each of the following E-R structures with its relational representation.

    a.   regular entity
    b.   weak entity
    c.   binary or unary 1:1 relationship
    d.   binary 1:N relationship
    e.   binary or unary M:N relationship or associative entity
    f.   binary or unary M:N relationship or associative entity with its own key

157.   Create a relation with a composite primary key that includes the primary key of the entity on which this entity depends and nonkey attributes.

                Answer: b   **Reference:** p. 404

158.   Create a relation with a composite primary key using the primary keys of the related entities, plus any nonkey attributes of the relationship or associative entity.

                Answer: e   **Reference:** p. 404

159.   Create a relation with the primary key associated with the relationship or associative entity, plus any nonkey attributes of the relationship or associative entity and the primary keys of the related entities.

                Answer: f   **Reference:** p. 404

160.   Place the primary key of the entity on the one side of the relationship as a foreign key in the relation for the entity on the many side.

                Answer: d   **Reference:** p. 404

161.   Create a relation with primary key and nonkey attributes.

                Answer: a   **Reference:** p. 404

162.   Place the primary key of either entity in the relation for the other entity or do this for both entities.

                Answer: c   **Reference:** p. 404

Match each of the following file organizations with a corresponding description. (Answers may occur more than once.)

    a.   indexed file organization
    b.   hashed file organization
    c.   sequential file organization

163.   Referencing storage space, this method has no wasted space.

Answer: c   **Reference:** p. 419

164.   Referencing sequential retrieval on the primary key, this method is impractical.

Answer: b   **Reference:** p. 419

165.   Referencing multiple key retrieval, this method is not possible.

Answer: b   **Reference:** p. 419

166.   Referencing updating rows, this method is easy but requires maintenance of indexes.

Answer: a   **Reference:** p. 419

167.   Referencing random retrieval on primary key, this method is moderately fast.

Answer: a   **Reference:** p. 419

Essay Questions

168.   *Define each of the following terms: relation, functional dependency, foreign key, and normalization.*

A relation is a named two-dimensional table of data. A particular relationship between two attributes is called a functional dependency. A foreign key is an attribute that appears as a nonkey attribute in one relation and as a primary key attribute (or part of a primary key) in another relation. Normalization is the process of converting complex data structures into simple, stable data structures.

169.   *Outline the four key steps in logical database modeling and design.*

The four key steps in logical database modeling and design are: (1) using normalization principles, develop a logical data model for each known user interface for the application; (2) combine all normalized user views into one consolidated logical database model; (3) translate the conceptual E-R data model for the application into normalized relations; and (4) compare the consolidated logical database design with the translated E-R model, and produce, through view integration, one final logical database model for the application.

170.   *Identify the five properties of a relation.*

The five properties that distinguish a relation from a nonrelational table are: (1) entries in columns are simple; (2) entries in columns are from the same set of values; (3) each row is unique; (4) the sequence of columns is insignificant; and (5) the sequence of rows is insignificant.

171. *Discuss the rules for normalization.*

Although first normal form is not directly mentioned in the textbook, it requires the removal of repeating data, so there is a single value at the intersection of each row and column of the relation. Relations are in second normal form if nonkey attributes require the whole key for identification. Relations are in third normal form if no transitive dependencies exist in the relation.

172. *Briefly identify the three file organizations.*

Sequential, indexed, and hashed are the three file organizations presented in the textbook. When using the sequential file organization, the rows in the file are stored in sequence according to a primary key value. When using the indexed file organization, the rows are stored either sequentially or nonsequentially, and an index is created that allows software to locate individual rows. The hashed file organization method uses an algorithm to determine the address for each row.

173. *Identify several advantages and disadvantages of using an index.*

By using an index, both random and sequential processing are possible. Since the index is separate from the data, multiple index structures can be built on the same data file. The disadvantages include the extra space needed to store the indexes and the extra time required to access and maintain the indexes.

174. *What are the four key physical database design decisions you will make?*

The four key physical database design decisions are selecting data types, data structures, file organizations, and media and structures for storing data.

175. *What is second normal form? What conditions determine if a relation is in second normal form?*

A relation is in second normal form if each nonkey attribute is functionally dependent on the whole primary key. Three conditions were mentioned in the textbook. These conditions are: (1) the primary key consists of only one attribute; (2) no nonprimary key attributes exist in the relation; and (3) every nonprimary key attribute is functionally dependent on the full set of primary key attributes.

176. *How is a binary one-to-one relationship represented?*

A binary one-to-one relationship can be represented in three ways: (1) the primary key of the first entity can serve as a foreign key of the second entity; (2) the primary key of the second entity can serve as a foreign key of the first entity; or (3) each entity's primary key can serve as a foreign key of the other entity.

177. *You have recently been hired by an appliance repair company. Your first task is to normalize the following relation.*

Client No.	Last Name	Street Address	City	State	Technician No.	Technician Last Name	Service Date	Type of Service

After normalization, students should identify at least four relations. Students may include additional fields.

CLIENT (<u>Client_No</u>, Last_Name, Street_Address, City, State)
TECHNICIAN (<u>Technician_No</u>, Tech_Last_Name)
PROVIDEDSERVICE (<u>Service_Date, Client_No, Service_No</u>)
SERVICE (<u>Service_No</u>, Service_Description)

Chapter 13
Designing Forms and Reports

True-False Questions

1. In general, forms are used to present or collect information on a single item.

    Answer: True   **Difficulty**: Med   **Reference**: p. 432

2. The contents of a form or report correspond to the data elements contained in an associated data flow located on a data flow diagram.

    Answer: True   **Difficulty**: Med   **Reference**: p. 434

3. The data on all forms and reports must consist of data elements in data stores and on the E-R data model for the application or else be computed from these data elements.

    Answer: True   **Difficulty**: Med   **Reference**: p. 434

4. Invoices and mailing labels are examples of forms.

    Answer: False   **Difficulty**: Med   **Reference**: p. 434

5. On the Internet, form interaction is the standard method of gathering and displaying information when consumers order products, request product information, or query account status.

    Answer: True   **Difficulty**: Med   **Reference**: p. 434

6. When preparing an initial prototype of a form or report, the structuring and refinement of the requirements requires much input from the end users.

    Answer: False   **Difficulty**: Med   **Reference**: p. 435

7. Often, the initial prototypes of forms and reports are mock screens that are not working modules or systems.

    Answer: True   **Difficulty**: Med   **Reference**: p. 435

8. The major deliverables from the designing forms and reports stage are logic models.

    Answer: False   **Difficulty**: Easy   **Reference**: p. 436

9. Structure charts, flowcharts, and dialogue diagrams are the major deliverables for the designing forms and reports stage.

    Answer: False   **Difficulty**: Med   **Reference**: p. 436

10. Designing usable forms and reports requires your active interaction with users.

    Answer: True   **Difficulty**: Easy   **Reference**: p. 439

11. The purpose of the testing and usability assessment section of a form design specification is to explain to those who will actually develop the final form why this form exists and how it will be used.

Answer: False   **Difficulty**: Med   **Reference**: p. 437

12. Notifying the user on the last page of a multipaged sequence is a guideline for designing forms and reports.

Answer: True   **Difficulty**: Med   **Reference**: p. 439

13. Gaining an understanding of the skills of the intended system users and the tasks they will be performing is invaluable when constructing a form or report.

Answer: True   **Difficulty**: Easy   **Reference**: p. 440

14. Highlighting techniques can be used singularly or in combination, depending upon the level of emphasis desired by the designer.

Answer: True   **Difficulty**: Med   **Reference**: p. 441

15. Highlighting should be used as often as possible to draw the user away from or to certain information.

Answer: False   **Difficulty**: Med   **Reference**: p. 441

16. Form designers should use highlighting as often as possible to distinguish the different categories of data.

Answer: False   **Difficulty**: Med   **Reference**: p. 441

17. Color, intensity, and size differences are methods of highlighting.

Answer: True   **Difficulty**: Med   **Reference**: p. 441

18. Highlighting methods should be consistently selected and used based upon the level of importance of the emphasized information.

Answer: True   **Difficulty**: Med   **Reference**: p. 442

19. Generally speaking, highlighting methods appear the same on all output devices.

Answer: False   **Difficulty**: Med   **Reference**: p. 442

20. In business-related systems, textual output is becoming less important as the text-based applications that use these systems are slowly disappearing.

Answer: False   **Difficulty**: Med   **Reference**: p. 443

21. Where possible, text should appear in all upper case on forms.

Answer: False   **Difficulty**: Med   **Reference**: p. 443

22. The guidelines for displaying text include case, spacing, and justification guidelines.

Answer: True   **Difficulty**: Easy   **Reference**: p. 443

23.   When designing textual output, the text's case should be displayed in mixed upper and lower case.

   Answer: True   **Difficulty**: Med   **Reference**: p. 443

24.   When designing textual output, you should use single spacing wherever possible.

   Answer: False   **Difficulty**: Med   **Reference**: p. 443

25.   When designing textual output, you should hyphenate words between lines.

   Answer: False   **Difficulty**: Med   **Reference**: p. 443

26.   When designing textual output, both the left and right margins should appear justified.

   Answer: False   **Difficulty**: Med   **Reference**: p. 443

27.   When displaying textual information, use abbreviations and acronyms as often as possible.

   Answer: False   **Difficulty**: Med   **Reference**: p. 443

28.   When using color, printing or conversion to other media, may not easily translate.

   Answer: True   **Difficulty**: Med   **Reference**: p. 443

29.   The context and meaning of tables and lists are significantly derived from the format of the information.

   Answer: True   **Difficulty**: Med   **Reference**: p. 445

30.   When displaying tables and lists, you should right-justify numeric data and align columns by decimal points or other delimiters.

   Answer: True   **Difficulty**: Med   **Reference**: p. 445

31.   When displaying tables and lists, you should break long sequences of alphanumeric data into small groups of three to four characters each.

   Answer: True   **Difficulty**: Med   **Reference**: p. 445

32.   Tables are very beneficial for analyzing data changes over time.

   Answer: False   **Difficulty**: Med   **Reference**: p. 447

33.   When selecting tables versus graphs, you should use graphs for reading individual values.

   Answer: False   **Difficulty**: Med   **Reference**: p. 447

34.   When selecting tables versus graphs, you should use graphs for detecting trends over time.

   Answer: True   **Difficulty**: Med   **Reference**: p. 447

35.   When selecting tables versus graphs, you should use tables to forecast activities.

   Answer: False   **Difficulty**: Med   **Reference**: p. 447

36. When selecting tables versus graphs, you should use tables to provide a quick summary of data.

    Answer: False   **Difficulty**: Med   **Reference**: p. 447

37. One of the primary advantages of impact printers is their ability to exactly replicate a screen report on paper.

    Answer: False   **Difficulty**: Med   **Reference**: p. 449

38. Reliability is an overall evaluation of how a system performs in supporting a particular user for a particular task.

    Answer: False   **Difficulty**: Med   **Reference**: p. 449

39. Referencing form and report usability, the consistency guideline means that formatting should be designed with an understanding of the task being performed and the intended user.

    Answer: False   **Difficulty**: Med   **Reference**: p. 449

40. Referencing form and report usability, special symbols, such as decimal places, dollar signs and +/- signs should be used as appropriate.

    Answer: True   **Difficulty**: Easy   **Reference**: p. 449

41. Referencing the general design guidelines for form and report usability, the ease usability factor means that information should be viewed and retrieved in a manner most convenient to the user.

    Answer: False   **Difficulty**: Hard   **Reference**: p. 449

42. When designing forms and reports, issues related to a user's experience, skills, motivation, education, and personality should not be considered.

    Answer: False   **Difficulty**: Med   **Reference**: p. 450

43. When designing the forms and reports for an Internet-based electronic commerce application, a prototyping design process is most appropriate.

    Answer: True   **Difficulty**: Med   **Reference**: p. 451

44. When designing the layout of Web pages, you should avoid using bleeding-edge technology.

    Answer: True   **Difficulty**: Med   **Reference**: p. 452

45. To avoid the nonstandard use of GUI widgets, make sure that users do not need the latest browsers or plug-ins to view your web site.

    Answer: False   **Difficulty**: Hard   **Reference**: p. 452

46. Nonstandard colors confuse the user and reduce ease of use.

    Answer: True   **Difficulty**: Med   **Reference**: p. 452

47. To avoid outdated information on your web site, you should make sure your site is continuously updated so that users feel that the site is regularly maintained and updated.

    Answer: True   **Difficulty**: Med   **Reference**: p. 452

48. Fixed-formatted text processing refers to the use of small simple images to allow a Web page to more quickly be displayed.

    Answer: False   **Difficulty**: Med   **Reference**: p. 452

49. XML icons are templates that display and process common attributes of higher-level, more abstract items.

    Answer: False   **Difficulty**: Med   **Reference**: p. 453

50. One key to designing quality business processes is the delivery of the right information to the right people, in the right format, at the right time.

    Answer: True   **Difficulty**: Easy   **Reference**: p. 453

Multiple Choice Questions

51. Presenting or collecting information on a single item is the purpose of a:

    a. diagram
    b. form
    c. report
    d. none of the above

    Answer: b   **Difficulty**: Med   **Reference**: p. 432

52. The type of document that is used to convey information on a collection of items is a:

    a. report
    b. diagram
    c. letter
    d. form

    Answer: a   **Difficulty**: Med   **Reference**: p. 432

53. Which of the following is not a true statement?

    a. Forms and reports are integrally related to various diagrams developed during requirements structuring.
    b. Every input form will be associated with a data flow leaving a process on a DFD.
    c. The contents of a form or report correspond to the data elements contained in an associated data flow.
    d. The data on all forms and reports must be data elements in data stores and on the E-R data model for the application, or must be computed from these data elements.

    Answer: b   **Difficulty**: Med   **Reference**: p. 434

54. A class registration sheet is an example of a:

a. report
b. diagram
c. memo
d. form

Answer: d   **Difficulty**: Med   **Reference**: p. 434

55. Which of the following is not a true statement concerning forms?

a. Most forms have a stylized format and are usually not in a simple row and column format.
b. Forms may be displayed on a video display and may be used for data display or data entry.
c. Forms are used to convey information on a collection of items.
d. Every output form will be a data flow produced by a process on a DFD.

Answer: c   **Difficulty**: Med   **Reference**: p. 434

56. A business document that contains some predefined data and may include some areas where additional data are to be filled in best describes a:

a. report
b. diagram
c. memo
d. form

Answer: d   **Difficulty**: Med   **Reference**: p. 434

57. A passive document that contains only predefined data best describes a:

a. report
b. diagram
c. form
d. none of the above

Answer: a   **Difficulty**: Med   **Reference**: p. 434

58. Which of the following is a true statement?

a. An employee application is an example of a report.
b. Reports are only for reading and often contain data about multiple unrelated records in a computer file.
c. Reports are used to convey information on a single item.
d. Generally, reports are only printed on paper.

Answer: b   **Difficulty**: Med   **Reference**: p. 434

59. A pie chart of population by age categories is an example of:

a. a statistical chart
b. a report
c. a form
d. regression analysis

Answer: b   **Difficulty**: Med   **Reference**: p. 434

60. Which of the following is a report?

    a. employment application
    b. class registration sheet
    c. product order form
    d. invoice

    Answer: d   **Difficulty**: Med   **Reference**: p. 434

61. When designing forms and reports, the first activity is to:

    a. gain an understanding of the intended user and task objectives by collecting initial requirements during requirements determination
    b. structure and refine the requirements independent from the users
    c. ask users to review and refine prototypes of the form or report
    d. structure and refine the requirements with the users

    Answer: a   **Difficulty**: Med   **Reference**: p. 434

62. Which of the following is a fundamental question to ask when designing forms and reports?

    a. Who will use the form or report?
    b. What is the purpose of the form or report?
    c. Where does the form or report need to be delivered and used?
    d. all of the above

    Answer: d   **Difficulty**: Easy   **Reference**: p. 435

63. The focus placed on forms and reports during logical design is on:

    a. the content and layout design of the forms and reports
    b. identifying how specific forms or reports should be implemented
    c. identifying the content, layout design, and implementation method
    d. none of the above

    Answer: a   **Difficulty**: Med   **Reference**: p. 435

64. In the case of designing forms and reports, the major deliverables are:

    a. the design specifications
    b. an updated baseline project plan and updated statement of work
    c. entity-relationship diagrams
    d. the implemented forms and reports

    Answer: a   **Difficulty**: Med   **Reference**: pp. 436-437

65. Which of the following is a design specification section?

    a. management issues
    b. system description
    c. testing and usability assessment
    d. feasibility assessment

    Answer: c   **Difficulty**: Med   **Reference**: p. 437

66. The section of a design specification that explains to those who will actually develop the final form why this form exists and how it will be used is called:

    a. testing and usability assessment
    b. rationale and benefit
    c. narrative overview
    d. usage and application

    Answer: c   **Difficulty**: Med   **Reference**: p. 437

67. If a form is delivered on a visual display terminal, which design specification section would describe the capabilities of this device?

    a. sample design
    b. narrative overview
    c. testing and usability
    d. management issues

    Answer: b   **Difficulty**: Med   **Reference**: p. 437

68. Clearly labeling all data and entry fields refers to the general guideline of:

    a. meaningful titles
    b. meaningful information
    c. balanced layout
    d. easy navigation

    Answer: c   **Difficulty**: Med   **Reference**: p. 439

69. Providing a valid date (or time) that identifies when the data in the form or report were accurate refers to the general guideline of:

    a. meaningful titles
    b. meaningful information
    c. balanced layout
    d. easy navigation

    Answer: a   **Difficulty**: Med   **Reference**: p. 439

70. All of the following are general guidelines for the design of forms and reports except:

    a. meaningful titles should be used
    b. extraneous information should be used to provide additional information as needed
    c. the user should be able to navigate easily through the document
    d. the layout should be balanced

    Answer: b   **Difficulty**: Med   **Reference**: p. 439

71. In general, highlighting:

    a. should not be used to warn users of errors in data entry or processing
    b. should not be used to provide warnings to users regarding possible problems such as unusual data values
    c. should not be used in tandem
    d. should be used sparingly to draw the user to or away from certain information and to group together related information

    Answer: d   **Difficulty**: Med   **Reference**: p. 441

72. Which of the following is a highlighting method?

    a. using all capital letters
    b. using different fonts
    c. underlining
    d. all of the above

    Answer: d   **Difficulty**: Easy   **Reference**: p. 441

73. Research conducted on highlighting suggests:

    a. highlighting should be used conservatively
    b. highlighting methods should be consistently used and selected based on the level of importance of the emphasized information
    c. blinking and audible tones should only be used to highlight critical information that requires an immediate response from the user
    d. all of the above are correct

    Answer: d   **Difficulty**: Med   **Reference**: p. 441

74. All of the following are problems with using color except:

    a. printing or conversion to other media may not easily translate
    b. evokes more emotional reactions
    c. resolution may degrade with different displays
    d. color pairings may washout or cause problems for some users

    Answer: b   **Difficulty**: Med   **Reference**: p. 443

75. Which of the following is not a benefit of using color?

    a. soothes or strikes the eye
    b. facilitates subtle discriminations in complex displays
    c. evokes more emotional reactions
    d. printing or conversion to other media may not easily translate

    Answer: d   **Difficulty**: Med   **Reference**: p. 443

76. Research conducted on the usage of color found that:

    a. color had positive effects on user task performance and perceptions when the user was under time constraints for the completion of a task
    b. color is universally better than no color
    c. the benefits of color are apparent regardless of the presentation format of the information
    d. limiting the number and amount of color is not a good idea

    Answer: a   **Difficulty**: Med   **Reference**: p. 443

77. When displaying text, a person should:

    a. right justify text
    b. hyphenate words between lines
    c. use double spacing if space permits
    d. use obscure abbreviations and acronyms

    Answer: c   **Difficulty**: Med   **Reference**: p. 443

78. Which of the following statements is not true?

    a. The context and meaning of tables and lists are significantly derived from the format of the information.
    b. The usability of information displayed in tables and alphanumeric lists is likely to be much more influenced by effective layout than most other types of information.
    c. Place a blank line between every ten rows in long columns.
    d. Use a single type face, except for emphasis.

    Answer: c   **Difficulty**: Med   **Reference**: p. 445

79. The general guidelines for displaying tables and lists include:

    a. providing meaningful labels for all columns and rows
    b. allowing white space on printed reports for users to write notes
    c. breaking long sequences of alphanumeric data into small groups of three to four characters each
    d. all of the above

    Answer: d   **Difficulty**: Med   **Reference**: p. 445

80. Tables should be used instead of graphs when the user will be:

    a. comparing points and patterns of different variables
    b. forecasting activities
    c. reading individual data values
    d. detecting trends over time

    Answer: c   **Difficulty**: Med   **Reference**: p. 447

81. Graphs should be used instead of tables for all of the following except:

    a. comparing points and patterns of different variables
    b. forecasting activities
    c. reading individual data values
    d. detecting trends over time

    Answer: c   **Difficulty**: Med   **Reference**: p. 447

82. Which of the following is not a true statement?

    a. Tables are best when the users' task is related to finding an individual data value from a larger data set.
    b. Line and bar graphs are more appropriate for gaining an understanding of data changes over time.
    c. Providing sufficient white space often entails printing a report in portrait rather than the landscape orientation.
    d. The key determination as to when you should select a table or a graph is the task being performed by the user.

    Answer: c   **Difficulty**: Med   **Reference**: pp. 447-448

83. All of the following are usability characteristics except:

    a. satisfaction
    b. completeness
    c. speed
    d. accuracy

    Answer: b   **Difficulty**: Med   **Reference**: p. 449

84. An overall evaluation of how a system performs for supporting a particular user for a particular task refers to:

    a. usability
    b. testing
    c. quality check
    d. feasibility assessment

    Answer: a   **Difficulty**: Med   **Reference**: p. 449

85. The general design guideline stating that information should be viewed and retrieved in a manner most convenient to the user is:

    a. efficiency
    b. ease
    c. flexibility
    d. format

    Answer: c   **Difficulty**: Med   **Reference**: p. 449

86. The general design guideline stating that outputs should be self-explanatory and not require users to remember information from prior outputs in order to complete tasks is:

    a. efficiency
    b. ease
    c. flexibility
    d. format

    Answer: b   **Difficulty**: Med   **Reference**: p. 449

87. The general design guideline stating that formatting should be designed with an understanding of the task being performed and the intended user refers to:

    a. efficiency
    b. ease
    c. flexibility
    d. format

    Answer: a   **Difficulty**: Med   **Reference**: p. 449

88. When designing forms and reports, the user characteristic addresses:

    a. issues related to experience, skills, motivation, education, and personality
    b. social issues such as the user's status and role, lighting, sound, task interruptions, temperature, and humidity
    c. job activities that differ in the amount of information that must be obtained from or provided to the user
    d. the platform in which the system is constructed, influencing interaction styles and devices

    Answer: a   **Difficulty**: Hard   **Reference**: p. 450

89. When designing forms and reports, the task characteristic addresses:

    a. issues related to experience, skills, motivation, education, and personality
    b. social issues such as the user's status and role, lighting, sound, task interruptions, temperature, and humidity
    c. activities that differ in the amount of information that must be obtained from or provided to the user
    d. the platform in which the system is constructed influencing interaction styles and devices

    Answer: c   **Difficulty**: Hard   **Reference**: p. 450

90. When designing forms and reports, the environment characteristic addresses:

    a. issues related to experience, skills, motivation, education, and personality
    b. social issues such as the user's status and role, lighting, sound, task interruptions, temperature, and humidity
    c. job activities that differ in the amount of information that must be obtained from or provided to the user
    d. the platform in which the system is constructed influencing interaction styles and devices

    Answer: b   **Difficulty**: Med   **Reference**: p. 450

91. When designing forms and reports, the system characteristic addresses:

    a. issues related to experience, skills, motivation, education, and personality
    b. social issues such as the user's status and role, lighting, sound, task interruptions, temperature, and humidity
    c. job activities that differ in the amount of information that must be obtained from or provided to the user
    d. the platform in which the system is constructed influencing interaction styles and devices

    Answer: d   **Difficulty**: Med   **Reference**: p. 450

92. Which of the following are methods used for assessing usability?

    a. subjective satisfaction
    b. speed of performance
    c. rate of errors
    d. all of the above

    Answer: d   **Difficulty**: Easy   **Reference**: p. 450

93. To assess usability, information can be collected by:

    a. observation
    b. interviews
    c. keystroke capturing
    d. all of the above

    Answer: d   **Difficulty**: Easy   **Reference**: p. 450

94. When designing Web pages, which of the following is the recommendation for avoiding nonstandard use of GUI Widgets?

    a. avoid using large images, lots of images, unnecessary animations, or other time-consuming content
    b. avoid scrolling text and animations since they are both hard to read and users often equate such content as advertising
    c. make sure that users do not need the latest browsers or plug-ins to view your site
    d. make sure that when using standard design items, that they behave in accordance to major interface design standards

    Answer: d   **Difficulty**: Hard   **Reference**: p. 452

95. When designing Web pages, which of the following is the recommendation for avoiding bleeding-edge technology?

    a. avoid using large images, lots of images, unnecessary animations, or other time-consuming content
    b. avoid scrolling text and animations since they are both hard to read and users often equate such content as advertising
    c. make sure that users do not need the latest browsers or plug-ins to view your site
    d. make sure you avoid designing any legitimate information in a manner that resembles advertising

    Answer: c   **Difficulty**: Hard   **Reference**: p. 452

96. When designing Web pages, which of the following is the recommendation for the displaying long lists as long pages error?

   a. avoid using large images, lots of images, unnecessary animations, or other time-consuming content
   b. show only *N* items at a time, use multiple pages, or use a scrolling container within the window
   c. make sure that users do not need the latest browsers or plug-ins to view your site
   d. make sure you avoid designing any legitimate information in a manner that resembles advertising

   Answer: b   **Difficulty**: Med   **Reference**: p. 452

97. When designing Web pages, which of the following is the recommendation for avoiding anything that looks like advertising?

   a. avoid using large images, lots of images, unnecessary animations, or other time-consuming content
   b. avoid scrolling text and animations since they are both hard to read and users often equate such content as advertising
   c. make sure that users do not need the latest browsers or plug-ins to view your site
   d. make sure you avoid designing any legitimate information in a manner that resembles advertising

   Answer: d   **Difficulty**: Med   **Reference**: p. 452

98. When designing Web pages, which of the following is the recommendation for avoiding slow download times?

   a. avoid using large images, lots of images, unnecessary animations, or other time-consuming content
   b. avoid scrolling text and animations since they are both hard to read and users often equate such content as advertising
   c. make sure that users do not need the latest browsers or plug-ins to view your site
   d. make sure you avoid designing any legitimate information in a manner that resembles advertising

   Answer: a   **Difficulty**: Med   **Reference**: p. 452

99. The use of small simple images to allow a Web page to be displayed more quickly best describes:

   a. icons
   b. lightweight graphics
   c. cookie crumbs
   d. MPEG files

   Answer: b   **Difficulty**: Med   **Reference**: p. 452

100. Templates used to display and process common attributes of a higher-level and more abstract items best describes:

   a. object-oriented templates
   b. CGI scripts
   c. Java
   d. template-based HTML

   Answer: d   **Difficulty**: Med   **Reference**: p. 453

Fill In the Blanks

101. A *form* is a business document that contains some predefined data and may include some areas where additional data are to be filled in.

    Difficulty: Easy   **Reference**: p. 434

102. A *report* is a business document that contains only predefined data; it is a passive document used only for reading or viewing.

    Difficulty: Easy   **Reference**: p. 434

103. Designing forms and reports is a user-focused activity that typically follows a *prototyping* approach.

    Difficulty: Med   **Reference**: p. 434

104. The three design specification sections are *narrative overview*, *sample design*, and *testing and usability assessment*.

    Difficulty: Hard   **Reference**: p. 437

105. The *narrative overview* section of a design specification provides a general overview of the characteristics of the target users, tasks, system, and environmental factors in which the form or report will be used.

    Difficulty: Med   **Reference**: p. 437

106. Guidelines for designing forms and reports address *using meaningful titles*, *including meaningful information*, *balancing the layout*, and *designing an easy navigation system*.

    Difficulty: Hard   **Reference**: p. 439

107. Guidelines for displaying text include *case*, *spacing*, *justification*, *hyphenation*, and *abbreviations*.

    Difficulty: Hard   **Reference**: p. 443

108. *Usability* is an overall evaluation of how a system performs in supporting a particular user for a particular task.

    Difficulty: Med   **Reference**: p. 449

109. The three usability characteristics are *speed*, *accuracy*, and *satisfaction*.

    Difficulty: Med   **Reference**: p. 449

110. The *flexibility* general design guideline for usability of forms and reports specifies that information should be viewed and retrieved in a manner most convenient to the user.

    Difficulty: Med   **Reference**: p. 449

111. The *efficiency* general design guideline for usability of forms and reports specifies that formatting should be designed with an understanding of the task being performed and the intended user.

    Difficulty: Med   **Reference**: p. 449

112.   The ***ease*** general design guideline for usability of forms and reports specifies that outputs should be self-explanatory and not require users to remember information from prior outputs in order to complete tasks.

Difficulty: Med   **Reference**: p. 449

113.   When designing forms and reports, the ***user*** characteristic suggests that issues related to experience, skills, motivation, education, and personality be considered.

Difficulty: Med   **Reference**: p. 450

114.   When designing forms and reports, the ***environment*** characteristic suggests that social issues be considered.

Difficulty: Med   **Reference**: p. 450

115.   ***Time to learn***, ***speed of performance***, ***rate of errors***, ***retention over time***, and ***subjective satisfaction*** are methods for assessing usability.

Difficulty: Hard   **Reference**: p. 450

116.   When assessing usability, you can collect information by ***observation***, ***interviews***, ***keystroke capture***, and ***questionnaires***.

Difficulty: Hard   **Reference**: p. 450

117.   ***Time to learn*** reflects how long it takes the average system user to become proficient using the system.

Difficulty: Med   **Reference**: p. 450

118.   Pine Valley Furniture's design guidelines for its WebStore included ***lightweight graphics***, ***forms and data integrity rules***, and ***template-based HTML***.

Difficulty: Hard   **Reference**: p. 451

119.   When designing the layout of Web pages, making sure that when using standard design items that they behave in accordance to major interface design standards is the recommendation for the ***nonstandard use of GUI Widgets*** error.

Difficulty: Hard   **Reference**: p. 452

120.   When designing the layout of Web pages, making sure that you avoid designing any legitimate information in a manner that resembles advertising is the recommendation for the ***anything that looks like advertising*** error.

Difficulty: Hard   **Reference**: p. 452

121.   When designing the layout of Web pages, making sure that users do not need the latest browsers or plug-ins to view your site is the recommendation for the ***bleeding-edge technology*** error.

Difficulty: Hard   **Reference**: p. 452

122. When designing the layout of Web pages, avoid scrolling text and animations since they are both hard to read and users often equate such content as advertising is the recommendation for the ***scrolling test and looping animations*** error.

Difficulty: Hard   **Reference**: p. 452

123. When designing the layout of Web pages, making sure your site is continuously updated so that users feel that the site is regularly maintained and updated is the recommendation for the ***outdated information*** error.

Difficulty: Med   **Reference**: p. 452

124. ***Lightweight graphics*** is the use of small simple images to allow a Web page to be displayed more quickly.

Difficulty: Med   **Reference**: p. 452

125. Templates to display and process common attributes of higher-level, more abstract items are called ***template-based HTML***.

Difficulty: Med   **Reference**: p. 453

Matching Questions

For each of the following statements, answer "a" if it is a problem using color, or answer "b" if it is a benefit.

126. Resolution may degrade with different displays.

Answer: a   **Reference**: p. 443

127. Emphasizes the logical organization of information.

Answer: b   **Reference**: p. 443

128. Draws attention to warnings.

Answer: b   **Reference**: p. 443

129. Evokes more emotional reactions.

Answer: b   **Reference**: p. 443

130. Printing or conversion to other media may not easily translate.

Answer: a   **Reference**: p. 443

131. Color pairings may washout or cause problems for some users.

Answer: a   **Reference**: p. 443

132. Soothes or strikes the eye.

Answer: b   **Reference**: p. 443

133.   Facilitates subtle discriminations in complex displays.

                          Answer: b   **Reference**: p. 443

134.   Accents an uninteresting display.

                          Answer: b   **Reference**: p. 443

135.   Color fidelity may degrade on different displays.

                          Answer: a   **Reference**: p. 443

Match each of the following common errors to its recommendation.

    a. bleeding-edge technology
    b. scrolling test and looping animations
    c. nonstandard link colors
    d. nonstandard use of GUI widgets
    e. anything that looks like advertising
    f. outdated information
    g. displaying long lists as long pages
    h. fixed-formatted text
    i. slow download times

136.   Avoid requiring users to scroll down a page to view information, especially navigational controls.

          Answer: g   **Reference:** p. 452

137.   Avoid fixed-formatted text that requires users to scroll horizontally to view content or links.

          Answer: h   **Reference:** p. 452

138.   Avoid using large images, lots of images, unnecessary animations, or other time-consuming content.

          Answer: i   **Reference:** p. 452

139.   Make sure your site is continuously updated so that users "feel" that the site is regularly maintained and updated.

          Answer: f   **Reference:** p. 452

140.   Avoid using nonstandard colors to show links and for showing links that users have already used.

          Answer: c   **Reference:** p. 452

141.   Avoid scrolling text and animations since they are both hard to read and users often equate such content as advertising.

          Answer: b   **Reference:** p. 452

142.   Make sure that your users do not need the latest browsers or plug-ins to view your site.

          Answer: a   **Reference:** p. 452

143.   Make sure that you avoid designing any legitimate information in a manner that resembles advertising.

          Answer: e   **Reference:** p. 452

144.   Make sure that when using standard design items, that they behave in accordance to major interface design standards.

          Answer: d   **Reference:** p. 452

Match each of the following usability factors with its description.

        a.   consistency
        b.   ease
        c.   efficiency
        d.   flexibility
        e.   format

145.   Formatting should be designed with an understanding of the task being performed and the intended user. Text and data should be aligned and sorted for efficient navigation and entry. Entry of data should be avoided where possible.

                Answer: c   **Reference:** p. 449

146.   Information should be viewed and retrieved in a manner most convenient to the user.

                Answer: d   **Reference:** p. 449

147.   Information format should be consistent between entry and display.

                Answer: e   **Reference:** p. 449

148.   Outputs should be self-explanatory and not require users to remember information from prior outputs in order to complete tasks.

                Answer: b   **Reference:** p. 449

149.   Use of terminology, abbreviations, formatting, titles, and navigation within and across outputs should be consistent.

                Answer: a   **Reference:** p. 449

For the following statements, answer "a" if the statement is a guideline for displaying text, or answer "b" if the statement is not a guideline.

150.   Hyphenate words between lines.

                        Answer: b   **Reference**: p. 443

151.   To shorten the message, use abbreviations and acronyms frequently.

                        Answer: b   **Reference**: p. 443

152.   Display text in mixed (upper and lower case), and use conventional punctuation.

                        Answer: a   **Reference**: p. 443

153.   Left- and right-justify text.

                        Answer: b   **Reference**: p. 443

154.   Use double spacing if space permits.

                        Answer: a   **Reference**: p. 443

For the following statements, answer "a" if the statement is a guideline for displaying tables and lists, or answer "b" if the statement is not a guideline.

155.   Left-justify textual data.

                        Answer: a   **Reference**: p. 445

156.   Break long sequences of alphanumeric data into small groups of three to four characters each.

                        Answer: a   **Reference**: p. 445

157.   Similar information displayed in multiple columns should be sorted vertically.

                        Answer: a   **Reference**: p. 445

158.   Labels should be separated from other information by using highlighting.

                        Answer: a   **Reference**: p. 445

159.   Re-display labels when the data extends beyond a single screen or page.

                        Answer: a   **Reference**: p. 445

Essay Questions

160. *Differentiate between a form and a report.*

Forms are defined as business documents that contain some predefined data and may include some areas where additional data are to be filled in. Examples of forms are order forms, employment applications, and class registration sheets. Reports are business documents that contain only predefined data. Reports are considered to be passive documents used only for reading or viewing. Examples of reports include invoices, a pie chart of population by age categories, and a weekly sales summary by region report.

161. *Identify several general guidelines for the design of forms and reports.*

The guidelines can be grouped into four categories: meaningful titles, meaningful information, balanced layout, and easy navigation. Clear and specific titles describe the content and use of the document. By providing a revision date or code, the document is distinguished from earlier versions. A valid date identifies on what date (or time) the data in the form or report was accurate. Only needed information should be displayed; information should be provided in a usable manner without requiring modification. Information should be balanced on the screen or page. Adequate spacing and margins should be used. Data and entry fields should be clearly labeled. Easy navigation is provided by clearly showing how to move forward and backward, clearly showing the user where he or she is, and by notifying the user when he or she is on the last page of a multipaged sequence.

162. *What are the general guidelines for displaying tables and lists?*

Three categories of guidelines were provided in the textbook, including using meaningful labels, formatting columns, rows, and text, and formatting numeric, textual, and alphanumeric data. Table 13-6 provides specific guidelines for each category.

163. *When should you use tables? When should you use graphs?*

Tables are recommended for reading individual data values. Graphs are recommended for providing a quick summary of data, detecting trends over time, comparing points and patterns of different variables, forecasting activities, and reporting vast amounts of information when relatively simple impressions are to be drawn.

164. *What is usability? Identify three characteristics for assessing usability.*

Usability is an overall evaluation of how a system performs in supporting a particular user for a particular task. Speed, accuracy, and satisfaction are the three characteristics.

165. *Identify nine common errors that occur when designing the layout of Web pages.*

The nine common errors are nonstandard use of GUI widgets, anything that looks like advertising, bleeding-edge technology, scrolling test and looping animations, nonstandard link colors, outdated information, slow download times, fixed-formatted text, and displaying long lists as long pages.

166. *Define template-based HTML. What is its advantage?*

Template-based HTML refers to templates that display and process common attributes of higher-level, more abstract items. HTML templates enable the easy maintenance of interfaces, allowing a module to be reused.

167. *Identify four problems from using color.*

Four problems were identified in the textbook, including color pairings may wash out or cause problems for some users, resolution may degrade with different displays, color fidelity may degrade on different displays, and printing or conversion to other media may not easily translate.

168. *Identify five guidelines for displaying text.*

The guidelines presented in the textbook include: (1) text should be displayed in mixed upper and lower case and use conventional punctuation; (2) when possible, double spacing should be used; (3) text should be left-justified; (4) words should not be hyphenated between lines; and (5) abbreviations and acronyms should be used only when they are widely understood by users and are significantly shorter than the full text.

169. *Identify five methods of highlighting.*

Ten methods were presented in the textbook; these include blinking and audible tones, color differences, intensity differences, size differences, font differences, reverse video, boxing, underlining, all capital letters, and offsetting the position of nonstandard information.

Chapter 14
Designing Interfaces and Dialogues

True-False Questions

1. Interface design focuses on how information is provided to and captured from users.

    Answer: True   **Difficulty**: Med   **Reference**: p. 460

2. The participatory design approach is the most widely used approach for designing interfaces and dialogues.

    Answer: False   **Difficulty**: Med   **Reference**: p. 461

3. Display sequence refers to the way a user can move from one display to another.

    Answer: False   **Difficulty**: Med   **Reference**: p. 461

4. The major deliverable from system interface and dialogue design is user acceptance testing results.

    Answer: False   **Difficulty**: Med   **Reference**: p. 462

5. A conversation is a method by which users interact with information systems.

    Answer: False   **Difficulty**: Med   **Reference**: p. 462

6. Command language interaction refers to a human-computer interaction method where a list of system options is provided and a specific command is invoked by user selection of a menu option.

    Answer: False   **Difficulty**: Med   **Reference**: p. 463

7. The variations in menu design are often related to the capabilities of the development environment, the skills of the developer, and the size and complexity of the system.

    Answer: True   **Difficulty**: Med   **Reference**: p. 463

8. A pop-up menu is a menu positioning method that places a menu near the current cursor position.

    Answer: True   **Difficulty**: Easy   **Reference**: p. 465

9. A linear menu is a menu positioning method that places the access point of the menu near the top line of the display.

    Answer: False   **Difficulty**: Med   **Reference**: p. 465

10. One guideline for menu design is making sure that command verbs clearly and specifically describe operations.

    Answer: True   **Difficulty**: Med   **Reference**: p. 466

11. Context-sensitive interaction is a highly intuitive human-computer interaction method whereby data fields are formatted in a manner similar to paper-based forms.

    Answer: False   **Difficulty**: Med   **Reference**: p. 468

12. Object-based interaction is the most commonly used method for data entry and retrieval in business-based systems.

    Answer: False   **Difficulty**: Med   **Reference**: p. 470

13. Menus are the most common method for implementing object-based interaction.

    Answer: False   **Difficulty**: Med   **Reference**: p. 470

14. The most fundamental and widely used interaction device is the keyboard.

    Answer: True   **Difficulty**: Easy   **Reference**: p. 471

15. The selection of devices users will use for interaction is made during implementation.

    Answer: False   **Difficulty**: Med   **Reference**: p. 471

16. A trackball is a small vertical lever mounted on a base that steers the cursor on a computer display.

    Answer: False   **Difficulty**: Med   **Reference**: p. 472

17. When using a touch screen, usability problems may occur in the areas of visual blocking, user fatigue and movement scaling.

    Answer: False   **Difficulty**: Hard   **Reference**: p. 472

18. When using a light pen, usability problems may occur in the areas of movement scaling, durability, and adequate feedback.

    Answer: False   **Difficulty**: Hard   **Reference**: p. 472

19. When using a mouse, usability problems may occur in the areas of movement scaling and adequate feedback.

    Answer: True   **Difficulty**: Hard   **Reference**: p. 472

20. When comparing input devices, a mouse is the most accurate for text selection.

    Answer: True   **Difficulty**: Med   **Reference**: p. 473

21. When comparing input devices, a touch screen is the most preferred for data entry.

    Answer: False   **Difficulty**: Med   **Reference**: p. 473

22. Data entry displays should be consistently formatted across applications to speed data entry and reduce errors.

    Answer: True   **Difficulty**: Med   **Reference**: p. 473

23. Referencing interface layout guidelines, the standard screen navigation that users use to move between fields should be from left-to-right and top-to-bottom.

    Answer: True   **Difficulty**: Med   **Reference**: p. 474

24. Referencing interface layout guidelines, data fields should be grouped into logical categories with labels describing the contents of the category.

    Answer: True   **Difficulty**: Med   **Reference**: p. 474

25. Referencing interface layout guidelines, users should not be able to access areas of the screen not used for data entry or commands.

    Answer: True   **Difficulty**: Med   **Reference**: p. 474

26. When designing the navigation procedures within a system, the primary concerns are dialogue flow and the instructional features.

    Answer: False   **Difficulty**: Hard   **Reference**: p. 474

27. Referencing interface layout guidelines, data should not be permanently saved by the system until the user makes an explicit request to do so.

    Answer: True   **Difficulty**: Med   **Reference**: p. 474

28. Functional capabilities for providing smooth and easy navigation within a form include cursor-control, editing, exit, and help capabilities.

    Answer: True   **Difficulty**: Med   **Reference**: p. 475

29. When structuring data entry, users should be required to enter the current date and time.

    Answer: False   **Difficulty**: Med   **Reference**: p. 475

30. When structuring data entry fields, captions are not always necessary.

    Answer: False   **Difficulty**: Med   **Reference**: p. 477

31. When structuring data entry fields, the system should automatically justify data entries.

    Answer: True   **Difficulty**: Med   **Reference**: p. 477

32. When an appending data error has occurred, characters have been lost from the field.

    Answer: False   **Difficulty**: Easy   **Reference**: p. 478

33. When a transcripting data error occurs, additional characters have been added to a field.

    Answer: False   **Difficulty**: Easy   **Reference**: p. 478

34. The values validation test makes sure that values come from a standard set of values.

    Answer: True   **Difficulty**: Med   **Reference**: p. 478

35. The size validation test checks for too few or too many characters.

    Answer: True   **Difficulty**: Med   **Reference**: p. 478

36. The range validation test makes sure that data are reasonable for a situation.

    Answer: False   **Difficulty**: Med   **Reference**: p. 478

37. A reasonableness validation test checks to see if a social security number is exactly nine digits.

    Answer: False   **Difficulty**: Med   **Reference**: p. 478

38. An expected values validation test checks to see if there is a quantity field on each line item of a customer order.

    Answer: False   **Difficulty**: Med   **Reference**: p. 478

39. An audit trail is a record of the sequence of data entries and the date of those entries.

    Answer: True   **Difficulty**: Med   **Reference**: pp. 479-480

40. System feedback provides status information, prompting cues, and error or warning messages.

    Answer: True   **Difficulty**: Med   **Reference**: p. 480

41. Error messages should appear in roughly the same format and placement each time.

    Answer: True   **Difficulty**: Med   **Reference**: p. 481

42. When designing usable help, use lists to break information into manageable pieces.

    Answer: True   **Difficulty**: Med   **Reference**: p. 481

43. Conversation refers to the sequence of interaction between a user and a system.

    Answer: False   **Difficulty**: Med   **Reference**: p. 484

44. Transition diagramming is a formal method for designing and representing human-computer dialogues using box and line diagrams.

    Answer: False   **Difficulty**: Med   **Reference**: p. 485

45. Building dialogue prototypes and assessing usability are often optional activities.

    Answer: True   **Difficulty**: Med   **Reference**: p. 486

46. When designing interfaces for Internet-based electronic commerce applications, the lack of maturity of Web scripting and programming languages and the limitations in commonly used Web GUI component libraries create problems for interface designers.

    Answer: True   **Difficulty**: Med   **Reference**: p. 491

47. When designing the interface and dialogues of Websites, complex URLs, orphan pages, and lack of navigation support are common errors.

     Answer: True   **Difficulty**: Med   **Reference**: p. 491

48. Placing a menu in the same location on ever Web page helps customers to more quickly become familiar with a Website and more rapidly navigate through the site.

     Answer: True   **Difficulty**: Med   **Reference**: p. 492

49. Cookie crumbs allow users to navigate to a point previously visited and will assure that they are not lost.

     Answer: True   **Difficulty**: Med   **Reference**: p. 492

50. Web tabbing is a technique for showing users where they are in a Website by placing a series of "tabs" on a Web page that shows the users where they are and where they have been.

     Answer: False   **Difficulty**: Med   **Reference**: p. 492

Multiple Choice Questions

51. Interface design focuses on:

     a.   how information is provided and captured from users
     b.   the design of forms and reports
     c.   the logical design of system files and databases
     d.   turning design specifications into working computer code

     Answer: a   **Difficulty**: Med   **Reference**: p. 460

52. The deliverable and outcome from system interface and dialogue design is:

     a.   structured descriptions and diagrams that outline the logic contained within each DFD process
     b.   the creation of a design specification
     c.   an updated baseline project plan that details the work necessary to turn the selected design strategy into the desired replacement information system
     d.   a set of coherent, interrelated data flow diagrams

     Answer: b   **Difficulty**: Med   **Reference**: p. 462

53. A method by which users interact with information systems defines:

     a.   dialogue
     b.   discussion
     c.   interface
     d.   session

     Answer: c   **Difficulty**: Med   **Reference**: p. 462

54. A human-computer interaction method where explicit statements are entered into a system to invoke operations refers to:

   a. command language interaction
   b. natural language interaction
   c. machine language interaction
   d. object-based interaction

   Answer: a   **Difficulty**: Med   **Reference**: p. 463

55. Command language interaction is good for:

   a. experienced users
   b. systems with a limited command set
   c. rapid interaction with the system
   d. all of the above

   Answer: d   **Difficulty**: Med   **Reference**: p. 463

56. A human-computer interaction method where a list of system options is provided and a specific command is invoked by user selection of a menu option is:

   a. natural language interaction
   b. menu interaction
   c. form interaction
   d. object-based interaction

   Answer: b   **Difficulty**: Med   **Reference**: p. 463

57. The most widely used interface method is:

   a. object-based interaction
   b. natural language interaction
   c. menu interaction
   d. command language interaction

   Answer: c   **Difficulty**: Med   **Reference**: p. 463

58. The variation of menu design is most often related to:

   a. the capabilities of the development environment
   b. the skills of the developer
   c. the size and complexity of the system
   d. all of the above

   Answer: d   **Difficulty**: Med   **Reference**: p. 463

59. The menu positioning method that places a menu near the current cursor position is the:

   a. pop-up menu
   b. drop-down menu
   c. box menu
   d. cursor menu

   Answer: a   **Difficulty**: Med   **Reference**: p. 465

60. This type of menu positioning method places the access point of the menu near the top line of the display; when accessed, menus open by dropping down onto the display.

    a. pop-up menu
    b. drop-down menu
    c. box menu
    d. cursor menu

    Answer: b   **Difficulty**: Hard   **Reference**: p. 465

61. Which of the following is not a menu design guideline?

    a. Command verbs should clearly and specifically describe operations.
    b. Menu items should be displayed in all upper-case letters and have a clear, unambiguous interpretation.
    c. A consistent organizing principle should be used that relates to the tasks the intended users perform.
    d. The number of menu choices should not exceed the length of the screen.

    Answer: b   **Difficulty**: Med   **Reference**: p. 466

62. Grouping related options together and requiring the same option to have the same wording and codes each time it appears refers to the:

    a. wording guideline for menu design
    b. selection guideline for menu design
    c. organization guideline for menu design
    d. highlighting guideline for menu design

    Answer: c   **Difficulty**: Med   **Reference**: p. 466

63. The premise of allowing users to "fill in the blanks" when working with a system refers to:

    a. form interaction
    b. fill-in-the-blank interaction
    c. field entry interaction
    d. command language interaction

    Answer: a   **Difficulty**: Med   **Reference**: p. 468

64. An effectively designed form:

    a. minimizes the need to scroll windows
    b. provides default values when practical
    c. displays data in appropriate field lengths
    d. does all of the above

    Answer: d   **Difficulty**: Easy   **Reference**: pp. 468-470

65. The most commonly used method for data entry and retrieval in business-based systems is:

    a. object-based interaction
    b. command language interaction
    c. form interaction
    d. menu interaction

    Answer: c   **Difficulty**: Med   **Reference**: p. 470

66. A highly intuitive human-computer interaction method where data fields are formatted in a manner similar to paper-based forms defines:

    a. form interaction
    b. menu interaction
    c. object-based interaction
    d. command language interaction

    Answer: a   **Difficulty**: Med   **Reference**: p. 468

67. A human-computer interaction method where symbols are used to represent commands or functions defines:

    a. form interaction
    b. menu interaction
    c. object-based interaction
    d. command language interaction

    Answer: c   **Difficulty**: Med   **Reference**: p. 470

68. An icon is:

    a. a small vertical lever mounted on a base that steers the cursor on a computer display
    b. a graphical picture that reflects specific functions within a system
    c. a button on the mouse that tells the system when an item is selected
    d. a sphere mounted on a fixed base that steers the cursor on a computer display

    Answer: b   **Difficulty**: Med   **Reference**: p. 470

69. Which of the following methods is the least viable interaction style?

    a. form interaction
    b. natural language interaction
    c. command language interaction
    d. object-based interaction

    Answer: b   **Difficulty**: Med   **Reference**: p. 470

70. A human-computer interaction method where inputs to and outputs from a computer-based application are in a conventional speaking language such as English refers to:

    a. natural language interaction
    b. command language interaction
    c. native language interaction
    d. assembly language interaction

    Answer: a   **Difficulty**: Med   **Reference**: p. 470

71. The selection of devices that the users will use for interaction is made during:

    a. analysis
    b. implementation
    c. design
    d. initiation and planning

    Answer: c   **Difficulty**: Med   **Reference**: p. 471

72. The most fundamental and widely used hardware device used to support system interaction is the:

    a. mouse
    b. trackball
    c. keyboard
    d. light pen

    Answer: c   **Difficulty**: Easy   **Reference**: p. 471

73. A sphere mounted on a fixed base that steers the cursor on a computer display is a:

    a. trackball
    b. mouse
    c. light pen
    d. joystick

    Answer: a   **Difficulty**: Med   **Reference**: p. 472

74. Potentially high usability problems for some applications exist for keyboards in all of the following areas except:

    a. adequate feedback
    b. speed
    c. movement scaling
    d. visual blocking

    Answer: d   **Difficulty**: Hard   **Reference**: p. 472

75. Little or no usability problems exist for light pens in all of the following areas except:

    a. movement scaling
    b. pointing accuracy
    c. durability
    d. speed

    Answer: b   **Difficulty**: Med   **Reference**: p. 472

76. The most preferred input device for text correction is the:

    a. mouse
    b. keyboard
    c. trackball
    d. light pen

    Answer: d   **Difficulty**: Med   **Reference**: p. 473

77. The input device that is most accurate for text selection is the:

    a. mouse
    b. keyboard
    c. trackball
    d. light pen

    Answer: a   **Difficulty**: Med   **Reference**: p. 473

78. When designing the navigation procedures within your system, the primary concerns are:

    a. the design of between-field navigation and the ability to provide feedback
    b. grouping data fields into logical categories and assigning group labels
    c. flexibility and consistency
    d. accuracy and reliability

    Answer: c   **Difficulty**: Med   **Reference**: p. 474

79. Which of the following functional requirements are required for providing smooth and easy navigation within a form?

    a. cursor control capabilities
    b. editing capabilities
    c. exit capabilities
    d. all of the above

    Answer: d   **Difficulty**: Med   **Reference**: p. 477

80. Which of the following is not a rule for structuring data entry fields?

    a. Never require the user to enter information that is already available within the system.
    b. Users should not be required to enter information that can be easily computed by the system.
    c. Require users to specify the dimensional units of a particular value.
    d. All data entered onto a screen should automatically justify in a standard format.

    Answer: c   **Difficulty**: Med   **Reference**: pp. 475-477

81. Movement to another screen requires the functional requirement of:

    a. cursor control capabilities
    b. editing capabilities
    c. exit capabilities
    d. help capabilities

    Answer: c   **Difficulty**: Med   **Reference**: p. 477

82. Which of the following is not a rule for structuring data entry fields?

a. Never require data that is already on-line or that can be computed.
b. Always provide default values when appropriate.
c. Never justify data entries.
d. Always place a caption adjacent to fields.

Answer: c   **Difficulty**: Med   **Reference**: p. 477

83. Reversing the sequence of one or more characters in a field is called:

a. transposing
b. transcripting
c. appending
d. truncating

Answer: a   **Difficulty**: Med   **Reference**: p. 478

84. Entering invalid data into a field describes:

a. transposing
b. transcripting
c. appending
d. truncating

Answer: b   **Difficulty**: Med   **Reference**: p. 478

85. Testing to assure that data is of proper type is the purpose of the:

a. expected values validation test
b. range validation test
c. class or composition validation test
d. values validation test

Answer: c   **Difficulty**: Med   **Reference**: p. 478

86. Testing to assure that data conforms to a standard format is the purpose of the:

a. missing data validation test
b. pictures templates validation test
c. reasonableness validation test
d. size validation test

Answer: b   **Difficulty**: Med   **Reference**: p. 478

87. "Please wait while I open the file" is an example of:

a. status information
b. a remark
c. a warning message
d. a prompting cue

Answer: a   **Difficulty**: Med   **Reference**: p. 480

88. Using lists to break information into manageable pieces conforms to the SOS guideline of:

    a. shortcuts
    b. organize
    c. simplicity
    d. show

    Answer: b   **Difficulty**: Med   **Reference**: p. 481

89. The ability to provide field-level help is often referred to as:

    a. context-sensitive help
    b. screen-level help
    c. systems-level help
    d. application-level help

    Answer: a   **Difficulty**: Med   **Reference**: p. 482

90. The sequence of interaction between a user and a system refers to:

    a. interface
    b. discussion
    c. dialogue
    d. session

    Answer: c   **Difficulty**: Med   **Reference**: p. 484

91. The three major steps for designing dialogues include each of the following except:

    a. assessing usability
    b. designing the dialogue sequence
    c. building a prototype
    d. implementing the dialogue

    Answer: d   **Difficulty**: Med   **Reference**: p. 484

92. All dialogue design rules are mitigated by the:

    a. feedback guideline
    b. consistency guideline
    c. ease guideline
    d. control guideline

    Answer: b   **Difficulty**: Med   **Reference**: p. 484

93. The guideline specifying that dialogues be logically grouped and have a beginning, middle, and end is:

    a. closure
    b. shortcuts and sequence
    c. consistency
    d. control

    Answer: a   **Difficulty**: Med   **Reference**: p. 484

94. The guideline specifying that dialogues be simple for users to enter information and navigate between screens is:

    a.   navigation
    b.   ease
    c.   shortcuts and sequence
    d.   reversal

    Answer: b   **Difficulty**: Med   **Reference**: p. 484

95. The technique where users must confirm their intention twice before being allowed to proceed is called:

    a.   double-confirmation
    b.   double-checking
    c.   replacement confirmation
    d.   validity confirmation

    Answer: a   **Difficulty**: Med   **Reference**: p. 485

96. A formal method for designing and representing human-computer dialogues using box and line diagrams is referred to as:

    a.   interface design
    b.   dialogue diagramming
    c.   state-transition diagramming
    d.   entity-relationship diagramming

    Answer: b   **Difficulty**: Med   **Reference**: p. 485

97. The first step to becoming an effective GUI designer requires:

    a.   being able to program competently using a third-generation language
    b.   becoming an expert user of the GUI environment
    c.   understanding the available resources and how they can be used
    d.   both b and c

    Answer: d   **Difficulty**: Med   **Reference**: p. 488

98. The common property of windows and forms in a graphical user interface environment that requires users to resolve the request for information before proceeding is:

    a.   maximize
    b.   movable
    c.   modality
    d.   system menu

    Answer: c   **Difficulty**: Med   **Reference**: p. 489

99.　How can you avoid a hidden links error?

    a.　Make sure users can use the back button to return to prior pages.
    b.　Make sure your pages conform to users expectations by providing commonly used icon links.
    c.　Make sure users know which links are internal anchor points versus external links and indicate if a link brings up a separate browser window from those that do not.
    d.　Make sure you leave a border around images that are links, do not change link colors from normal defaults, and avoid embedding links within long blocks of text.

Answer: d　　　　　**Difficulty**: Hard　　　　　**Reference**: p. 491

100.　A technique for showing a user where they are in a Web site by placing a series of "tabs" on a Web page that shows a user where they are and where they have been best describes:

    a.　icons
    b.　lightweight images
    c.　cookie crumbs
    d.　MPEG files

Answer: b　　　　　**Difficulty**: Med　　　　　**Reference**: p. 492

Fill In the Blanks

101.　***Interface design*** focuses on how information is provided to and captured from users.

Difficulty: Med　　　　　**Reference**: p. 460

102.　An ***interface*** is a method by which users interact with information systems.

Difficulty: Med　　　　　**Reference**: p. 462

103.　***Command language interaction*** refers to a human-computer interaction method where users enter explicit statements into a system to invoke operations.

Difficulty: Med　　　　　**Reference**: p. 463

104.　***Menu interaction*** refers to a human-computer interaction method where a list of system options is provided and a specific command is invoked by user selection of a menu option.

Difficulty: Med　　　　　**Reference**: p. 463

105.　A ***pop-up menu*** is a menu positioning method that places a menu near the current cursor position.

Difficulty: Med　　　　　**Reference**: p. 465

106.　A ***drop-down menu*** is a menu positioning method that places the access point of the menu near the top line of the display; when accessed, menus open by dropping down onto the display.

Difficulty: Easy　　　　　**Reference**: p. 465

107. **_Form interaction_** is a highly intuitive human-computer interaction method whereby data fields are formatted in a manner similar to paper-based forms.

                    Difficulty: Med   **Reference**: p. 468

108. **_Object-based interaction_** is a human-computer interaction method where symbols are used to represent commands or functions.

                    Difficulty: Med   **Reference**: p. 470

109. **_Icon_** refers to graphical pictures that represent specific functions within a system.

                    Difficulty: Easy   **Reference**: p. 470

110. **_Natural language interaction_** is a human-computer interaction method whereby inputs to and outputs from a computer-based application are in a conventional speaking language such as English.

                    Difficulty: Med   **Reference**: p. 470

111. When designing the navigation procedures within your system, **_flexibility_** and **_consistency_** are primary concerns.

                    Difficulty: Med   **Reference**: p. 474

112. **_Appending_** is the type of data error that adds additional characters to a field.

                    Difficulty: Med   **Reference**: p. 478

113. **_Truncating_** is the type of data error that loses characters from a field.

                    Difficulty: Med   **Reference**: p. 478

114. **_Transcripting_** is the type data error that occurs when invalid data are entered into a field.

                    Difficulty: Med   **Reference**: p. 478

115. A **_transposition_** data error occurs when the sequence of one or more characters in a field is reversed.

                    Difficulty: Med   **Reference**: p. 478

116. A **_combinations_** validation test checks to see if the value combinations of two or more data fields are appropriate or make sense.

                    Difficulty: Hard   **Reference**: p. 478

117. A **_missing data_** validation test checks for the existence of data items in all fields of a record.

                    Difficulty: Med   **Reference**: p. 478

118. A **_pictures/templates_** validation test assures that data conform to a standard format.

                    Difficulty: Easy   **Reference**: p. 478

119. A _**self-checking digits**_ validation test is a test where an extra digit is added to a numeric field in which its value is derived using a standard formula.

    Difficulty: Hard   **Reference**: p. 478

120. An _**audit trail**_ is a record of the sequence of data entries and the date of those entries.

    Difficulty: Med   **Reference**: pp. 479-480

121. _**Status information**_, _**prompting cues**_, and _**error and warning messages**_ are three types of system feedback.

    Difficulty: Hard   **Reference**: p. 480

122. The sequence of interaction between a user and a system is called a _**dialogue**_.

    Difficulty: Med   **Reference**: p. 484

123. _**Dialogue diagramming**_ is a formal method for designing and representing human-computer dialogues using box and line diagrams.

    Difficulty: Med   **Reference**: p. 485

124. The _**modality**_ common property of windows and forms in a graphical user interface environment requires users to resolve the request for information before proceeding.

    Difficulty: Hard   **Reference**: p. 489

125. _**Cookie crumbs**_ is a technique for showing users where they are in a Web site by placing a series of "tabs" on a Web page that shows users where they are and where they have been.

    Difficulty: Med   **Reference**: p. 492

Matching Questions

Match each of the following validation tests and techniques with corresponding examples.

    a.   class or composition
    b.   combinations
    c.   expected values
    d.   missing data
    e.   pictures templates
    f.   range
    g.   reasonableness
    h.   self-checking digits
    i.   size
    j.   values

126.   Making sure that hyphens are in the right places for a student ID number.

                      Answer: e   **Reference:** p. 478

127.   Making sure that the pay rate for a specific type of employee is within reason.

                      Answer: g   **Reference:** p. 478

128.   Determining if the social security number contains exactly nine digits.

                      Answer: i   **Reference:** p. 478

129.   Determining if the state abbreviation is from the set of standard two-letter state codes.

                      Answer: j   **Reference:** p. 478

130.   Determining if the student's grade point average is between 0 and 4.0.

                      Answer: f   **Reference:** p. 478

131.   Determining if there is a quantity field on each line item of a customer order.

                      Answer: d   **Reference:** p. 478

132.   Matching data with existing customer names.

                      Answer: c   **Reference:** p. 478

133.   Evaluating the quantity sold to determine if it makes sense given the type of product.

                      Answer: b   **Reference:** p. 478

134.   Making sure that all data are numeric as opposed to alphabetic.

                      Answer: a   **Reference:** p. 478

135.   Using a standard formula to derive and add an extra digit to a part number.

                      Answer: h   **Reference:** p. 478

Match each of the input devices listed below to the areas where little or no usability problems exist for it.
(Answer may occur more than once. Questions may have multiple answers.)

     a. visual blocking
     b. user fatigue
     c. movement scaling
     d. durability
     e. adequate feedback
     f. speed
     g. pointing accuracy

136. keyboard

    Answer: a, b, d, g   **Reference**: p. 472

137. mouse

    Answer: a, b, d, f, g   **Reference**: p. 472

138. joystick

    Answer: a, b, d, f   **Reference**: p. 472

139. trackball

    Answer: a, b, f, g   **Reference**: p. 472

140. touch screen

    Answer: c, e, f   **Reference**: p. 472

141. light pen

    Answer: c, d, e, f   **Reference**: p. 472

142. graphics tablet

    Answer: a, b, d, f, g   **Reference**: p. 472

143. voice

    Answer: a, b, d, f   **Reference**: p. 472

Match each of the input devices listed below to the potentially high usability problems associated with it. (Answers may occur more than once. Questions may have multiple answers.)

    a.   visual blocking
    b.   user fatigue
    c.   movement scaling
    d.   durability
    e.   adequate feedback
    f.   speed
    g.   pointing accuracy

144. keyboard

    Answer: c, e, f   **Reference:** p. 472

145. mouse

    Answer: c, e   **Reference:** p. 472

146. joystick

    Answer: c, e, g   **Reference:** p. 472

147. trackball

    Answer: c, d, e   **Reference:** p. 472

148. touch screen

    Answer: a, b, d, g   **Reference:** p. 472

149. light pen

    Answer: a, b, g   **Reference:** p. 472

150. graphics tablet

    Answer: c, e   **Reference:** p. 472

151. voice

    Answer: c, e, g   **Reference:** p. 472

Match each of the following guidelines for structuring data entry fields with corresponding examples.

    a.   entry
    b.   defaults
    c.   units
    d.   replacement
    e.   captioning
    f.   format
    g.   justify
    h.   help

152.   Allow the user to look up the value in a table or automatically fill in the value once the user enters enough significant characters.

                   Answer: d   **Reference:** p. 477

153.   Assume today's date for a new sales invoice, or use the standard product price unless overridden.

                   Answer: b   **Reference:** p. 477

154.   Numbers are right justified and aligned on decimal points, and text is left justified.

                   Answer: g   **Reference:** p. 477

155.   Captions are placed adjacent to fields.

                   Answer: e   **Reference:** p. 477

156.   Automatically show standard embedded symbols, decimal points, credit symbol, or dollar sign.

                   Answer: f   **Reference:** p. 477

157.   Provide a hot key, such as the F1 key, that opens the help system on an entry that is most closely related to where the cursor is on the display.

                   Answer: h   **Reference:** p. 477

158.   Quantity in tons, dozens, or pounds is clearly identified.

                   Answer: c   **Reference:** p. 477

159.   The system calculates the extended order price.

                   Answer: a   **Reference:** p. 477

Match each of the following terms with its corresponding definition.

  a. command language interaction
  b. cookie crumbs
  c. dialogue
  d. dialogue diagramming
  e. drop-down menu
  f. form interaction
  g. icon
  h. interface
  i. menu interaction
  j. natural language interaction
  k. object-based interaction
  l. pop-up menu

160. A highly intuitive human-computer interaction method whereby data fields are formatted in a manner similar to paper-based forms

        Answer: f   **Reference:** p. 468

161. A technique for showing users where they are in a Web site by placing a series of "tabs" on a Web page that shows users where they are and where they have been

        Answer: b   **Reference:** p. 492

162. A formal method for designing and representing human-computer dialogues using box and line diagrams

        Answer: d   **Reference:** p. 485

163. The sequence of interaction between a user and a system

        Answer: c   **Reference:** p. 484

164. A human-computer interaction method where users enter explicit statements into a system to invoke operations

        Answer: a   **Reference:** p. 463

165. A menu positioning method that places the access point of the menu near the top line of the display; when accessed, menus open by dropping down onto the display

        Answer: e   **Reference:** p. 465

166. A human-computer interaction method where a list of system options is provided and a specific command is invoked by user selection of a menu option

        Answer: i   **Reference:** p. 463

167. A human-computer interaction method whereby inputs to and outputs from a computer-based application are in a conventional speaking language such as English

        Answer: j   **Reference:** p. 470

168.   Graphical pictures that represent specific functions within a system

               Answer: g   **Reference**: p. 470

169.   A human-computer interaction method where symbols are used to represent commands or functions

               Answer: k   **Reference**: p. 470

170.   A menu positioning method that places a menu near the current cursor position

               Answer: l   **Reference**: p. 465

171.   A method by which users interact with information systems

               Answer: h   **Reference**: p. 462

Essay Questions

172.   *Briefly identify and define the five most widely used interaction methods.*

The five interaction methods identified in the text are command language, menu, form, object, and natural language. Command language interaction refers to a human-computer interaction method where explicit statements are entered into a system to invoke operations. While this type of interaction places a substantial burden on the user (remembering names, syntax, and operations), command languages are good for experienced users, for systems with a limited command set, and for rapid interaction with the system. Menu interaction refers to a human-computer interaction method where a list of system options are provided and a specific command is invoked by user selection of a menu option. Menus have become the most widely used interface. The design and complexity of menus differs due to the capabilities of the development environment, developer skills, and size and complexity of the system. Form interaction refers to a highly intuitive human-computer interaction method where data fields are formatted in a manner similar to paper-based forms. This method is the most commonly used method for data entry and retrieval in business-based systems. Object-based interaction is a human-computer interaction method where symbols are used to represent commands or functions. The implementation of object-based interaction is usually through the use of icons. Natural language interaction is a human-computer interaction method where inputs to and outputs from a computer-based application are in a conventional speaking language such as English. Currently, this is not as viable an interaction method as the other methods.

173.   *Briefly identify eight common devices for interacting with an information system.*

The common devices for interacting with an information system are keyboard, mouse, joystick, trackball, touch screen, light pen, graphics tablet, and voice. Keyboards require users to push an array of small buttons that represent symbols that are then translated into words and commands. The mouse is a small plastic box that users push across a flat surface and whose movements are translated into cursor movement on a computer display. The joystick is a small vertical lever mounted on a base that steers the cursor on a computer display. A trackball is a sphere mounted on a fixed base that steers the cursor on a computer display. On a touch sensitive screen, selections are made by touching a computer display. With a light pen, selections are made by pressing a pen-like device against the screen. Using a graphics tablet involves moving a pen-like device across a flat tablet to steer the cursor on a computer display. The voice device captures spoken words.

174. *Identify four sources of data errors.*

Sources of data errors include appending, truncating, transcripting, and transposing. Appending is the addition of extra characters to a field. Losing characters from a field is called truncating. Transcripting is defined as entering invalid data into a field. Transposing involves reversing the sequence of one or more characters in a field.

175. *Briefly discuss the SOS guidelines.*

The authors provided their SOS guidelines for the design of system help. SOS stands for simplicity, organize, and show. Simplicity refers to using short, simple wording, common pronunciation, and complete sentences. Organize suggests using lists to break information into manageable pieces. Show recommends providing examples of proper use and the outcomes of such use.

176. *Identify the eight guideline categories for the design of human-computer dialogues.*

The eight categories are consistency, shortcuts and sequence, feedback, closure, error handling, reversal, control, and ease.

177. *Identify ten validation tests and techniques used to enhance the validity of data input.*

Class or composition, combinations, expected values, missing data, pictures/templates, range, reasonableness, self-checking digits, size, and values are ten validation tests and techniques. The class or composition test checks to assure that data are of proper type. The combinations test checks to see if the value combinations of two or more data fields are appropriate or make sense. The expected values test checks to see if data are what is expected. The missing data test checks for existence of data items in all fields of a record. The picture/templates test assures that data conform to a standard format. The range test assures that data are within a proper range of values. The reasonableness test assures that data are reasonable for a situation. The self-checking digits test is a test where an extra digit is added to a numeric field in which its value is derived using a standard formula. Testing for too few or too many characters is referred to as a size test. A values test checks to make sure values come from a set of standard values.

178. *Identify nine common errors that might occur when designing the interface and dialogues of Web sites.*

Opening a new browser window, breaking or slowing down the back button, complex URLs, orphan pages, scrolling navigation pages, lack of navigation support, hidden links, links that do not provide enough information, and buttons that provide no click feedback are the nine common errors mentioned in the textbook.

179. *As a Website designer, how can you avoid errors caused by links that do not provide enough information?*

The textbook provides three recommendations: (1) not turning off link marking borders so that the links clearly show which links users have clicked and which they have not; (2) making sure users know which links are internal anchor points versus external links and indicating if a link brings up a separate browser window from those that do not; and (3) making sure link images and text provide enough information to users so that they understand the meaning of the link.

180. *As a Website designer, how can you avoid errors caused by hidden links?*

The textbook provides three recommendations: (1) making sure you leave a border around images that are links; (2) not changing link colors from normal defaults, and (3) not embedding links within long blocks of text.

181. *Prepare a dialogue diagram for an ATM machine.*

A suggested answer is provided below.

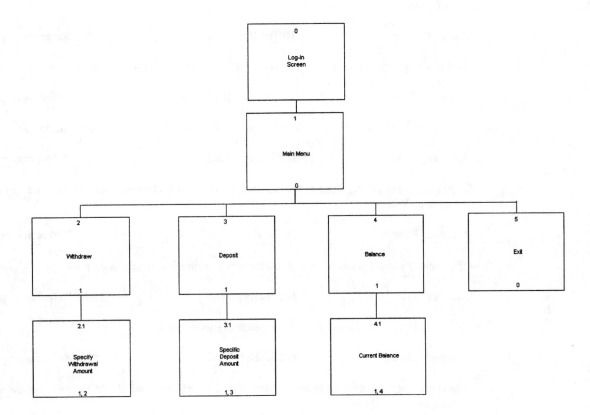

Chapter 15
Finalizing Design Specifications

True-False Questions

1. Traditionally, design specifications were paper-based and contained thorough descriptions of the different software modules that were to complete the new system, along with detailed descriptions of their functions.

   Answer: True   **Difficulty**: Med   **Reference**: p. 499

2. Today, design specifications are delivered to programmers in forms other than paper.

   Answer: True   **Difficulty**: Med   **Reference**: p. 499

3. Today, the lines between analysis and design, and between design and implementation, are blurring.

   Answer: True   **Difficulty**: Med   **Reference**: p. 499

4. Today, there are clearly defined breaks between analysis and design, and between design and implementation.

   Answer: False   **Difficulty**: Med   **Reference**: p. 500

5. Throwaway prototypes are one method for representing design specifications.

   Answer: True   **Difficulty**: Med   **Reference**: p. 500

6. Logic models are methods for finalizing design specifications.

   Answer: False   **Difficulty**: Med   **Reference**: p. 500

7. The specification document is one of the major deliverables from the design phase of the systems development life cycle.

   Answer: True   **Difficulty**: Med   **Reference**: p. 500

8. System testing results are one of the major deliverables from the design phase of the systems development life cycle.

   Answer: False   **Difficulty**: Med   **Reference**: p. 500

9. It is possible for a design specifications document to be filled with quality requirements that are poorly represented by the requirements statements that describe them.

   Answer: True   **Difficulty**: Med   **Reference**: p. 501

10. Correct, feasible, and necessary are quality requirement characteristics.

    Answer: False   **Difficulty**: Hard   **Reference**: p. 501

11. Referencing the quality requirement statement characteristics, each requirement must be something the users really need.

    Answer: True   **Difficulty**: Med   **Reference**: p. 501

12. Referencing the quality requirement statement characteristics, each requirement should be assigned a priority rating, which reflects how important it is to the final product.

    Answer: True   **Difficulty**: Med   **Reference**: p. 501

13. Complete, consistent, and traceable are characteristics of quality requirements.

    Answer: True   **Difficulty**: Med   **Reference**: p. 502

14. Referencing quality requirement characteristics, a quality requirement must be traceable to its original source.

    Answer: True   **Difficulty**: Med   **Reference**: p. 502

15. Referencing quality requirement characteristics, a quality requirement is not missing any key description information.

    Answer: True   **Difficulty**: Med   **Reference**: p. 502

16. A design specification document contains a section describing the platform costs associated with the project.

    Answer: False   **Difficulty**: Med   **Reference**: p. 502

17. A design specification document describes the overall system description, interface requirements, system features, and nonfunctional requirements for the new system.

    Answer: True   **Difficulty**: Med   **Reference**: p. 502

18. A major section on a design specification document is the Management Issues section.

    Answer: False   **Difficulty**: Med   **Reference**: p. 502

19. When finalizing design specifications, logic models are a key deliverable.

    Answer: False   **Difficulty**: Med   **Reference**: p. 502

20. When finalizing design specifications, a set of physical design specifications for the entire system is a key deliverable.

    Answer: True   **Difficulty**: Med   **Reference**: p. 502

21. A complete design specification is comprehensive.

    Answer: True   **Difficulty**: Easy   **Reference**: p. 502

22. Data flow diagrams are useful design specification documents.

    Answer: False   **Difficulty**: Med   **Reference**: p. 503

23. A structure chart is a useful design specification document.

     Answer: True   **Difficulty**: Med   **Reference**: p. 503

24. It is common for design specification documents to be represented in graphical form.

     Answer: True   **Difficulty**: Med   **Reference**: p. 503

25. The most common architecture for representing the physical structure of a system is vertical.

     Answer: False   **Difficulty**: Med   **Reference**: p. 503

26. A structure chart is a graphical representation of a decision situation in which decision situation points
     are connected together by arcs and terminate in ovals.

     Answer: False   **Difficulty**: Med   **Reference**: p. 503

27. A structure chart is a hierarchical diagram that shows how an information system is organized.

     Answer: True   **Difficulty**: Med   **Reference**: p. 503

28. The purpose of a structure chart is to show graphically how the parts of a system or program are
     related to each other, in terms of passing data and in terms of the basic components of structured
     programming.

     Answer: True   **Difficulty**: Med   **Reference**: p. 503

29. The structure of programs written in newer object-oriented or event-driven programming languages is
     usually represented by decision tables, decision trees, and state-transition diagrams.

     Answer: False   **Difficulty**: Med   **Reference**: p. 506

30. Structure charts are used to show the breakdown of a system into programs and the internal structure
     of programs written in third- and fourth-generation languages.

     Answer: True   **Difficulty**: Med   **Reference**: p. 506

31. Modules are called in order from right to left.

     Answer: False   **Difficulty**: Med   **Reference**: p. 506

32. When naming a module, it is appropriate to use conjunctions.

     Answer: False   **Difficulty**: Med   **Reference**: p. 506

33. In a structure chart, a rounded rectangle represents a module.

     Answer: False   **Difficulty**: Med   **Reference**: p. 506

34. In a structure chart, modules may have multiple entry points and multiple exit points.

     Answer: False   **Difficulty**: Med   **Reference**: p. 506

35. Modules may represent separately compiled programs, subprograms, or identifiable internal procedures.

    Answer: True   **Difficulty**: Med   **Reference**: p. 506

36. Modules at the lowest levels call other modules.

    Answer: False   **Difficulty**: Med   **Reference**: p. 506

37. In a structure chart, a COBOL section is represented as a module.

    Answer: True   **Difficulty**: Med   **Reference**: p. 506

38. In a structure chart, a data couple's circle is filled in.

    Answer: False   **Difficulty**: Med   **Reference**: p. 507

39. In a structure chart, parameters take the form of data couples and flags.

    Answer: True   **Difficulty**: Med   **Reference**: p. 507

40. In a structure chart, a flag's circle is not filled in.

    Answer: False   **Difficulty**: Med   **Reference**: p. 507

41. In a structure chart, a flag represents one module telling another module what to do.

    Answer: False   **Difficulty**: Med   **Reference**: p. 507

42. In a structure chart, a flag represents information the system needs for processing.

    Answer: True   **Difficulty**: Med   **Reference**: p. 507

43. A diamond shape at the bottom of a module means that the module's subordinates are called over and over again until some terminal condition is encountered.

    Answer: False   **Difficulty**: Med   **Reference**: p. 507

44. In a structure chart, a predefined module is represented with a vertical bar drawn down each side.

    Answer: True   **Difficulty**: Med   **Reference**: p. 507

45. When finalizing design specifications, it is appropriate to represent the processing logic inside each module with Structured English.

    Answer: False   **Difficulty**: Med   **Reference**: p. 510

46. Pseudocode is a method for representing the instructions in a module with language very similar to computer programming code.

    Answer: True   **Difficulty**: Med   **Reference**: p. 510

47. In the Planning Game, Development is represented by those actually designing and constructing the system.

   Answer: True   **Difficulty**: Easy   **Reference**: p. 518

48. Referencing eXtreme programming, programmers and end users play the Iteration Planning Game.

   Answer: False   **Difficulty**: Hard   **Reference**: p. 519

49. Exploration, commitment, and steering are the three phases of the Iteration Planning Game.

   Answer: True   **Difficulty**: Hard   **Reference**: p. 519

50. The RAD approach captures requirements during JAD workshops and formalizes these requirements in prototype construction using CASE tools.

   Answer: True   **Difficulty**: Med   **Reference**: p. 520

Multiple Choice Questions

51. Which of the following has caused the design and implementation phases to overlap?

   a. the use of logic models
   b. object-oriented analysis and design
   c. user interface design
   d. the desire for rapid development

   Answer: d   **Difficulty**: Med   **Reference**: p. 500

52. Which of the following is a method for finalizing design specifications?

   a. evolutionary prototypes
   b. throwaway prototypes
   c. structure charts
   d. all of the above

   Answer: d   **Difficulty**: Med   **Reference**: p. 500

53. Which of the following is one of the major deliverables from the design phase of the systems development life cycle?

   a. decision table
   b. statement of work
   c. design specification document
   d. program code

   Answer: c   **Difficulty**: Easy   **Reference**: p. 500

54. Which of the following is a quality requirements statement characteristic?

   a. traceable
   b. consistent
   c. complete
   d. verifiable

   Answer: d   **Difficulty**: Hard   **Reference**: p. 501

55. Which of the following is not a quality requirements statement characteristic?

   a. traceable
   b. correct
   c. necessary
   d. prioritized

   Answer: a   **Difficulty**: Hard   **Reference**: p. 501

56. Which of the following is a quality requirement statement characteristic?

   a. prioritized
   b. necessary
   c. unambiguous
   d. all of the above

   Answer: d   **Difficulty**: Med   **Reference**: p. 501

57. Which of the following is a true statement?

   a. Each requirement statement should accurately describe the functionality to be developed.
   b. Each requirement statement should be assigned a priority rating, which reflects how important it is to the final product.
   c. Each requirement should be clear to anyone who reads its description.
   d. All of the above are true statements.

   Answer: d   **Difficulty**: Med   **Reference**: p. 501

58. Which of the following is not a true statement?

   a. A quality requirement cannot be altered.
   b. A quality requirement must be traceable to its original source.
   c. A quality requirement does not conflict with any other requirement specified for the system.
   d. A quality requirement is not missing any key description information.

   Answer: a   **Difficulty**: Med   **Reference**: p. 502

59. Which of the following is a quality requirement characteristic?

   a. modifiable
   b. complete
   c. traceable
   d. all of the above

   Answer: d   **Difficulty**: Med   **Reference**: p. 502

60.   Which of the following is not a quality requirement characteristic?

    a.   complete
    b.   modifiable
    c.   verifiable
    d.   traceable

Answer: c   **Difficulty**: Med   **Reference**: p. 502

61.   Which of the following is a true statement?

    a.   A quality requirement can be altered.
    b.   A quality requirement does not conflict with any other requirement specified for the system.
    c.   A quality requirement is not missing any key description information.
    d.   All of the above are true statements.

Answer: d   **Difficulty**: Med   **Reference**: p. 502

62.   The contents of a design specification document address each of the following areas except:

    a.   nonfunctional requirements
    b.   management issues
    c.   interface requirements
    d.   system features

Answer: b   **Difficulty**: Med   **Reference**: p. 502

63.   Which of the following is an area addressed by a design specification document?

    a.   project scope
    b.   feasibility
    c.   nonfunctional requirements
    d.   management issues

Answer: c   **Difficulty**: Med   **Reference**: p. 502

64.   When finalizing design specifications, one key deliverable is:

    a.   a statement of work
    b.   a set of logical design specifications for the entire system
    c.   logic models for the entire system
    d.   a set of physical design specifications for the entire system

Answer: d   **Difficulty**: Med   **Reference**: p. 502

65.   The most common architecture for representing the physical structure of a system is:

    a.   perpendicular
    b.   horizontal
    c.   hierarchical
    d.   vertical

Answer: c   **Difficulty**: Med   **Reference**: p. 503

66. Showing graphically how the parts of a system or program are related to each other, in terms of passing data and in terms of the basic components of structured programming, is the purpose of:

    a. decision tables
    b. structure charts
    c. data flow diagrams
    d. entity-relationship diagrams

    Answer: b   **Difficulty:** Med   **Reference:** p. 503

67. Each of the following is a true statement except:

    a. Structure charts show the breakdown of a system into programs and the internal structure of programs written in third- and fourth-generation languages.
    b. The most common architecture for representing the physical structure of a system is hierarchical.
    c. The structure of programs written in newer object-oriented or event-driven programming languages is usually represented by decision tables, decision trees, and state-transition diagrams.
    d. It is common for many aspects of design specifications to be represented in graphical form.

    Answer: c   **Difficulty:** Hard   **Reference:** p. 506

68. A hierarchical diagram that shows how an information system is organized is a:

    a. state-transition diagram
    b. structure chart
    c. data flow diagram
    d. entity-relationship diagram

    Answer: b   **Difficulty:** Med   **Reference:** p. 503

69. Modules may represent:

    a. separately compiled programs
    b. subprograms
    c. COBOL sections
    d. all of the above

    Answer: d   **Difficulty:** Easy   **Reference:** p. 506

70. Which of the following is a true statement about modules?

    a. Modules are executed as units.
    b. Modules may represent separately complied programs, subprograms, or identifiable internal procedures.
    c. In most instances, modules have a single point of entry and a single point of exit.
    d. All of the above are true statements.

    Answer: d   **Difficulty:** Med   **Reference:** p. 506

71. Each of the following is a true statement except:

    a. Middle-level modules do not perform processing, serving only as coordinating modules for lower-level modules.
    b. Modules at the lowest levels do not call any other modules; instead they only perform specific tasks.
    c. In a structure chart, a module is represented as a rectangle containing a descriptive name of its function.
    d. Modules are called in order from left to right.

    Answer: a   **Difficulty**: Hard   **Reference**: p. 506

72. In a structure chart, a module is represented as a(n):

    a. oval
    b. diamond
    c. rectangle
    d. circle

    Answer: c   **Difficulty**: Med   **Reference**: p. 506

73. Each of the following is a true statement except:

    a. modules may represent separately compiled programs, subprograms, or identifiable internal procedures
    b. modules at the lowest levels do not call any other modules; instead they only perform specific tasks
    c. it is appropriate to use conjunctions when naming a module
    d. in a structure chart, a module is represented as a rectangle containing a descriptive name of its function

    Answer: c   **Difficulty**: Med   **Reference**: p. 506

74. In a structure chart, COBOL sections are represented as:

    a. processes
    b. modules
    c. flags
    d. relationships

    Answer: b   **Difficulty**: Med   **Reference**: p. 506

75. For object-oriented programming languages, a module is roughly a(n):

    a. object
    b. method
    c. relationship
    d. entity

    Answer: b   **Difficulty**: Med   **Reference**: p. 506

76. A self-contained component of a system, defined by function is the definition for:

    a. module
    b. option
    c. flag
    d. data couple

    Answer: a   **Difficulty**: Med   **Reference**: p. 506

77. Modules in a structure chart communicate with each other through:

    a. methods
    b. data couples and flags
    c. data flows
    d. objects

    Answer: b   **Difficulty**: Med   **Reference**: p. 507

78. Referencing a structure chart, which of the following is not a true statement?

    a. The arrow indicates the direction of movement of the data couple between modules.
    b. Data couples are drawn as circles with arrows coming out of them.
    c. A flag is processed.
    d. A data couple is usually a single data element.

    Answer: c   **Difficulty**: Med   **Reference**: p. 507

79. In a structure chart, data couples are represented as:

    a. ellipses
    b. rectangles
    c. ovals
    d. unfilled circles with arrows coming out of them

    Answer: d   **Difficulty**: Med   **Reference**: p. 507

80. A data couple represents a(n):

    a. single data element
    b. data structure
    c. entire record
    d. all of the above

    Answer: d   **Difficulty**: Easy   **Reference**: p. 507

81. In a structure chart, flags are represented as:

    a. rectangles
    b. filled-in circles with arrows coming out of them
    c. arrows
    d. straight lines

    Answer: b   **Difficulty**: Med   **Reference**: p. 507

82. Which of the following is not a true statement?

a. Flags are processed.
b. Flags represent information the system needs for processing.
c. Flags should never represent one module telling another module what to do.
d. Flags are represented as filled-in circles with arrows coming out of them.

Answer: a   **Difficulty**: Med   **Reference**: p. 507

83. A diagrammatic representation of the data exchanged between two modules in a structure chart best defines:

a. flag
b. data couple
c. statement
d. data flow

Answer: b   **Difficulty**: Med   **Reference**: p. 507

84. A diagrammatic representation of a message passed between two modules best defines:

a. flag
b. data couple
c. statement
d. data flow

Answer: a   **Difficulty**: Med   **Reference**: p. 507

85. In a structure chart, a vertical bar drawn down each side of the module signifies:

a. only one of the subordinates attached to the module will be called
b. that the module's subordinates are called over and over again until some terminal condition is reached
c. that the module is predefined
d. subordinates are called only once

Answer: c   **Difficulty**: Med   **Reference**: p. 507

86. In a structure chart, a diamond shape at the bottom of the module means that:

a. only one of the subordinates attached to the diamond will be called
b. that the module's subordinates are called over and over again until some terminal condition is reached
c. the module is predefined
d. subordinates are called only once

Answer: a   **Difficulty**: Med   **Reference**: p. 507

87. In a structure chart, repetition is indicated by:

    a. placing a diamond shape at the bottom of a module
    b. drawing clear circles with arrows attached
    c. placing vertical bars down the sides of the module
    d. drawing a curved line through the arrows connecting the module to the subordinates that are called over and over

    Answer: d   **Difficulty**: Med   **Reference**: p. 507

88. In a structure chart, selection is indicated by:

    a. placing a diamond shape at the bottom of a module
    b. drawing clear circles with arrows attached
    c. placing vertical bars down the sides of the module
    d. drawing a curved line through the arrows connecting the module to the subordinates that are called over and over

    Answer: a   **Difficulty**: Med   **Reference**: p. 507

89. In a structure chart, printing to a specific type of printer is represented as a(n):

    a. embedded module
    b. repetition module
    c. selection module
    d. predefined module

    Answer: d   **Difficulty**: Med   **Reference**: p. 507

90. In a structure chart, a "hat" means that:

    a. there is a condition statement in the module's code that determines which subordinate module to call
    b. the module's subordinates are called over and over again until some terminal condition is reached
    c. the function in the subordinate module is important logically to the system, but so few lines of code are needed to perform the function, the code itself is actually contained in the boss module
    d. the module's function is predefined

    Answer: c   **Difficulty**: Med   **Reference**: p. 507

91. In a structure chart, a coordinating module is also called a:

    a. referring module
    b. boss module
    c. supervisory module
    d. method module

    Answer: b   **Difficulty**: Med   **Reference**: p. 508

92. A method for representing the instructions in a module with language very similar to computer programming code best describes:

   a. UML
   b. sequence diagramming
   c. pseudocode
   d. Structured English

   Answer: c   **Difficulty**: Med   **Reference**: p. 510

93. When the prototype serves as the basis for the production system itself, this is referred to as:

   a. cumulative prototyping
   b. iterative prototyping
   c. throwaway prototyping
   d. evolutionary prototyping

   Answer: d   **Difficulty**: Med   **Reference**: p. 510

94. When the prototype is used as a reference and is then discarded after it has been used, this is referred to as:

   a. cumulative prototyping
   b. iterative prototyping
   c. throwaway prototyping
   d. evolutionary prototyping

   Answer: c   **Difficulty**: Med   **Reference**: p. 510

95. Which of the following is not a true statement?

   a. Analysts must choose prototyping languages and tools that are consistent with the development environment for the production system.
   b. When developing an evolutionary prototype, you often begin with those parts of the system that are most difficult and uncertain.
   c. Prototypes often do not reflect database access, database integrity, system security, and networking.
   d. Most prototypes are designed to handle exceptional cases.

   Answer: d   **Difficulty**: Hard   **Reference**: p. 511

96. Which of the following was developed by Kent Beck, and is distinguished by its short cycles, its incremental planning approach, its focus on automated tests written by programmers and customers to monitor the process of development, and its reliance on an evolutionary approach to development that lasts throughout the lifetime of the system?

   a. eXtreme programming
   b. evolutionary prototyping
   c. rapid application development
   d. object-oriented analysis and design

   Answer: a   **Difficulty**: Med   **Reference**: p. 518

97. Referencing eXtreme programming, which of the following is a stylized approach to development that seeks to maximize fruitful interaction between those who need a new system and those who built it?

    a. Iteration Planning Game
    b. Planning Game
    c. eXtreme Walkthrough
    d. eXtreme JAD

    Answer: b   **Difficulty**: Hard   **Reference**: p. 518

98. Referencing eXtreme programming, which of the following is not a Planning Game phase?

    a. exploration
    b. design
    c. commitment
    d. steering

    Answer: b   **Difficulty**: Hard   **Reference**: p. 518

99. Referencing eXtreme programming, which of the following is the final phase of the Planning Game?

    a. exploration
    b. design
    c. commitment
    d. steering

    Answer: d   **Difficulty**: Hard   **Reference**: p. 519

100. Referencing eXtreme programming, who plays the Iteration Planning Game?

    a. programmers
    b. business managers and analysts
    c. end users, business managers, and analysts
    d. programmers, analysts, and end users

    Answer: a   **Difficulty**: Med   **Reference**: p. 519

Fill In the Blanks

101. The most common architecture for representing the physical structure of a system is ***hierarchical***.

    Difficulty: Med   **Reference**: p. 503

102. A ***structure chart*** is a hierarchical diagram that shows how an information system is organized.

    Difficulty: Med   **Reference**: p. 503

103. The structure of programs written in newer object-oriented or event-driven programming languages is usually depicted by ***state-transition diagrams*** and ***Structured English***.

    Difficulty: Med   **Reference**: p. 506

104.   A *module* is a self-contained component of a system, defined by function.

                            Difficulty: Med   **Reference**: p. 506

105.   In a structure chart, each module is represented by a *rectangle*.

                            Difficulty: Med   **Reference**: p. 506

106.   Modules are called in order from *left to right*.

                            Difficulty: Med   **Reference**: p. 506

107.   In a structure chart, parameters are represented as *data couples* and *flags*.

                            Difficulty: Med   **Reference**: p. 507

108.   A *data couple* is a diagrammatic representation of the data exchanged between two modules in a
        structure chart.

                            Difficulty: Med   **Reference**: p. 507

109.   A *flag* is a diagrammatic representation of a message passed between two modules.

                            Difficulty: Med   **Reference**: p. 507

110.   Selection is shown in structure charts by using *diamonds*.

                            Difficulty: Med   **Reference**: p. 507

111.   Repetition is shown in structure charts by a *curved line drawn through the arrows connecting the
        module to its subordinates*.

                            Difficulty: Hard   **Reference**: p. 507

112.   A predefined module is represented by *drawing a vertical line down each side of the module*.

                            Difficulty: Hard   **Reference**: p. 507

113.   In a structure chart, a *hat* means that the function in the subordinate module is important logically to
        the system, but so few lines of code are needed to perform the function that the code itself is actually
        contained in the superior module.

                            Difficulty: Hard   **Reference**: p. 507

114.   The order in which the modules are called is determined by the *placement of the arrows connecting
        the modules*.

                            Difficulty: Hard   **Reference**: p. 508

115.   A coordinating module is often called a *boss* module.

                            Difficulty: Med   **Reference**: p. 508

116. *Pseudocode* is a method for representing the instructions in a module with language very similar to computer programming code.

Difficulty: Med   **Reference**: p. 510

117. An *evolutionary* prototype serves as the basis for the production system.

Difficulty: Med   **Reference**: p. 510

118. A *throwaway* prototype serves as a reference for the construction of the actual system and is discarded after it has been used.

Difficulty: Med   **Reference**: p. 510

119. *RAD* and *eXtreme programming* are two approaches that may not produce design specification documents.

Difficulty: Hard   **Reference**: p. 518

120. *eXtreme programming* is an approach developed by Kent Beck, and is distinguished by its short cycles, its incremental planning approach, its focus on automated tests written by programmers and customers to monitor the process of development, and its reliance on an evolutionary approach to development that lasts throughout the lifetime of the system.

Difficulty: Hard   **Reference**: p. 518

121. Referencing eXtreme programming, the *Planning Game* is a stylized approach to development that seeks to maximize fruitful interaction between those who need a new system and those who build it.

Difficulty: Med   **Reference**: p. 518

122. *Exploration*, *commitment*, and *steering* are the three phases of the Planning Game.

Difficulty: Hard   **Reference**: p. 518

123. *Exploration*, *commitment*, and *steering* are the three phases of the Iteration Planning Game.

Difficulty: Hard   **Reference**: p. 519

124. Referencing the Iteration Planning Game, programmers will accept responsibility for tasks and balance their workloads during the *commitment* phase.

Difficulty: Hard   **Reference**: p. 519

125. The four RAD life-cycle phases are: *planning*, *design*, *construction*, and *cutover*.

Difficulty: Med   **Reference**: p. 520

Matching Questions

Match each of the following terms with its corresponding definition.

a. structure chart
b. pseudocode
c. flag
d. module
e. data couple
f. eXtreme programming
g. evolutionary prototype
h. throwaway prototype

126. A diagrammatic representation of the data exchanged between two modules in a structure chart

    Answer: e   **Reference**: p. 507

127. A hierarchical diagram that shows how an information system is organized

    Answer: a   **Reference**: p. 503

128. A diagrammatic representation of a message passed between two modules

    Answer: c   **Reference**: p. 507

129. A method for representing the instructions in a module with language very similar to computer programming code

    Answer: b   **Reference**: p. 510

130. A self-contained component of a system, defined by function

    Answer: d   **Reference**: p. 506

131. An approach developed by Kent Beck, and is distinguished by its short cycles, its incremental planning approach, its focus on automated tests written by programmers and customers to monitor the process of development, and its reliance on an evolutionary approach to development that lasts throughout the lifetime of the system

    Answer: f   **Reference**: p. 518

132. A prototype that serves as the basis for the production system

    Answer: g   **Reference**: p. 510

133. A prototype that serves as a reference for the construction of the actual system and is discarded after it has been used

    Answer: h   **Reference**: p. 510

Match each of the following structure chart elements with its corresponding representation.

    a. data couple
    b. flag
    c. repetitive call of subordinates
    d. conditional call of subordinates
    e. predefined module
    f. embedded module

134.

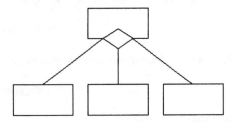

Answer: d   **Reference**: p. 508

135.

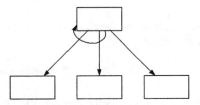

Answer: c   **Reference**: p. 508

136.

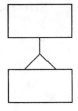

Answer: f   **Reference**: p. 508

137.

Answer: a   **Reference**: p. 507

138.

Answer: b   **Reference**: p. 507

139.

Answer: e   **Reference**: p. 508

Match each of the following eXtreme programming terms with its corresponding description.

    a.   Business
    b.   Development
    c.   exploration
    d.   commitment
    e.   steering

140.   Refers to the phase where Business sorts the Story Cards according to the type of features.

Answer: d   **Reference:** p. 519

141.   Refers to the phase where Business creates a Story Card for something it wants to do.

Answer: c   **Reference:** p. 518

142.   Refers to those who are designing and constructing the system.

Answer: b   **Reference:** p. 518

143.   Refers to the phase where Business has a chance to see how the development process is progressing and to work with Development to adjust the plan accordingly.

Answer: e   **Reference:** p. 519

144.   Refers to the customer, and is represented by someone who knows the processes to be supported by the system being developed

Answer: a   **Reference:** p. 518

For each of the following characteristics, answer "a" if it is a quality requirement statement characteristic, or answer "b" if it is a quality requirement characteristic.

145.   modifiable

         Answer: b   **Reference**: p. 502

146.   feasible

         Answer: a   **Reference**: p. 501

147.   traceable

         Answer: b   **Reference**: p. 502

148.   correct

         Answer: a   **Reference**: p. 501

149.   necessary

         Answer: a   **Reference**: p. 501

150.   complete

         Answer: b   **Reference**: p. 502

151.   prioritized

         Answer: a   **Reference**: p. 501

152.   unambiguous

         Answer: a   **Reference**: p. 501

153.   verifiable

         Answer: a   **Reference**: p. 501

154.   consistent

         Answer: b   **Reference**: p. 502

For each of the following descriptions, answer "a" if it best exemplifies a quality requirement statement characteristic, or answer "b" if it best exemplifies a quality requirement characteristic.

155.   Is not missing any key description information

                  Answer: b   **Reference:** p. 502

156.   Can be altered, with a history of the changes made

                  Answer: b   **Reference:** p. 502

157.   Must be something the users really need

                  Answer: a   **Reference:** p. 501

158.   Should be clear to anyone who reads its description

                  Answer: a   **Reference:** p. 501

159.   Should be possible to determine if each requirement has been successfully implemented in the system

                  Answer: a   **Reference:** p. 501

Essay Questions

160.   *Illustrate how an embedded module is represented in a structure chart.*

    A suggested answer is provided below.

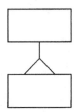

161.   *Illustrate how repetitive calls of subordinates are represented a structure chart.*

    A suggested answer is provided below.

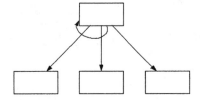

162.   *Illustrate how conditional calls of subordinates are made in a structure chart.*

A suggested answer is provided below.

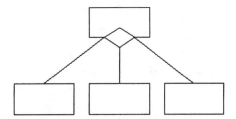

163.   *Differentiate between evolutionary prototyping and throwaway prototyping.*

While an evolutionary prototype is used as the basis for the production system, a throwaway prototype is only used for reference and is discarded after it has been used.

164.   *What is eXtreme programming?*

eXtreme programming is an approach developed by Kent Beck. This approach is distinguished by its short cycles, its incremental planning approach, its focus on automated tests written by programmers and customers to monitor the process of development, and its reliance on an evolutionary approach to development that lasts throughout the lifetime of the system.

165.   *What is a structure chart? What are its major constructs?*

A structure chart is a hierarchical diagram that shows how an information system is organized. The primary symbol is the rectangle which represents a module. Data couples and flags are represented as circles with arrows coming out of them. While data flags do not have their circles filled in, flags have their circles filled in. Additionally, a structure chart is able to represent the three structured programming constructs.

166.   *What are the characteristics of quality requirement statements?*

Correct, feasible, necessary, prioritized, unambiguous, and verifiable are six characteristics of quality requirement statements.

167.   *What are the characteristics of quality requirements?*

The four characteristics of quality requirements are complete, consistent, modifiable, and traceable.

168.   *Briefly discuss the contents of a design specification document.*

Although design specifications may take different formats, the design specification document may address the overall system, interface requirements, system features, nonfunctional requirements, and other requirements. Supporting diagrams and modules may be included.

169.   *How might design specifications be represented?*

Design specifications are presented to programmers in several ways. These include textual representations, structure charts, evolutionary prototypes, or throwaway prototypes. Additionally, development approaches, such as RAD or eXtreme programming, may be used.

Chapter 16
Designing Distributed and Internet Systems

True-False Questions

1. Upsizing is the process of linking previous stand-alone computers together to form networks that support workgroup computing.

    Answer: True   **Difficulty**: Med   **Reference**: p. 527

2. Downsizing is the process of migrating mainframe applications to personal computers, workstations, and networks.

    Answer: True   **Difficulty**: Med   **Reference**: p. 527

3. Corporate downsizing has lessened the individual manager's span of control.

    Answer: False   **Difficulty**: Med   **Reference**: p. 528

4. When designing distributed and Internet systems, the primary deliverables from this stage are decision tables, structure charts, and throwaway prototypes.

    Answer: False   **Difficulty**: Med   **Reference**: p. 528

5. When designing distributed and Internet systems, you should consider information about the site, processing, and data for each location.

    Answer: True   **Difficulty**: Med   **Reference**: p. 530

6. Private network refers to the cabling, hardware, and software used to connect workstations, computers, and file servers located in a confined geographical area.

    Answer: False   **Difficulty**: Easy   **Reference**: p. 530

7. In a basic LAN environment, all data manipulation occurs on the file server.

    Answer: False   **Difficulty**: Med   **Reference**: p. 530

8. In a file server environment, each PC stores a copy of the database.

    Answer: False   **Difficulty**: Med   **Reference**: p. 530

9. In a file server environment, the DBMS runs only on the file server.

    Answer: False   **Difficulty**: Med   **Reference**: p. 530

10. The primary characteristic of a client-based LAN is that all data manipulation is performed at the client PC, not at the file server.

    Answer: True   **Difficulty**: Med   **Reference**: p. 530

11. In a client-based LAN, the file server acts as a shared data storage device, provides additional resources, supports collaborative applications, and provides access to shared data.

    Answer: True   **Difficulty**: Med   **Reference**: p. 530

12. In a client-based LAN, the file server handles all data manipulations.

    Answer: False   **Difficulty**: Med   **Reference**: p. 531

13. When using file servers on local area networks, excessive data movement is one limitation.

    Answer: True   **Difficulty**: Med   **Reference**: p. 531

14. An advantage to using file servers on local area networks is the ability to use thin clients.

    Answer: False   **Difficulty**: Med   **Reference**: p. 531

15. An advantage to using file servers on local area networks is the ability to centralize data control.

    Answer: False   **Difficulty**: Med   **Reference**: p. 531

16. File server-based architectures benefit from having a very fast hard disk and cache memory in both clients and the server, enhancing their ability to transfer files to and from the network, RAM, and hard disk.

    Answer: True   **Difficulty**: Med   **Reference**: p. 532

17. In the client/server architecture, the client workstation is most often responsible for managing the user interface.

    Answer: True   **Difficulty**: Med   **Reference**: p. 532

18. In a typical client/server architecture, all database recovery, security and access management is localized at the client.

    Answer: False   **Difficulty**: Med   **Reference**: p. 532

19. The database engine is the front-end portion of the client/server database system that provides the user interface and data manipulation functions.

    Answer: False   **Difficulty**: Med   **Reference**: p. 532

20. In the client/server architecture, the server executes all requests for data so that only data that match the requested criteria are passed across the network to client stations.

    Answer: True   **Difficulty**: Med   **Reference**: p. 532

21. The primary difference between an application built using the client/server architecture and a centralized database system on a mainframe is that each client is an intelligent part of the application processing system.

    Answer: True   **Difficulty**: Hard   **Reference**: p. 532

22. An advantage of client/server architectures is the ability to decouple the client environment from the server environment.

    Answer: True   **Difficulty**: Med   **Reference**: p. 533

23. XML refers to software building blocks that are used to assure that common system capabilities like user interfaces and printing are standardized as well as modules for facilitating the data exchange between clients and servers.

    Answer: False   **Difficulty**: Med   **Reference**: p. 533

24. A benefit of the client/server architecture is that it allows most processing to be performed close to the source of the processed data, thereby improving response times and reducing network traffic.

    Answer: True   **Difficulty**: Med   **Reference**: p. 533

25. When migrating relational DBMSs and other LAN-based technologies into the client/server environment, issues such as compatibility of data types, query optimization, distributed databases, data administration of distributed data, CASE tool code generators, and cross operating system integration may arise.

    Answer: True   **Difficulty**: Hard   **Reference**: p. 534

26. A file server architecture is most appropriate for applications that are relatively small in size with little or no concurrent data access by multiple users.

    Answer: True   **Difficulty**: Easy   **Reference**: p. 534

27. When comparing file server and client/server architectures, the file server architecture requires greater coordination between the client and server.

    Answer: False   **Difficulty**: Hard   **Reference**: p. 534

28. The data analysis function manages all interaction between software and files and databases, including data retrieval/querying, updating, security, concurrency control, and recovery.

    Answer: False   **Difficulty**: Med   **Reference**: p. 535

29. API refers to a combination of hardware, software, and communication technologies that bring together data management, presentation, and analysis into a three-tiered client/server environment.

    Answer: False   **Difficulty**: Med   **Reference**: p. 535

30. An application server is a computing server where data analysis functions primarily reside.

    Answer: True   **Difficulty**: Med   **Reference**: p. 535

31. The remote presentation approach to designing client/server architectures places all data presentation functions on the client machine so that the client has total responsibility for formatting data.

    Answer: True   **Difficulty**: Hard   **Reference**: p. 538

32. BIND is a method for translating Internet domain names into Internet Protocol addresses.

    Answer: True   **Difficulty**: Med   **Reference**: p. 539

33. Designers can create vocabularies for any type of application in XML.

    Answer: True   **Difficulty**: Med   **Reference**: p. 540

34. Network PCs are examples of thin clients.

    Answer: True   **Difficulty**: Easy   **Reference**: p. 540

35. XML is the most basic way to implement a standard style design within a Website.

    Answer: False   **Difficulty**: Med   **Reference**: p. 542

36. XSL allows designers to dictate how Web pages are displayed and the type of client device.

    Answer: True   **Difficulty**: Med   **Reference**: p. 542

37. XSL-based formatting consists of methods for transforming XML documents into a generic comprehensive form and formatting the generic comprehensive form into a device specific form.

    Answer: True   **Difficulty**: Hard   **Reference**: p. 543

38. Usually, link titles should be less than 80 characters.

    Answer: True   **Difficulty**: Easy   **Reference**: p. 544

39. Having a Website that is connected to the rest of the Web is one way designers can convey trustworthiness in a Website.

    Answer: True   **Difficulty**: Med   **Reference**: p. 545

40. Providing Internet content to users based upon knowledge of that customer defines customization.

    Answer: False   **Difficulty**: Med   **Reference**: p. 545

41. Customer bookmarks, links from other sites, search engines referrals, and old content adds value are four reasons why Web pages must live forever.

    Answer: True   **Difficulty**: Med   **Reference**: p. 546

42. Integration depth is a method that helps you to better understand how a system fits within existing business activities and data.

    Answer: False   **Difficulty**: Med   **Reference**: p. 548

43. On-line transaction processing is the immediate automated responses to the requests of users.

    Answer: True   **Difficulty**: Med   **Reference**: p. 549

44. The primary purpose of an informational system is to run the business on a current basis.

    Answer: False   **Difficulty**: Med   **Reference**: p. 551

45. The primary users of an operational system are managers, business analysts, and customers.

    Answer: False   **Difficulty**: Med   **Reference**: p. 551

46. The design goal of an informational system is performance.

     Answer: False   **Difficulty**: Hard   **Reference**: p. 551

47. A data warehouse is a subject-oriented, integrated, time-variant, nonvolatile collection of data used in support of management decision making.

     Answer: True   **Difficulty**: Med   **Reference**: p. 551

48. A major difference between two-level and three-level data warehouses is the creation of an enterprise data warehouse.

     Answer: True   **Difficulty**: Med   **Reference**: p. 553

49. Generally speaking, an enterprise data warehouse is directly accessible by end users.

     Answer: False   **Difficulty**: Med   **Reference**: p. 553

50. In a three-layer data warehouse architecture, users access the data that have been derived from the enterprise data warehouse that are stored in data marts.

     Answer: True   **Difficulty**: Med   **Reference**: p. 554

Multiple Choice Questions

51. The process of linking together previous stand-alone personal computers to form networks that support workgroup computing is sometimes called:

     a. upsizing
     b. downsizing
     c. upgrading
     d. communicating

     Answer: a   **Difficulty**: Med   **Reference**: p. 527

52. The process of migrating mainframe applications to personal computers, workstations, and networks is sometimes called:

     a. upsizing
     b. downsizing
     c. downgrading
     d. resizing

     Answer: b   **Difficulty**: Med   **Reference**: p. 527

53. When designing distributed and Internet systems, the deliverable is:

    a. an updated Baseline Project Plan that details the work necessary to turn the selected design strategy into the desired replacement information system
    b. a set of structured descriptions and diagrams that outline the logic contained within each DFD process
    c. a set of physical design specifications for each separate part of the system
    d. a document that will consolidate the information that must be considered when implementing a system design

    Answer: d   **Difficulty**: Med   **Reference**: p. 528

54. The biggest driver for developing new types of systems is:

    a. electronic commerce
    b. corporate mergers
    c. downsizing
    d. CASE tools

    Answer: a   **Difficulty**: Med   **Reference**: p. 528

55. Information that must be considered when designing distributed and Internet systems includes:

    a. site information for each location in the distributed environment
    b. processing information for each location in the distributed environment
    c. data information for each location in the distributed environment
    d. all of the above

    Answer: d   **Difficulty**: Med   **Reference**: p. 530

56. To support concurrent access from multiple users of a shared database, the LAN modules of a DBMS add:

    a. concurrent access controls
    b. extra security features
    c. query or transaction queuing management
    d. all of the above

    Answer: d   **Difficulty**: Med   **Reference**: p. 530

57. The cabling, hardware, and software used to connect workstations, computers, and file servers located in a confined geographical area describes a:

    a. metropolitan area network
    b. wide area network
    c. local area network
    d. company network

    Answer: c   **Difficulty**: Med   **Reference**: p. 530

58. In a basic LAN environment, all data manipulation occurs:

   a. on the mainframe where the data are stored
   b. on the file server where the data are stored
   c. at the workstations where the data are requested
   d. on the superserver where the data are stored

   Answer: c　　　　　**Difficulty**: Med　　　　　**Reference**: p. 530

59. A device that manages file operations and is shared by each client PC that is attached to a LAN best describes a:

   a. file server
   b. print server
   c. data server
   d. minicomputer

   Answer: a　　　　　**Difficulty**: Med　　　　　**Reference**: p. 530

60. The primary characteristic of a client-based LAN is that:

   a. all data manipulation is performed at the file server, not at the client PC
   b. all data manipulation is performed at the client PC, not at the file server
   c. each client has a copy of the database and performs all data manipulations
   d. the database is stored on the file server and all data manipulations are performed by the file server

   Answer: b　　　　　**Difficulty**: Med　　　　　**Reference**: p. 530

61. When using a DBMS in a file server environment:

   a. data security checks and file and record locking are done at the file server
   b. data security checks and file and record locking are done on the mainframe
   c. data security checks and file and record locking are done at the client PCs
   d. data security checks are performed at the file server, and file and record locking are done at the client PCs

   Answer: c　　　　　**Difficulty**: Med　　　　　**Reference**: p. 531

62. Which of the following is a file server limitation?

   a. decentralized data control
   b. need for powerful client workstations
   c. excessive data movement
   d. all of the above

   Answer: d　　　　　**Difficulty**: Med　　　　　**Reference**: p. 531

63. A LAN-based computing environment in which a central database server or engine performs all database commands sent to it from client workstations, and in which application programs on each client concentrate on user interface functions, describes a:

    a. file server environment
    b. client/server architecture
    c. bus architecture
    d. metropolitan area network

    Answer: b   **Difficulty**: Med   **Reference**: p. 532

64. In the typical client/server architecture:

    a. all database recovery, security, and concurrent access management is centralized at the server
    b. all database recovery, security, and concurrent access management is moved to the client
    c. only database recovery and concurrent access management is centralized at the server
    d. database security and recovery are provided by the client

    Answer: a   **Difficulty**: Med   **Reference**: p. 532

65. Client-based deliveries of applications to users using PCs and workstations are called:

    a. client-delivery applications
    b. local applications
    c. front-end applications
    d. back-end applications

    Answer: c   **Difficulty**: Med   **Reference**: p. 532

66. The back-end portion of the client/server database system running on the server and providing database processing and shared access functions describes a(n):

    a. intelligent agent
    b. server
    c. database engine
    d. client

    Answer: c   **Difficulty**: Med   **Reference**: p. 532

67. The front-end portion of the client/server database system that provides the user interface and data manipulation functions describes a(n):

    a. client
    b. server
    c. database engine
    d. application program interface

    Answer: a   **Difficulty**: Med   **Reference**: p. 532

68. The primary difference between an application built using the client/server architecture and a centralized database system on a mainframe is that:

    a. in a mainframe environment, all interactions with the user and local devices are handled by local intelligent terminals
    b. in a client/server environment, each client is an intelligent part of the application processing system
    c. in a client/server environment, all parts of the information system are managed and executed by the central computer
    d. none of the above

    Answer: b   **Difficulty**: Med   **Reference**: p. 532

69. Software building blocks that are used to assure that common system capabilities like user interfaces and printing are standardized as well as modules for facilitating the data exchange between clients and servers best describes:

    a. firmware
    b. a software patch
    c. a database management system
    d. an application program interface

    Answer: d   **Difficulty**: Med   **Reference**: p. 533

70. Which of the following is not a benefit of adopting a client/server architecture?

    a. Companies can leverage the benefits of microcomputer technology.
    b. Numerous tools for systems design and performance monitoring are available in a client/server environment.
    c. It facilitates the use of graphical user interfaces.
    d. It allows for and encourages the acceptance of open systems.

    Answer: b   **Difficulty**: Hard   **Reference**: p. 533

71. Which of the following statements regarding the differences between file server and client/server architectures is true?

    a. While the file server architecture involves efficient data transfers, the client/server architecture has large file and data transfers.
    b. Servers and clients perform processing in a file server architecture. Only servers perform processing in a client/server architecture.
    c. While database security and integrity on a file server architecture is high, it is low on the client/server architecture.
    d. While software maintenance on the file server architecture is considered low, software maintenance on the client/server architecture is mixed since some new parts must be delivered to each client.

    Answer: d   **Difficulty**: Hard   **Reference**: p. 534

72. Which of the following statements regarding the differences between file server and client/server architectures is true?

    a. While database security and integrity are low on a file server architecture, they are high on a client/server architecture.
    b. While network usage involves efficient data transfers on a file server architecture, it is not efficient on a client/server architecture.
    c. In terms of hardware and system software flexibility, there is less need for coordination between the client and server on a client/server architecture than on a file server architecture.
    d. In terms of concurrent data access, concurrent data access is managed by the client in a client/server architecture.

    Answer: a   **Difficulty**: Med   **Reference**: p. 534

73. Which of the following functions manages all interaction between software and files and databases, including data retrieval/querying, updating, security, concurrency control, and recovery?

    a. data analysis
    b. data presentation
    c. data management
    d. transport management

    Answer: c   **Difficulty**: Med   **Reference**: p. 535

74. Which of the following functions transforms inputs into outputs, including simple summarization to complex mathematical modeling like regression analysis?

    a. data analysis
    b. data presentation
    c. data management
    d. transport management

    Answer: a   **Difficulty**: Med   **Reference**: p. 535

75. Which of the following functions manages just the interface between system users and the software, including the display and printing of forms and reports and possibly validating system inputs?

    a. data analysis
    b. data presentation
    c. data management
    d. transport management

    Answer: b   **Difficulty**: Med   **Reference**: p. 535

76. A computing server where data analysis functions primarily reside best defines:

    a. file server
    b. analytical server
    c. dedicated server
    d. application server

    Answer: d   **Difficulty**: Med   **Reference**: p. 535

77. Which of the following combines three logical and distinct applications (data management, presentation, and analysis) into a single information system application?

    a. analytical server
    b. application server
    c. three-tiered client/server
    d. trinity server

    Answer: c   **Difficulty**: Med   **Reference**: p. 535

78. Which of the following is a combination of hardware, software, and communication technologies that bring together data management, presentation, and analysis into a three-tiered client/server environment?

    a. middleware
    b. transparency software
    c. presentation software
    d. partitioning software

    Answer: a   **Difficulty**: Med   **Reference**: p. 535

79. Which of the following is a primary reason for creating three-tiered client/server architectures?

    a. Applications can be partitioned in a way that best fits the organizational computing needs.
    b. Making global changes or customizing processes for individual users is relatively easy.
    c. Because data analysis is separate from the user interface, it is a lot easier to change one or both without affecting the other.
    d. all of the above

    Answer: d   **Difficulty**: Med   **Reference**: p. 535

80. Which of the following client/server architectures freshens up the delivery of existing server-based applications to distributed clients?

    a. distributed function
    b. remote presentation
    c. remote data management
    d. distributed presentation

    Answer: d   **Difficulty**: Hard   **Reference**: p. 538

81. Which of the following client/server architectures places all data presentation functions on the client machine so that the client has total responsibility for formatting data?

    a. distributed function
    b. remote presentation
    c. remote data management
    d. distributed presentation

    Answer: b   **Difficulty**: Hard   **Reference**: p. 538

82. Which of the following client/server architectures places all software on the client except for the data management functions?

    a. distributed function
    b. remote presentation
    c. remote data management
    d. distributed processing

    Answer: c   **Difficulty**: Hard   **Reference**: p. 538

83. Which of the following client/server architectures splits analysis functions between the client and server, leaving all presentation on the client and all data management on the server?

    a. distributed function
    b. distributed database
    c. remote data management
    d. distributed processing

    Answer: a   **Difficulty**: Hard   **Reference**: p. 538

84. Which of the following client/server architectures places all functionality on the client, except data storage and management, which is divided between client and server?

    a. distributed function
    b. distributed database
    c. remote data management
    d. distributed processing

    Answer: b   **Difficulty**: Hard   **Reference**: p. 538

85. Which of the following client/server architectures combines the best features of the distributed function and distributed database by splitting both of these across client and server, with presentation functions under the exclusive responsibility of the client machine?

    a. distributed presentation
    b. remote data management
    c. distributed management
    d. distributed processing

    Answer: d   **Difficulty**: Hard   **Reference**: p. 538

86. Which of the following is not an Internet standard?

    a. BIND
    b. HTML
    c. HTTP
    d. OOAD

    Answer: d   **Difficulty**: Easy   **Reference**: p. 539

87. A method for translating Internet domain names into Internet Protocol addresses best defines:

a. HTTP
b. BIND
c. HTML
d. XML

Answer: b   **Difficulty**: Med   **Reference**: p. 539

88. A communication protocol for exchanging information on the Internet best describes:

a. HTTP
b. BIND
c. HTML
d. XML

Answer: a   **Difficulty**: Med   **Reference**: p. 539

89. An Internet authoring language that allows designers to create customized tags, enabling the definition, transmission, validation, and interpretation of data between applications best describes:

a. HTTP
b. BIND
c. HTML
d. XML

Answer: d   **Difficulty**: Med   **Reference**: p. 540

90. Which of the following is a method of implementing standard page styles through a Website?

a. XSL
b. HTTP
c. HTML
d. VRML

Answer: a   **Difficulty**: Med   **Reference**: p. 542

91. Which of the following is not a method for conveying trustworthiness in a Website?

a. up-front disclosure
b. connected to the rest of the Web
c. use of state of the art technology
d. design quality

Answer: c   **Difficulty**: Med   **Reference**: p. 545

92. Providing Internet content to users based upon knowledge of that customer best describes:

a. micromarketing
b. personalization
c. customization
d. profiling

Answer: b   **Difficulty**: Med   **Reference**: p. 545

93. A method that helps you to better understand how a system fits within existing business activities and data best defines:

    a. system granularity
    b. context development
    c. integration depth
    d. organizational breadth

    Answer: b   **Difficulty**: Med   **Reference**: p. 548

94. A measurement that tracks the core business functions affected by a system best defines:

    a. system granularity
    b. context development
    c. integration depth
    d. organizational breadth

    Answer: d   **Difficulty**: Med   **Reference**: p. 548

95. The use of graphical software tools that provide complex analysis of data stored in a database best defines:

    a. on-line knowledge analysis
    b. on-line transaction processing
    c. on-line analytical processing
    d. on-line critical processing

    Answer: c   **Difficulty**: Med   **Reference**: p. 550

96. Systems that are used to interact with customers and run a business in real time best defines:

    a. operational systems
    b. intelligent systems
    c. informational systems
    d. dynamic systems

    Answer: a   **Difficulty**: Med   **Reference**: p. 551

97. A subject-oriented, integrated, time-variant, nonvolatile collection of data used in support of management decision making best describes a(n):

    a. information desk
    b. data warehouse
    c. data mart
    d. data center

    Answer: b   **Difficulty**: Med   **Reference**: p. 551

98. A three-level data warehouse has each of the following components except:

a. operational systems and data
b. enterprise data warehouse
c. knowledge engine
d. data marts

Answer: c   **Difficulty**: Hard   **Reference**: p. 552

99. A centralized, integrated data warehouse that is the control point and single source of all data made available to end users for decision-support applications throughout the entire organization best describes a(n):

a. information desk
b. enterprise data warehouse
c. centralized data mart
d. data center

Answer: b   **Difficulty**: Med   **Reference**: p. 553

100. A data warehouse that is limited in scope and whose data are obtained by selecting and summarizing data from the enterprise data warehouse best describes a(n):

a. information desk
b. rule base
c. data mart
d. data center

Answer: c   **Difficulty**: Med   **Reference**: p. 554

Fill In the Blanks

101. The cabling, hardware, and software used to connect workstations, computers, and file servers located in a confined geographical area best describes a ***local area network***.

Difficulty: Easy   **Reference**: p. 530

102. A ***file server*** is a device that manages file operations and is shared by each client PC attached to a LAN.

Difficulty: Med   **Reference**: p. 530

103. The ***client/server architecture*** is a LAN-based computing environment in which a central database server or engine performs all database commands sent to it from client workstations, and application programs on each client concentrate on user interface functions.

Difficulty: Med   **Reference**: p. 532

104. A ***database engine*** is the back-end portion of the client/server database system running on the server and providing database processing and shared access functions.

Difficulty: Med   **Reference**: p. 532

105.   A *client* is the front-end portion of the client/server database system that provides the user interface and data manipulation functions.

Difficulty: Easy   **Reference**: p. 532

106.   *Application program interface* refers to software building blocks that are used to assure that common system capabilities like user interfaces and printing are standardized as well as modules for facilitating the data exchange between clients and servers.

Difficulty: Hard   **Reference**: p. 533

107.   An *application server* is a computing server where data analysis functions primarily reside.

Difficulty: Med   **Reference**: p. 535

108.   *Three-tiered client/server* refers to advanced client/server architectures in which there are three logical and distinct applications—data management, presentation, and analysis—which are combined to create a single information system.

Difficulty: Med   **Reference**: p. 535

109.   *Middleware* is a combination of hardware, software, and communication technologies that bring together data management, presentation, and analysis into a three-tiered client/server environment.

Difficulty: Med   **Reference**: p. 535

110.   The *domain naming system* is a method for translating Internet domain names into Internet Protocol (IP) addresses.

Difficulty: Med   **Reference**: p. 539

111.   *HTTP* is a communications protocol for exchanging information on the Internet.

Difficulty: Easy   **Reference**: p. 539

112.   *XML* is an Internet authoring language that allows designers to create customized tags, enabling the definition, transmission, validation, and interpretation of data between applications.

Difficulty: Med   **Reference**: p. 540

113.   A *thin client* is a client device designed so that most processing and data storage occurs on the server.

Difficulty: Med   **Reference**: p. 540

114.   *Cascading style sheets* are a set of style rules that tells a Web browser how to present a document.

Difficulty: Med   **Reference**: p. 542

115.   *XSL* is a specification for separating style from content when generating HTML documents.

Difficulty: Med   **Reference**: p. 542

116. Providing Internet content to users based upon knowledge of that customer best describes *personalization*.

                              Difficulty: Med   **Reference**: p. 545

117. Internet sites that allow a user to customize information to their personal preferences best describes *customization*.

                              Difficulty: Easy   **Reference**: p. 546

118. *Context development* is a method that helps you to better understand how a system fits within existing business activities and data.

                              Difficulty: Med   **Reference**: p. 548

119. *Integration depth* is a measurement of how far into the existing technology infrastructure a system penetrates.

                              Difficulty: Hard   **Reference**: p. 548

120. *Organizational breadth* is a measurement that tracks the core business functions affected by a system.

                              Difficulty: Hard   **Reference**: p.548

121. *On-line transaction processing* is the immediate automated responses to the request of users.

                              Difficulty: Med   **Reference**: p. 549

122. *On-line analytical processing* is the use of graphical software tools that provide complex analysis of data stored in a database.

                              Difficulty: Med   **Reference**: p. 550

123. A *data warehouse* is a subject-oriented, integrated, time-variant, nonvolatile collection of data used in support of management decision making.

                              Difficulty: Med   **Reference**: p. 551

124. An *enterprise data warehouse* is a centralized, integrated data warehouse that is the control point and single source of all data made available to end users for decision-support applications throughout the entire organization.

                              Difficulty: Med   **Reference**: p. 553

125. A *data mart* is a data warehouse that is limited in scope; whose data are obtained by selecting and summarizing data from the enterprise data warehouse.

                              Difficulty: Med   **Reference**: p. 554

Matching Questions

Match each of the following terms with its corresponding definition.

        a.   application program interface
        b.   application server
        c.   file server
        d.   middleware
        e.   three-tiered client server
        f.   client/server architecture

126.   A LAN-based computing environment in which a central database server or engine performs all database commands sent to it from client workstations, and application programs on each client concentrate on user interface functions.

                  Answer: f   **Reference:** p. 532

127.   Software building blocks that are used to assure that common system capabilities like user interfaces and printing are standardized as well as modules for facilitating the data exchange between clients and servers.

                  Answer: a   **Reference:** p. 533

128.   A computing server where data analysis functions primarily reside.

                  Answer: b   **Reference:** p. 535

129.   A combination of hardware, software, and communication technologies that bring together data management, presentation, and analysis into a three-tiered client/server environment.

                  Answer: d   **Reference:** p. 535

130.   Advanced client/server architectures in which there are three logical and distinct application--data management, presentation, and analysis--which are combined to create a single information system.

                  Answer: e   **Reference:** p. 535

131.   A device that manages file operations and is shared by each client PC attached to a LAN.

                  Answer: c   **Reference:** p. 530

Match each of the following terms with its corresponding definition.

    a.   BIND
    b.   EDW
    c.   XSL
    d.   HTTP
    e.   XML

132.   A communications protocol for exchanging information on the Internet.

          Answer: d   **Reference**: p. 539

133.   A method for translating Internet domain names into Internet Protocol addresses.

          Answer: a   **Reference**: p. 539

134.   An Internet authoring language that allows designers to create customized tags, enabling the definition, transmission, validation, and interpretation of data between applications.

          Answer: e   **Reference**: p. 540

135.   A centralized, integrated data warehouse that is the control point and single source of all data made available to end users for decision-support applications throughout the entire organization.

          Answer: b   **Reference**: p. 553

136.   A specification for separating style from content when generating HTML documents.

          Answer: c   **Reference**: p. 542

Match each of the following terms with its corresponding definition.

    a.   context development
    b.   customization
    c.   integration depth
    d.   organizational breadth
    e.   personalization

137.   Internet sites that allow a user to customize information to their personal preferences.

                  Answer: b   **Reference**: p. 546

138.   A measurement of how far into the existing technology infrastructure a system penetrates.

                  Answer: c   **Reference**: p. 548

139.   Providing Internet content to users based upon knowledge of that customer.

                  Answer: e   **Reference**: p. 545

140.   A method that helps you to better understand how a system fits within existing business activities and data.

                  Answer: a   **Reference**: p. 548

141.   A measurement that tracks the core business functions affected by a system.

                  Answer: d   **Reference**: p. 548

Match each of the following terms with its corresponding definition.

    a.   data mart
    b.   data warehouse
    c.   enterprise data warehouse
    d.   informational system
    e.   on-line analytical processing
    f.   on-line transaction processing
    g.   operational system

142.   A subject-oriented, integrated, time-variant, nonvolatile collection of data used in support of management decision making.

Answer: b   **Reference**: p. 551

143.   A system designed to support decision making based on stable point-in-time or historical data.

Answer: d   **Reference**: p. 551

144.   A centralized, integrated data warehouse that is the control point and single source of all data made available to end users for decision-support applications throughout the entire organization.

Answer: c   **Reference**: p. 553

145.   The use of graphical software tools that provide complex analysis of data stored in a database.

Answer: e   **Reference**: p. 550

146.   A system that is used to interact with customers and run a business in real time.

Answer: g   **Reference**: p. 551

147.   A data warehouse that is limited in scope; whose data are obtained by selecting and summarizing data from the enterprise data warehouse.

Answer: a   **Reference**: p. 554

148.   The immediate automated responses to the requests of users.

Answer: f   **Reference**: p. 549

Match each of the following approaches to its corresponding description.

     a.   distributed database
     b.   distributed function
     c.   distributed presentation
     d.   distributed processing
     e.   remote data management
     f.   remote presentation

149.   This form of client/server architecture places all software on the client except for the data management functions.

           Answer: e   **Reference**: p. 538

150.   This form of client/server architecture is used to freshen up the delivery of existing server-based applications to distributed clients.

           Answer: c   **Reference**: p. 538

151.   This form of client/server architecture splits analysis functions between the client and server, leaving all presentation on the client and all data management on the server.

           Answer: b   **Reference**: p. 538

152.   This form of client/server architecture places all functionality on the client, except data storage and management which is divided between the client and server.

           Answer: a   **Reference**: p. 538

153.   This form of client/server architecture combines the best features of distributed function and distributed database by splitting both of these across client and server, with presentation functions under the exclusive responsibility of the client machine.

           Answer: d   **Reference**: p. 538

154.   This form of client/server architecture places all data presentation functions on the client machine so that the client has total responsibility for formatting data.

           Answer: f   **Reference**: p. 538

Essay Questions

155. *Describe six approaches to designing server architectures.*

The six approaches are distributed presentation, remote presentation, remote data management, distributed function, distributed database, and distributed processing. Distributed presentation is used to freshen up the delivery of existing server-based applications to distributed clients. Remote presentation places all data presentation functions on the client machine so that the client has total responsibility for formatting data. Remote data management places all software on the client except for the data management functions. Distributed function splits analysis functions between the client and server, leaving all presentation on the client and all data management on the server. Distributed database places all functionality on the client, except data storage and management which is divided between the client and server. Distributed processing combines the best features of distributed function and distributed database by splitting both of these across client and server, with presentation functions under the exclusive responsibility of the client machine.

156. *Identify three reasons for creating a three-tiered client/server architecture.*

Three reasons are application partitioning, easier customization, and easier maintenance.

157. *What is middleware? Provide an example to illustrate the usefulness of middleware.*

Middleware is a combination of hardware, software, and communication technologies that bring together data management, presentation, and analysis into a three-tiered client/server environment. The example from the textbook shows how ODBC drivers enable an Access query to retrieve data from Oracle and Informix databases.

158. *Differentiate between file server and client/server architectures.*

These architectures differ in terms of processing, concurrent data access, network usage, database security and integrity, software maintenance, and hardware and system software flexibility. The file server architecture supports only the distribution of data, while the client/server architecture supports both the distribution of data and processing. In a file server architecture, concurrent data access is managed by the client; in a client/server architecture, concurrent data access is managed by the server. While the client/server architecture supports efficient data transfers, the file server architecture requires large file and data transfers. Database security and integrity are low for the file server architecture; the client/server has high database security and integrity. Software maintenance for a file server architecture is low, although it is mixed for the client/server architecture. In terms of hardware and system software flexibility, the client and server can be decoupled and mixed in a file server architecture. In a client/server architecture, there is a need for greater coordination between client and server.

159. *When adopting a client/server architecture, identify four benefits that may occur.*

A client server architecture: (1) allows companies to leverage the benefits of microcomputer technology; (2) allows most processing to be performed close to the source of processed data, thereby improving response times and reducing network traffic; (3) facilitates the use of graphical user interfaces and visual presentation techniques commonly available for workstations; and (4) allows for and encourages the acceptance of open systems.

160. *What is a database engine? What is a client?*

A database engine is the back-end portion of the client/server database system running on the server and providing database processing and shared access functions. A client is the front-end portion of the client/server database system that provides the user interface and data manipulation functions.

161. *What is a data warehouse? What are the four steps to building a two-level data warehouse architecture?*

A data warehouse is a subject-oriented, integrated, time-variant, nonvolatile collection of data used in support of management decision making. The four steps are: (1) extract data from the various source systems files and databases; (2) transform and integrate the extracted data before loading into the warehouse; (3) organize the read-only database for decision support; and (4) provide a variety of query languages and analytical tools for users to access the data warehouse.

162. *How do operational and informational systems differ?*

These systems differ in their primary purposes, data types, primary users, usage scope, and design goals. The operational system runs the business on a current basis; provides a current representation of the state of the business; is used primarily by on-line customers, clerks, salespersons, and administrators; has a narrow scope of usage; and has a performance design goal. In contrast, an informational system supports managerial decision making; provides historical or point-in-time data; has managers, business analysts, and customers as its primary users; supports a broad usage scope; and has an easy access and use design goal.

163. *What is an enterprise data warehouse? What is its purpose?*

An enterprise data warehouse is a centralized, integrated data warehouse that is the control point and single source of all data made available to end users for decision-support applications throughout the entire organization. Its purpose is to serve as a centralized control point ensuring the quality and integrity of data and providing an accurate, consolidated historical record of business, for time-sensitive data.

164. *Distinguish between personalization and customization. Provide an example of each.*

Personalization provides Internet content to users based upon knowledge of that customer. When visiting an on-line department store, information about your visit and purchases are stored. Each time you visit that site, the stored information is used to provide personalized information to you. If you have purchased clothing and toys for your two-year old child, the site may alert you to new sale items for toddlers. Customization refers to Internet sites that allow a user to customize information to their personal preferences. Customization requires more active involvement on the part of the customer. For instance, you can ask a portal to deliver specific stock, sports, and weather information to you each time you visit that site.

Chapter 17
System Implementation

True-False Questions

1. After maintenance, the implementation phase of the systems development life cycle is the most expensive and time-consuming phase of the entire life cycle.

   Answer: True   **Difficulty**: Med   **Reference**: p. 570

2. Documentation is one of the six major activities associated with systems implementation.

   Answer: True   **Difficulty**: Med   **Reference**: p. 571

3. Test planning is often done during systems design.

   Answer: False   **Difficulty**: Med   **Reference**: p. 572

4. The development of a new version of the software and new versions of all design documents are the major deliverables associated with the coding, testing, and installation stage.

   Answer: False   **Difficulty**: Med   **Reference**: p. 573

5. The systems administration plan answers such questions as when and where the new system will be installed, what people and resources are required, which data will be converted and cleansed, and how long the installation process will take.

   Answer: False   **Difficulty**: Med   **Reference**: p. 573

6. Information systems personnel and end users are the two audiences for the final systems documentation.

   Answer: True   **Difficulty**: Easy   **Reference**: p. 574

7. According to Bloor, embedded software programmers are professionals and technicians who program as part of their main duties.

   Answer: False   **Difficulty**: Med   **Reference**: p. 574

8. System and user documentation, a user training plan, user training modules, and a user support plan are deliverables for documenting the system, training, and supporting users.

   Answer: True   **Difficulty**: Easy   **Reference**: p. 575

9. A master test plan is developed during design.

   Answer: False   **Difficulty**: Med   **Reference**: p. 575

10. Testing managers are responsible for developing test plans, establishing testing standards, integrating testing and development activities in the life cycle, and ensuring that test plans are completed.

    Answer: True   **Difficulty**: Med   **Reference**: p. 576

11. During an inspection test, exactly what the code does is investigated.

Answer: False   **Difficulty**: Med   **Reference**: p. 577

12. The purpose of a walkthrough is to detect and correct errors.

Answer: False   **Difficulty**: Med   **Reference**: p. 577

13. Walkthroughs are a very effective method for identifying errors in code.

Answer: True   **Difficulty**: Med   **Reference**: p. 577

14. Desk checking is a testing technique in which the program code is sequentially executed manually by the reviewer.

Answer: True   **Difficulty**: Med   **Reference**: p. 577

15. Unit testing does not require automated code execution.

Answer: False   **Difficulty**: Med   **Reference**: p. 578

16. A systems analyst or programmer typically does syntax checking.

Answer: False   **Difficulty**: Med   **Reference**: p. 578

17. System testing is the process of bringing together all of the modules that a program comprises for testing purposes.

Answer: False   **Difficulty**: Med   **Reference**: p. 578

18. Integration testing brings together all of the programs that a system comprises for testing purposes.

Answer: False   **Difficulty**: Med   **Reference**: p. 578

19. Unit testing is a technique used in testing modules, especially where modules are written and tested in a top-down fashion, where a few lines of code are used to substitute for subordinate modules.

Answer: False   **Difficulty**: Med   **Reference**: p. 578

20. System testing is intended to demonstrate whether a system meets its requirements.

Answer: False   **Difficulty**: Hard   **Reference**: p. 578

21. The focus of integration testing is on the interrelationships among modules.

Answer: True   **Difficulty**: Med   **Reference**: p. 578

22. A test case is a specific scenario of transactions, queries, or navigation paths that represent a typical, critical, or abnormal use of the system.

Answer: True   **Difficulty**: Med   **Reference**: p. 579

23. The people who create the test cases should be the same people who have coded and will test the system.

    Answer: False   **Difficulty**: Med   **Reference**: p. 580

24. A symbolic debugger allows a program to be run on-line, allowing the programmer to observe how different areas of data are affected as the instructions are executed.

    Answer: True   **Difficulty**: Med   **Reference**: p. 581

25. Software testing tools can compare the results of one test run with those from prior test cases to identify errors or to highlight the results of new features.

    Answer: True   **Difficulty**: Med   **Reference**: p. 581

26. During alpha testing users test a completed information system using simulated data.

    Answer: True   **Difficulty**: Med   **Reference**: p. 582

27. During beta testing, users test a completed information system using real data in the real user environment.

    Answer: True   **Difficulty**: Med   **Reference**: p. 582

28. During recovery testing, the analysts try to break the system.

    Answer: False   **Difficulty**: Med   **Reference**: p. 582

29. During stress testing, the analysts try to determine how the system performs on the range of possible environments on which it may be used.

    Answer: False   **Difficulty**: Med   **Reference**: p. 582

30. The purpose of system testing is to determine whether the software, documentation, technical support, and training activities work as intended.

    Answer: False   **Difficulty**: Hard   **Reference**: p. 583

31. Installation is the organizational process of changing over from the current information system to a new one.

    Answer: True   **Difficulty**: Easy   **Reference**: p. 583

32. The coexistence of the old and new systems is characteristic of the parallel installation approach.

    Answer: True   **Difficulty**: Med   **Reference**: p. 585

33. The key advantage of a direct installation is that it limits potential damage and potential cost by limiting the effects to a single site.

    Answer: False   **Difficulty**: Med   **Reference**: p. 585

34. A positive aspect of the direct installation approach is that there is a high interest in making installation a success.

    Answer: True   **Difficulty**: Med   **Reference**: p. 585

35. A positive aspect of the phased installation approach is that learning can occur and problems can be fixed by concentrating on one site.

    Answer: False   **Difficulty**: Med   **Reference**: p. 586

36. A positive aspect of the phased installation approach is that it limits potential harm and costs from system error or failure to certain business activities or functions.

    Answer: True   **Difficulty**: Med   **Reference**: p. 586

37. Installation is an organizational change process.

    Answer: True   **Difficulty**: Easy   **Reference**: p. 587

38. According to Bell and Evans, the resource requirement specification is finalized during systems development phase.

    Answer: False   **Difficulty**: Hard   **Reference**: p. 587

39. According to Bell and Evans, the release description is finalized during the detailed design and implementation stage of the systems development generic life cycle phase.

    Answer: False   **Difficulty**: Hard   **Reference**: p. 587

40. System documentation is the detailed information about a system's design specifications, its internal workings, and its functionality.

    Answer: True   **Difficulty**: Med   **Reference**: p. 588

41. Internal documentation is system documentation that includes the outcome of structured diagramming techniques such as data flow and entity-relationship diagrams.

    Answer: False   **Difficulty**: Med   **Reference**: p. 588

42. A system administrator's guide is an example of external system documentation.

    Answer: False   **Difficulty**: Med   **Reference**: p. 588

43. A release description is an example of user documentation.

    Answer: True   **Difficulty**: Med   **Reference**: p. 588

44. The purpose of a user's guide is to provide information on how users can use computer systems to perform specific tasks.

    Answer: True   **Difficulty**: Med   **Reference**: p. 589

45.   An acceptance sign-off allows users to test for proper system installation and then signify their acceptance of the new system with their signatures.

Answer: True   **Difficulty**: Med   **Reference**: p. 590

46.   Network architecture refers to all the resources and practices required to help people adequately use computer systems to do their primary work.

Answer: False   **Difficulty**: Med   **Reference**: p. 593

47.   According to Henderson and Treacy, training and support are most important during the later stages of end-user computing growth and less so in the earlier stages.

Answer: False   **Difficulty**: Hard   **Reference**: p. 593

48.   Many organizations tend to underinvest in computing skills training.

Answer: True   **Difficulty**: Med   **Reference**: p. 593

49.   The extent to which a system is used and the user's satisfaction with the system are two ways to determine if implementation has been successful.

Answer: True   **Difficulty**: Med   **Reference**: p. 601

50.   User demographics, performance, and satisfaction are factors that influence the extent to which a system is used.

Answer: True   **Difficulty**: Med   **Reference**: p. 601

Multiple Choice Questions

51.   After maintenance, which of the following is the most expensive and most time consuming phase of the entire life cycle?

   a.   implementation
   b.   physical design
   c.   logical design
   d.   analysis

Answer: a   **Difficulty**:   **Reference**: p. 570

52.   Which of the following affect the implementation process?

   a.   the work habits of an organization's members
   b.   the personal goals of an organization's members
   c.   the beliefs of an organization's members
   d.   all of the above

Answer: d   **Difficulty**: Med   **Reference**: p. 571

53. The purpose of coding, testing, and installation is to:

    a. transform the logical specifications of the system into technology specific details from which all programming and system construction can be done
    b. convert the final physical system specifications into working and reliable software and hardware
    c. systematically repair and improve the information system
    d. study and propose alternative replacement systems

    Answer: b   **Difficulty**: Med   **Reference**: p. 571

54. Who is responsible for ensuring that coding, testing, and installation are properly planned and executed?

    a. programmers
    b. management
    c. systems analysts
    d. end-users

    Answer: c   **Difficulty**: Med   **Reference**: p. 571

55. The process whereby the physical design specifications created by the analysis team is turned into working computer code is referred to as:

    a. coding
    b. testing
    c. implementation
    d. analysis

    Answer: a   **Difficulty**: Med   **Reference**: p. 572

56. Which of the following statements is true regarding testing?

    a. The coding process should be completed, and then the testing process can begin.
    b. Once coding has begun, the testing process can begin and proceed in parallel.
    c. The testing process is performed first, then the coding process begins.
    d. None of the above is correct.

    Answer: b   **Difficulty**: Med   **Reference**: p. 572

57. The process in which the current system is replaced by the new system best describes:

    a. the systems development life cycle
    b. installation
    c. physical design
    d. set-up

    Answer: b   **Difficulty**: Easy   **Reference**: p. 572

58. The deliverables for coding, testing, and installation are:

    a.   the creation of a document that will consolidate the information that must be considered when implementing a physically distributed systems design
    b.   structured descriptions and diagrams that outline the logic contained within each DFD process
    c.   the code, program documentation, test scenarios and test data, results of program and system testing, user guides, user training plan, and an installation and conversion plan
    d.   a system service request, a statement of work, and a baseline project plan

    Answer: c   **Difficulty**: Med   **Reference**: p. 573

59. A strategy for training users so they can quickly learn the new system is a(n):

    a.   training plan
    b.   installation plan
    c.   user guide
    d.   training curriculum

    Answer: a   **Difficulty**: Med   **Reference**: p. 573

60. Training on the use of the system begins during the early stages of the:

    a.   analysis phase
    b.   logical design phase
    c.   implementation phase
    d.   project initiation and planning phase

    Answer: c   **Difficulty**: Med   **Reference**: p. 573

61. This plan lays out a strategy for moving from the old system to the new, from the beginning to end of the process.

    a.   baseline project plan
    b.   installation plan
    c.   training plan
    d.   testing plan

    Answer: b   **Difficulty**: Med   **Reference**: p. 573

62. This type of future programmer includes professionals and technicians who program as part of their main duties.

    a.   secondary programmer
    b.   embedded software programmer
    c.   part-time programmer
    d.   occasional programmer

    Answer: d   **Difficulty**: Med   **Reference**: p. 574

63.   A master test plan is developed during:

    a.   implementation
    b.   analysis
    c.   logical design
    d.   physical design

Answer: b   **Difficulty**: Med   **Reference**: p. 575

64.   Which of the following are testing managers responsible for?

    a.   developing testing plans
    b.   integrating testing and development activities in the life cycle
    c.   establishing testing standards
    d.   all of the above

Answer: d   **Difficulty**: Med   **Reference**: p. 576

65.   The type of testing that does not execute the code is called:

    a.   static testing
    b.   dynamic testing
    c.   referential testing
    d.   manual testing

Answer: a   **Difficulty**: Med   **Reference**: p. 576

66.   The results of running the code are not an issue for this particular type of test.

    a.   static testing
    b.   dynamic testing
    c.   referential testing
    d.   none of the above

Answer: a   **Difficulty**: Med   **Reference**: p. 576

67.   The type of testing that involves the execution of code is called:

    a.   code testing
    b.   static testing
    c.   dynamic testing
    d.   execution testing

Answer: c   **Difficulty**: Med   **Reference**: p. 576

68.   A testing technique in which participants examine program code for predictable language-specific errors defines:

    a.   walkthrough
    b.   inspections
    c.   desk checking
    d.   syntax checking

Answer: b   **Difficulty**: Med   **Reference**: p. 576

69. The type of testing responsible for determining what the code does is:

    a. walkthrough
    b. inspection
    c. system testing
    d. syntax checking

    Answer: a   **Difficulty**: Med   **Reference**: p. 577

70. A testing technique in which the program code is sequentially executed manually by the reviewer is referred to as:

    a. inspection
    b. system testing
    c. desk checking
    d. syntax checking

    Answer: c   **Difficulty**: Easy   **Reference**: p. 577

71. Testing each module alone in an attempt to discover any errors that may exist in the module's code is referred to as:

    a. unit testing
    b. system testing
    c. stub testing
    d. singular testing

    Answer: a   **Difficulty**: Med   **Reference**: p. 578

72. The process of bringing together all of the modules that comprise a program for testing purposes is referred to as:

    a. unity testing
    b. integration testing
    c. system testing
    d. implementation

    Answer: b   **Difficulty**: Med   **Reference**: p. 578

73. The bringing together of all the programs that comprise a system for testing describes:

    a. unity testing
    b. integration testing
    c. system testing
    d. implementation

    Answer: c   **Difficulty**: Med   **Reference**: p. 578

74. A technique used in testing modules, especially where modules are written and tested in a top-down fashion, where a few lines of code are used to substitute for subordinate modules describes:

    a. module testing
    b. unit testing
    c. top-down testing
    d. stub testing

    Answer: d   **Difficulty**: Med   **Reference**: p. 578

75. The purpose of acceptance testing is to:

    a. determine if new requirements must be added to the newly completed system
    b. determine if the system meets user requirements
    c. determine if the system meets its objectives
    d. do none of the above

    Answer: b   **Difficulty**: Hard   **Reference**: p. 582

76. The most complete acceptance testing will include:

    a. alpha testing
    b. beta testing
    c. a system audit
    d. all of the above

    Answer: d   **Difficulty**: Med   **Reference**: p. 582

77. The process whereby actual users test a completed information system, the end result of which is the users' acceptance of it, best describes:

    a. acceptance testing
    b. alpha testing
    c. beta testing
    d. system testing

    Answer: a   **Difficulty**: Med   **Reference**: p. 582

78. User testing of a completed information system using simulated data refers to:

    a. acceptance testing
    b. alpha testing
    c. beta testing
    d. system testing

    Answer: b   **Difficulty**: Med   **Reference**: p. 582

79. User testing of a completed information system using real data in the real user environment refers to:

    a. acceptance testing
    b. alpha testing
    c. beta testing
    d. system testing

    Answer: c   **Difficulty**: Med   **Reference**: p. 582

80. Which of the following are designed during alpha testing and try to break the system?

a. stress tests
b. performance tests
c. recovery tests
d. security tests

Answer: a   **Difficulty**: Med   **Reference**: p. 582

81. The organizational process of changing over from the current information system to a new one best defines:

a. reorganization
b. physical design
c. installation
d. replacement

Answer: c   **Difficulty**: Med   **Reference**: p. 583

82. Changing over from the old information system to a new one by turning off the old system as the new one is turned on best describes:

a. phased installation
b. single location installation
c. parallel installation
d. direct installation

Answer: d   **Difficulty**: Med   **Reference**: p. 583

83. All of the following are types of user documentation except:

a. release description
b. reference guide
c. acceptance sign-off
d. management plan

Answer: d   **Difficulty**: Med   **Reference**: p. 588

84. System documentation is intended primarily for:

a. maintenance programmers
b. end users
c. systems analysts
d. system operators

Answer: a   **Difficulty**: Med   **Reference**: p. 588

85. Written or other visual information about an application system, how it works, and how to use it best defines:

    a. system documentation
    b. user documentation
    c. internal documentation
    d. external documentation

    Answer: b   **Difficulty**: Med   **Reference**: p. 588

86. System documentation that is part of the program source code or is generated at compile time best defines:

    a. program statements
    b. user documentation
    c. internal documentation
    d. external documentation

    Answer: c   **Difficulty**: Med   **Reference**: p. 588

87. System documentation that includes the outcome of such structured diagramming techniques as data flow and entity-relationship diagrams best defines:

    a. system documentation
    b. user documentation
    c. internal documentation
    d. external documentation

    Answer: d   **Difficulty**: Med   **Reference**: p. 588

88. Which of the following is an exhaustive list of the system's functions and commands, usually in alphabetical order?

    a. reference guide
    b. user's guide
    c. release description
    d. system administrator's guide

    Answer: a   **Difficulty**: Med   **Reference**: p. 588

89. This type of user documentation contains information about a new system release, including a list of complete documentation for the new release, features and enhancements, known problems and how they have been dealt with in the new release, and information about installation.

    a. reference guide
    b. user's manual
    c. release description
    d. system administrator's guide

    Answer: c   **Difficulty**: Med   **Reference**: p. 590

90. This type of user documentation is intended primarily for those who will install and administer a new system and contains information about the network on which the system will run, software interfaces for peripherals such as printers, troubleshooting, and setting up user accounts.

    a. external documentation
    b. user's manual
    c. system documentation
    d. system administrator's guide

    Answer: d   **Difficulty**: Med   **Reference**: p. 590

91. This type of user documentation allows users to test for proper system installation and then signify their acceptance of the new system with their signatures.

    a. acceptance sign-off
    b. user contract
    c. RFP
    d. system verification

    Answer: a   **Difficulty**: Med   **Reference**: p. 590

92. Most user documentation is now delivered:

    a. on-line, in hypertext format
    b. through paper manuals
    c. by calling technical support numbers
    d. through help desks

    Answer: a   **Difficulty**: Easy   **Reference**: p. 591

93. Which of the following is one of the four fundamental issues IS managers must address?

    a. IS specialist salaries
    b. career preparation
    c. computing infrastructure
    d. an organization's mission

    Answer: c   **Difficulty**: Med   **Reference**: p. 593

94. According to research studies cited in the text, which of the following statements is true?

    a. Training and support are not as important in the early stages of end user computing growth as they are in the later stages.
    b. Training and support are equally important throughout the stages of end-user computing growth.
    c. Training and support are most important in the early stages of end user computing growth and less so later on.
    d. Training is best offered during the design phase.

    Answer: c   **Difficulty**: Hard   **Reference**: p. 593

95. Which of the following statements is true about intermittent users?

    a. Support mechanisms are a good way to provide training for intermittent users of a system.
    b. Intermittent users are not interested in, nor would they profit from, typical user training methods.
    c. Intermittent users must be provided "point of need support."
    d. All of the above are true statements.

    Answer: d   **Difficulty**: Med   **Reference**: p. 593

96. The factor identified by Rivard and Huff as being most closely related to overall satisfaction with user development of computer-based applications was:

    a. user satisfaction with support provided by the information systems department
    b. the correct diagnosis of current information system requirements
    c. active user participation during the analysis of the current system
    d. management participation in the planning process

    Answer: a   **Difficulty**: Med   **Reference**: p. 593

97. Which of the following is true regarding information system training?

    a. Many organizations tend to over invest in computing skills training.
    b. On average, organizations tend to invest appropriate amounts of time and money in computing skills training.
    c. Many organizations tend to under invest in computing skills training.
    d. Information system training is not a costly expense for the organization.

    Answer: c   **Difficulty**: Med   **Reference**: p. 593

98. A component of a software package or application in which training and educational information is embedded best defines:

    a. resident expert
    b. computer-aided instruction
    c. electronic tutorial
    d. electronic performance support system

    Answer: d   **Difficulty**: Med   **Reference**: p. 595

99. Based on a research study cited in the text, which of the following is the number one criterion that contributes to user satisfaction with personal computing?

    a. type of training manual
    b. training time
    c. user support
    d. training method

    Answer: c   **Difficulty**: Med   **Reference**: p. 596

100.   An organizational unit whose mission is to support users in exploiting information technology best
        defines:

    a.   development center
    b.   information center
    c.   computer center
    d.   management information systems department

Answer: b   **Difficulty**: Med   **Reference**: p. 596

Fill In the Blanks

101.   *Inspections* are a testing technique in which participants examine program code for predictable
        language-specific errors.

                                       Difficulty: Med   **Reference**: p. 576

102.   *Desk checking* is a testing technique in which the program code is sequentially executed manually by
        the reviewer.

                                       Difficulty: Med   **Reference**: p. 577

103.   *Stub testing* is a technique used in testing modules, especially where modules are written and tested in
        a top-down fashion, where a few lines of code are used to substitute for subordinate modules.

                                       Difficulty: Hard   **Reference**: p. 578

104.   In *unit testing*, each module is tested alone in an attempt to discover any errors in its code.

                                       Difficulty: Med   **Reference**: p. 578

105.   *Integration testing* is the process of bringing together all of the modules that a program comprises for
        testing purposes; the modules are typically integrated in a top-down, incremental fashion.

                                       Difficulty: Hard   **Reference**: p. 578

106.   *System testing* is the process of bringing together all of the programs that a system comprises for
        testing purposes; programs are typically integrated in a top-down, incremental fashion.

                                       Difficulty: Med   **Reference**: p. 578

107.   *Acceptance testing* is the process whereby actual users test a completed information system, the end
        result of which is the user's acceptance of it.

                                       Difficulty: Med   **Reference**: p. 582

108.   *Alpha testing* refers to user testing of a completed information system using simulated data.

                                       Difficulty: Med   **Reference**: p. 582

109. **_Beta testing_** refers to user testing of a completed information system using real data in the real user environment.

Difficulty: Med **Reference**: p. 582

110. **_Installation_** is the organizational process of changing over from the current information system to a new one.

Difficulty: Easy **Reference**: p. 583

111. **_Direct_**, **_parallel_**, **_single location_**, and **_phased_** are the four approaches to installation.

Difficulty: Med **Reference**: p. 583

112. **_Direct installation_** refers to changing over from the old information system to a new one by turning off the old system when the new one is turned on.

Difficulty: Easy **Reference**: p. 583

113. **_Parallel installation_** refers to running the old information system and the new one at the same time until management decides the old system can be turned off.

Difficulty: Easy **Reference**: p. 585

114. **_Single location installation_** refers to trying out a new information system at one site and using the experience to decide if and how the new system should be deployed throughout the organization.

Difficulty: Med **Reference**: p. 585

115. **_Phased installation_** refers to changing from the old information system to the new one incrementally, starting with one or a few functional components and then gradually extending the installation to cover the whole new system.

Difficulty: Med **Reference**: p. 586

116. **_System documentation_** and **_user documentation_** are the two basic types of documentation.

Difficulty: Easy **Reference**: p. 588

117. **_System documentation_** is the detailed information about a system's design specifications, its internal workings, and its functionality.

Difficulty: Med **Reference**: p.588

118. **_Internal documentation_** is system documentation that is part of the program source code or is generated at compile time.

Difficulty: Med **Reference**: p. 588

119. **_External documentation_** is system documentation that includes the outcome of structured diagramming techniques such as data flow and entity-relationship diagrams.

Difficulty: Med **Reference**: p. 588

120. **_User documentation_** is written or other visual information about an application system, how it works, and how to use it.

                    Difficulty: Easy   **Reference**: p. 588

121. **_Support_** refers to providing ongoing educational and problem-solving assistance to information system users.

                    Difficulty: Easy   **Reference**: p. 593

122. **_Computing infrastructure_** refers to all the resources and practices required to help people adequately use computer systems to do their primary work.

                    Difficulty: Med   **Reference**: p. 593

123. An **_electronic performance support system_** is a component of a software package or application in which training and educational information is embedded.

                    Difficulty: Hard   **Reference**: p. 595

124. An **_information center_** is an organizational unit whose mission is to support users in exploiting information technology.

                    Difficulty: Med   **Reference**: p. 596

125. A **_help desk_** is a single point of contact for all user inquiries and problems about a particular information system or for all users in a particular department.

                    Difficulty: Med   **Reference**: p. 598

Matching Questions

Match each of the following terms with its corresponding definition.

a. acceptance testing
b. alpha testing
c. beta testing
d. desk checking
e. direct installation
f. inspections
g. installation
h. integration testing
i. parallel installation
j. phased installation
k. single location installation
l. stub testing
m. support

126. Changing over from the old information system to a new one incrementally, starting with one or a few functional components and then gradually extending the installation to cover the whole new system.

                    Answer: j   **Reference**: p. 586

127. The process of bringing together all of the modules that comprise a program for testing purposes. The modules are typically integrated in a top-down, incremental fashion.

                    Answer: h   **Reference:** p. 578

128. User testing of a completed information system using simulated data.

                    Answer: b   **Reference:** p. 582

129. The organizational process of changing over from the current information system to a new one.

                    Answer: g   **Reference:** p. 583

130. Trying out a new information system at one site and using the experience to decide if and how the new system should be deployed throughout the organization.

                    Answer: k   **Reference:** p. 585

131. A testing technique in which the program code is sequentially executed manually by the reviewer.

                    Answer: d   **Reference:** p. 577

132. Running the old information system and the new one at the same time until management decides the old system can be turned off.

                    Answer: i   **Reference:** p. 585

133. Changing over from the old information system to a new one by turning off the old system as the new one is turned on.

                    Answer: e   **Reference:** p. 583

134. A testing technique in which participants examine program code for predictable language-specific errors.

                    Answer: f   **Reference:** p. 576

135. Providing ongoing educational and problem-solving assistance to information systems users.

                    Answer: m   **Reference:** p. 593

136. The process whereby actual users test a completed information system, the end result of which is the users' acceptance of it.

                    Answer: a   **Reference:** p. 582

137. A technique used in testing modules, especially where modules are written and tested in a top-down fashion, where a few lines of code are used to substitute for subordinate modules.

                    Answer: l   **Reference:** p. 578

138. User testing of a completed information system using real data in the real user environment.

                    Answer: c   **Reference:** p. 582

Based on the information adapted from Bloor, 1994, match each of the following future programmer categories with its corresponding description. (Answers may occur more than once.)

      a.   embedded software programmers
      b.   IS department programmers
      c.   occasional programmers
      d.   software company programmers

139.   These programmers work for consulting and packaged software companies.

                Answer: d   **Reference**: p. 574

140.   Of the four categories of programmers mentioned in the article, this is the only programmer category that is expected to decline.

                Answer: b   **Reference**: p. 574

141.   This group will likely dramatically increase from several million in 1994 to over 10 million by 2010.

                Answer: a   **Reference**: p. 574

142.   This group includes professionals and technicians who program as part of their main duties.

                Answer: c   **Reference**: p. 574

143.   These individuals work for the IS function.

                Answer: b   **Reference**: p. 574

144.   These programmers produce code that is contained in other products, like cars, office equipment, and consumer electronics.

                Answer: a   **Reference**: p. 574

145.   This group will rise from roughly 20 million in 1994 to over 100 million in 2010.

                Answer: c   **Reference**: p. 574

146.   The number of programmers in this category will likely rise from roughly 600,000 in 1994 to several million by 2010.

                Answer: d   **Reference**: p. 574

Using Mosley's categorization of test types, classify each of the tests listed below.

    a.   static, manual
    b.   static, automated
    c.   dynamic, manual
    d.   dynamic, automated

147.   Unit test

        Answer: d   **Reference:** p. 576

148.   Syntax checking

        Answer: b   **Reference:** p. 576

149.   Walkthroughs

        Answer: c   **Reference:** p. 576

150.   Desk checking

        Answer: c   **Reference:** p. 576

151.   Integration test

        Answer: d   **Reference:** p. 576

152.   Inspections

        Answer: a   **Reference:** p. 576

153.   System test

        Answer: d   **Reference:** p. 576

Match each of the following types of testing with its corresponding description.

    a.   integration testing
    b.   system testing
    c.   stub testing
    d.   acceptance testing
    e.   alpha testing
    f.   beta testing
    g.   recovery testing
    h.   security testing
    i.   stress testing
    j.   performance testing

154.   This type of testing verifies protection mechanisms built into the system will protect it from improper penetration.

                   Answer: h   **Reference:** p. 582

155.   User testing of a completed information system using real data in the real user environment.

                   Answer: f   **Reference:** p. 582

156.   The process whereby actual users test a completed information system, the end result of which is the users' acceptance of it.

                   Answer: d   **Reference:** p. 582

157.   This type of testing determines how the system performs on the range of possible environments in which it may be used.

                   Answer: j   **Reference:** p. 583

158.   This type of test tries to break the system.

                   Answer: i   **Reference:** p. 582

159.   The process of bringing together all of the modules that comprise a program for testing purposes. Modules are typically integrated in a top-down, incremental fashion.

                   Answer: a   **Reference:** p. 578

160.   This type of test forces the software (or environment) to fail in order to verify that recovery is properly performed.

                   Answer: g   **Reference:** p. 582

161.   User testing of a completed information system using simulated data.

                   Answer: e   **Reference:** p. 582

162.   A technique used in testing modules, especially where modules are written and tested in a top-down fashion, where a few lines of code are used to substitute for subordinate modules.

                   Answer: c   **Reference:** p. 578

163.   The bringing together of all the programs that a system comprises for testing purposes; programs are typically integrated in a top-down, incremental fashion.

Answer: b   **Reference:** p. 578

Match each of the following terms with its corresponding description.

a.   direct installation
b.   installation
c.   parallel installation
d.   phased installation
e.   single location installation

164.   Running the old information system and the new one at the same time until management decides the old system can be turned off.

Answer: c   **Reference:** p. 585

165.   The organizational process of changing over from the current information system to a new one.

Answer: b   **Reference:** p. 583

166.   Trying out a new information system at one site and using the experience to decide if and how the new system should be deployed throughout the organization.

Answer: e   **Reference:** p. 585

167.   Changing over from the old information system to a new one incrementally, starting with one or a few functional components and then gradually extending the installation to cover the whole new system.

Answer: d   **Reference:** p. 586

168.   Changing over from the old information system to a new one by turning off the old system as the new one is turned on.

Answer: a   **Reference:** p. 583

Essay Questions

169.   *Briefly identify the four types of installation.*

The four types of installation are direct, parallel, single location, and phased. Changing over from the old information system to a new one by turning off the old system as the new one is turned on is called direct installation. Parallel installation involves running the old information system and the new one at the same time until management decides the old system can be turned off. Single location installation involves trying out a new information system at one site and using the experience to decide if and how the new system should be deployed throughout the organization. Changing over from the old information system to a new one incrementally, starting with one or a few functional components and then gradually extending the installation to cover the whole new system is commonly called phased installation.

170. *Briefly identify and categorize the seven different types of tests as proposed by Mosley.*

Software application testing includes several different types of tests. As indicated in the text, Mosley (1993) classifies the techniques based on whether they use static or dynamic techniques, and whether the test is automated or manual. While static means the code being tested is not executed, dynamic does involve the execution of code. Automation indicates that the computer performs the testing; manual means that people perform the testing. Four distinct categories are identified: (1) static, manual, (2) static, automated, (3) dynamic, manual, and (4) dynamic, automated. The first category contains inspections; the second category contains syntax checking. The third category contains walkthroughs and desk checking; the fourth category contains unit test, integration test, and system test.

171. *Define system documentation, user documentation, internal documentation, and external documentation.*

System documentation is detailed information about a system's design specifications, its internal workings, and its functionality. Internal documentation and external documentation are two types of system documentation. Internal documentation is system documentation that is part of the program source code or is generated at compile time. External documentation is system documentation that includes the outcome of such structured diagramming techniques as data flow and entity-relationship diagrams. User documentation refers to written or other visual information about an application system, how it works, and how to use it.

172. *Identify several types of user documentation.*

The text identified several types of user documentation. These types include a reference guide, a user's guide, a release description, a systems administrator's guide, and an acceptance sign-off. A reference guide consists of an exhaustive list of the system's functions and commands and is usually in alphabetical order. This purpose of the user's guide is to provide information on how users can use computer systems to perform specific tasks. A release description provides information about a new system release, including a list of complete documentation for the new release, features and enhancements, known problems and how they have been dealt with in the new release, and information about installation. The systems administrator's guide is intended for individuals who will install and administer the system. It contains information about the network on which the system will run, software interfaces for peripherals, troubleshooting, and setting up user accounts. Users demonstrate their approval by recording their signatures on an acceptance sign-off.

173. *Briefly identify the tasks associated with closing down the project.*

The first task encompasses many activities. These activities include team member evaluations, team member reassignments, and notifying affected parties of the project ending. The second task encompasses post-project reviews with both management and customers; its purpose is to critique the project, its methods, its deliverables, and its management. The third task involves closing out the customer contract.

174. *What are the six factors, identified by Lucas, that influence the extent to which a system is used?*

Lucas identified user's personal stake, system characteristics, user demographics, organization support, performance, and satisfaction.

175. *What is a help desk? What are the top two valued skills help desk personnel should have?*

A help desk is a single point of contact for all user inquiries and problems about a particular information system or for all users in a particular department. The top two valued skills are related to communication and customer service.

176. *What is an electronic performance support system? What forms might this system take?*

An electronic performance support system is a component of a software package or application in which training and educational information is embedded. An EPSS can be implemented as a tutorial, expert system shell, or hypertext jumps to reference material.

177. *What factors influence implementation success?*

While management support and user involvement impact the successful implementation of a new system, other factors play a part. Commitment to the project, commitment to change, the extent of project definition, user expectations, and political environment impact the implementation process. Additionally, Lucas identified six factors that influence the extent to which a system is used; these include user's personal stake, system characteristics, user demographics, organization support, performance, and satisfaction.

178. *How can you support intermittent users of a system?*

Intermittent system users require "point of need support." Their needs can be addressed through the system interface and on-line help facilities.

Chapter 18
Maintaining Information Systems

True-False Questions

1. Today more programmers work on maintenance activities than work on new development.

    Answer: True   **Difficulty**: Med   **Reference**: p. 615

2. Overcoming internal processing errors and providing better support for changing business needs are two reasons why systems are maintained.

    Answer: True   **Difficulty**: Med   **Reference**: p. 615

3. Maintenance activities are limited to software changes.

    Answer: False   **Difficulty**: Easy   **Reference**: p. 615

4. Implementation is the last phase of the systems development life cycle.

    Answer: False   **Difficulty**: Med   **Reference**: p. 616

5. The decision to either maintain a system or replace it is often an issue of economics.

    Answer: True   **Difficulty**: Med   **Reference**: p. 616

6. Installation is one of the four major maintenance activities.

    Answer: False   **Difficulty**: Med   **Reference**: p. 616

7. Obtaining maintenance requests, transforming requests into changes, designing changes and implementing changes are the four major maintenance activities.

    Answer: True   **Difficulty**: Med   **Reference**: p. 616

8. Transforming requests into changes is a major maintenance activity.

    Answer: True   **Difficulty**: Med   **Reference**: p. 616

9. Many similarities exist between the SDLC and the activities within the maintenance process.

    Answer: True   **Difficulty**: Easy   **Reference**: p. 618

10. The project identification and planning and analysis SDLC phases are analogous to the maintenance process of transforming requests into changes.

    Answer: False   **Difficulty**: Hard   **Reference**: p. 618

11. The systems analysis SDLC phase is analogous to the maintenance process of obtaining maintenance requests.

    Answer: False   **Difficulty**: Hard   **Reference**: p. 618

12. The systems design SDLC phase is analogous to the maintenance process of designing changes.

     Answer: True   **Difficulty**: Easy   **Reference**: p. 618

13. The systems implementation SDLC phase is analogous to the maintenance process of implementing changes.

     Answer: True   **Difficulty**: Med   **Reference**: p. 618

14. The maintenance phase's primary deliverables are finalized design specifications.

     Answer: False   **Difficulty**: Hard   **Reference**: p. 619

15. One way to distinguish maintenance from new development is that maintenance reuses most existing system modules in producing the new system version.

     Answer: True   **Difficulty**: Med   **Reference**: p. 619

16. A significant portion of the expenditures for information systems within organizations goes to the maintenance of existing systems.

     Answer: True   **Difficulty**: Med   **Reference**: p. 619

17. Corrective maintenance modifies the system to environmental changes.

     Answer: False   **Difficulty**: Med   **Reference**: p. 620

18. Corrective maintenance repairs design and programming errors.

     Answer: True   **Difficulty**: Easy   **Reference**: p. 620

19. Adaptive maintenance modifies the system to environmental changes.

     Answer: True   **Difficulty**: Med   **Reference**: p. 620

20. Adaptive maintenance evolves the system to solve new problems or take advantage of new opportunities.

     Answer: False   **Difficulty**: Hard   **Reference**: p. 620

21. Perfective maintenance evolves the system to solve new problems or take advantage of new opportunities.

     Answer: True   **Difficulty**: Med   **Reference**: p. 620

22. Preventive maintenance safeguards a system from future problems.

     Answer: True   **Difficulty**: Easy   **Reference**: p. 620

23. Preventive maintenance repairs design and programming errors.

     Answer: False   **Difficulty**: Med   **Reference**: p. 620

24. Adaptive maintenance accounts for as much as 75 percent of all maintenance activity.

    Answer: False   **Difficulty**: Med   **Reference**: p. 620

25. Corrective maintenance focuses on removing defects from an existing system without adding new functionality.

    Answer: True   **Difficulty**: Med   **Reference**: p. 620

26. Adaptive maintenance is a significant part of an organization's maintenance effort.

    Answer: False   **Difficulty**: Med   **Reference**: p. 620

27. Both perfective and preventive maintenance typically have a much higher priority than corrective maintenance.

    Answer: False   **Difficulty**: Hard   **Reference**: p. 620

28. The number of customers for a given system influences most of the costs associated with maintaining a system.

    Answer: False   **Difficulty**: Hard   **Reference**: p. 621

29. Transitive defects are the number of unknown errors existing in the system after it is installed.

    Answer: False   **Difficulty**: Med   **Reference**: p. 621

30. The number of latent defects in a system influences most of the costs associated with maintaining a system.

    Answer: True   **Difficulty**: Med   **Reference**: p. 621

31. The number of customers for a given system influences maintenance costs.

    Answer: True   **Difficulty**: Easy   **Reference**: p. 621

32. The quality of system documentation influences maintenance costs.

    Answer: True   **Difficulty**: Easy   **Reference**: p. 622

33. Software structure is a cost element of maintenance.

    Answer: True   **Difficulty**: Med   **Reference**: p. 622

34. Management support is one of the major cost elements of maintenance.

    Answer: False   **Difficulty**: Med   **Reference**: p. 622

35. Separate, combined, and functional are types of maintenance organizational structures.

    Answer: True   **Difficulty**: Med   **Reference**: p. 623

36. An advantage of the combined maintenance organizational structure is the formal transfer of systems between groups improving the system and documentation quality.

    Answer: False   **Difficulty**: Hard   **Reference**: p. 623

37. A disadvantage associated with the separate maintenance organizational structure is that documentation and testing thoroughness suffers due to a lack of a formal transfer of responsibility.

    Answer: False   **Difficulty**: Hard   **Reference**: p. 623

38. An advantage to the functional maintenance organizational structure is that the maintenance group knows or has access to all assumptions and decisions behind the system's original design.

    Answer: False   **Difficulty**: Hard   **Reference**: p. 623

39. It is now common to rotate individuals in and out of maintenance activities.

    Answer: True   **Difficulty**: Easy   **Reference**: p. 624

40. Mean time between failures is a measurement of error occurrences that can be tracked over time to indicate the quality of a system.

    Answer: True   **Difficulty**: Med   **Reference**: p. 624

41. Over time, the MTBF should rapidly decrease after a few months of system use.

    Answer: False   **Difficulty**: Hard   **Reference**: p. 624

42. Managing maintenance requests is a maintenance activity.

    Answer: True   **Difficulty**: Easy   **Reference**: p. 625

43. The queue of maintenance tasks is dynamic.

    Answer: True   **Difficulty**: Med   **Reference**: p. 625

44. Changes to a system are usually implemented in batches.

    Answer: True   **Difficulty**: Med   **Reference**: p. 626

45. Configuration management is the process of assuring that only authorized changes are made to a system.

    Answer: True   **Difficulty**: Med   **Reference**: p. 627

46. Build routines are software modules that have been tested, documented, and approved to be included in the most recently created version of a system.

    Answer: False   **Difficulty**: Hard   **Reference**: p. 627

47. Baseline routines are guidelines that list the instructions to construct an executable system from the baseline source code.

    Answer: False   **Difficulty**: Hard   **Reference**: p. 627

48. A primary objective of using CASE and other automated tools for systems development and maintenance is to change radically how code and documentation are modified and updated.

   Answer: True   **Difficulty**: Med   **Reference**: p. 628

49. Reverse engineering and reengineering tools are primarily used to maintain older systems that have incomplete documentation or that were developed prior to CASE use.

   Answer: True   **Difficulty**: Med   **Reference**: p. 628

50. Locking out the use of pages in a portion of a Website can be done by inserting a "Temporary Out of Service" notice on the main page of the section being maintained and disabling all links within that segment.

   Answer: True   **Difficulty**: Med   **Reference**: p. 629

Multiple Choice Questions

51. The largest systems development expenditure for many organizations is:

   a. systems maintenance
   b. project planning
   c. implementation
   d. requirements structuring

   Answer: a   **Difficulty**: Med   **Reference**: p. 615

52. Once an information system is installed, it is essentially in the:

   a. implementation phase
   b. redesign phase
   c. maintenance phase
   d. system renewal phase

   Answer: c   **Difficulty**: Med   **Reference**: p. 616

53. The last phase of the systems development life cycle is:

   a. operation
   b. implementation
   c. maintenance
   d. analysis

   Answer: c   **Difficulty**: Easy   **Reference**: p. 616

54. Which of the following is a major activity that occurs during maintenance?

    a. coding
    b. transforming requests into changes
    c. conversion
    d. training and supporting users

    Answer: b   **Difficulty**: Med   **Reference**: p. 616

55. All of the following are major activities that occur during maintenance except:

    a. transforming requests into changes
    b. designing changes
    c. implementing changes
    d. structuring requirements

    Answer: d   **Difficulty**: Med   **Reference**: p. 616

56. Which of the following is a major activity occurring during maintenance?

    a. obtaining maintenance requests
    b. transforming requests into changes
    c. designing changes
    d. all of the above

    Answer: d   **Difficulty**: Med   **Reference**: p. 616

57. An SSR or similar document can be used to:

    a. request new development
    b. report problems
    c. request new system features with an existing system
    d. all of the above

    Answer: d   **Difficulty**: Med   **Reference**: p. 616

58. The first phase of the SDLC, project identification and selection, is analogous to the maintenance process of:

    a. obtaining maintenance requests
    b. transforming requests into changes
    c. designing changes
    d. implementing changes

    Answer: a   **Difficulty**: Med   **Reference**: p. 619

59. The SDLC phases of project initiation and planning and analysis are analogous to the maintenance process of:

    a. obtaining maintenance requests
    b. transforming requests into changes
    c. designing changes
    d. implementing changes

    Answer: b   **Difficulty**: Med   **Reference**: p. 619

60. The SDLC design phase is analogous to the maintenance process of:

    a. obtaining maintenance requests
    b. transforming requests into changes
    c. designing changes
    d. implementing changes

    Answer: c   **Difficulty**: Easy   **Reference**: p. 619

61. The SDLC phase of implementation is analogous to the maintenance process of:

    a. obtaining maintenance requests
    b. transforming requests into changes
    c. designing changes
    d. implementing changes

    Answer: d   **Difficulty**: Easy   **Reference**: p. 619

62. Which of the following best identifies the deliverables for the maintenance phase?

    a. The creation of a document that will consolidate the information that must be considered when implementing a physical distributed systems design.
    b. The development of a new version of the software and new versions of all design documents that were developed or modified during the maintenance process.
    c. Structured descriptions and diagrams that outline the logic contained within each DFD process.
    d. Documentation, a user training plan, user training modules, and a user support plan.

    Answer: b   **Difficulty**: Med   **Reference**: p. 619

63. Which of the following types of maintenance accounts for as much as 75 percent of all maintenance activity?

    a. preventive maintenance
    b. corrective maintenance
    c. adaptive maintenance
    d. perfective maintenance

    Answer: b   **Difficulty**: Med   **Reference**: p. 620

64. Changes made to a system to fix or enhance its functionality best defines:

    a. maintenance
    b. support
    c. repair
    d. installation

    Answer: a   **Difficulty**: Med   **Reference**: p. 620

65. Changes made to a system to repair flaws in its design, coding, or implementation describes:

     a. corrective maintenance
     b. adaptive maintenance
     c. preventive maintenance
     d. perfective maintenance

     Answer: a   **Difficulty**: Med   **Reference**: p. 620

66. Which of the following is a type of maintenance?

     a. preventive
     b. perfective
     c. corrective
     d. all of the above

     Answer: d   **Difficulty**: Easy   **Reference**: p. 620

67. All of the following are types of maintenance except:

     a. supportive maintenance
     b. corrective maintenance
     c. adaptive maintenance
     d. perfective maintenance

     Answer: a   **Difficulty**: Med   **Reference**: p. 620

68. Modifying a system to reflect environmental changes describes:

     a. corrective maintenance
     b. adaptive maintenance
     c. preventive maintenance
     d. perfective maintenance

     Answer: b   **Difficulty**: Med   **Reference**: p. 620

69. Evolving the system to solve new problems or take advantage of new opportunities describes:

     a. corrective maintenance
     b. adaptive maintenance
     c. preventive maintenance
     d. perfective maintenance

     Answer: d   **Difficulty**: Med   **Reference**: p. 620

70. Changes made to a system to evolve its functionality to changing business needs or technologies best describes:

     a. corrective maintenance
     b. adaptive maintenance
     c. preventive maintenance
     d. perfective maintenance

     Answer: b   **Difficulty**: Med   **Reference**: p. 620

71. Changes made to a system to add new features or to improve performance best describes:

    a. corrective maintenance
    b. adaptive maintenance
    c. preventive maintenance
    d. perfective maintenance

    Answer: d   **Difficulty**: Med   **Reference**: p. 620

72. Which of the following typically is assigned the highest priority?

    a. preventive maintenance
    b. perfective maintenance
    c. corrective maintenance
    d. adaptive maintenance

    Answer: c   **Difficulty**: Med   **Reference**: p. 620

73. Changes made to a system to avoid possible future problems best describes:

    a. corrective maintenance
    b. adaptive maintenance
    c. preventive maintenance
    d. perfective maintenance

    Answer: c   **Difficulty**: Med   **Reference**: p. 620

74. Which of the following is felt by many systems professionals to be new development, not maintenance?

    a. perfective maintenance
    b. preventive maintenance
    c. adaptive maintenance
    d. corrective maintenance

    Answer: a   **Difficulty**: Hard   **Reference**: p. 620

75. Which of the following is a true statement?

    a. In the 1990s, maintenance accounted for 10 - 20 percent of the software budget.
    b. In the 1990s, maintenance accounted for 30 - 40 percent of the software budget.
    c. In the 1990s, maintenance accounted for 50 - 60 percent of the software budget.
    d. In the 1990s, maintenance accounted for 70 - 80 percent of the software budget.

    Answer: d   **Difficulty**: Hard   **Reference**: p. 621

76. Which of the following maintenance cost elements is the most significant?

    a. tools
    b. software structure
    c. personnel
    d. customers

    Answer: d   **Difficulty**: Med   **Reference**: p. 621

77. Which of the following influences most of the costs associated with maintaining a system?

    a. personnel
    b. documentation quality
    c. number of latent defects
    d. number of customers

    Answer: c   **Difficulty:** Med   **Reference:** p. 621

78. The ease with which software can be understood, corrected, adapted, and enhanced best describes:

    a. maintenance
    b. maintainability
    c. adaptability
    d. comfort level

    Answer: b   **Difficulty:** Med   **Reference:** p. 621

79. Which of the following is not a cost element of maintenance?

    a. defects
    b. documentation
    c. personnel
    d. time

    Answer: d   **Difficulty:** Med   **Reference:** p. 622

80. Which of the following are cost elements of maintenance?

    a. defects
    b. documentation
    c. personnel
    d. all of the above

    Answer: d   **Difficulty:** Med   **Reference:** p. 622

81. According to research mentioned in the textbook:

    a. in the year 2000, there were approximately 5 million programmers working on new programs, as opposed to 3 million programmers working on maintenance
    b. in the year 2000, there were approximately 14 million programmers working on new programs, as opposed to 16 million programmers working on maintenance
    c. in the year 2000, there were approximately 1 million programmers working on new programs, as opposed to 2 million programmers working on maintenance
    d. in the year 2000, there were approximately 4 million programmers working on new programs, as opposed to 6 million programmers working on maintenance

    Answer: d   **Difficulty:** Hard   **Reference:** p. 623

82. Which of the following is not a maintenance organizational structure?

    a.   separate
    b.   combined
    c.   vertical
    d.   functional

    Answer: c   **Difficulty**: Med   **Reference**: p. 623

83. Which of the following maintenance organizational structures has as its advantage the formal transfer of systems between groups improves the system and documentation quality?

    a.   separate
    b.   combined
    c.   functional
    d.   none of the above

    Answer: a   **Difficulty**: Med   **Reference**: p. 623

84. The lack of thoroughness in documentation and testing caused by the absence of a formal transfer of responsibility is a disadvantage of:

    a.   the separate maintenance organizational structure
    b.   the combined maintenance organizational structure
    c.   the functional maintenance organizational structure
    d.   none of the above

    Answer: b   **Difficulty**: Med   **Reference**: p. 623

85. The maintenance group knowing or having access to all assumptions and decisions behind the system's original design is an advantage of:

    a.   the separate maintenance organizational structure
    b.   the combined maintenance organizational structure
    c.   the functional maintenance organizational structure
    d.   all of the maintenance organizational structures

    Answer: b   **Difficulty**: Med   **Reference**: p. 623

86. All things not being documented, so the maintenance group may not know critical information about the system is a disadvantage of:

    a.   the separate maintenance organizational structure
    b.   the combined maintenance organizational structure
    c.   the functional maintenance organizational structure
    d.   all of the maintenance organizational structures

    Answer: a   **Difficulty**: Med   **Reference**: p. 623

87. Personnel having limited job mobility and lacking access to adequate human and technical resources is a disadvantage of:

    a. the separate maintenance organizational structure
    b. the combined maintenance organizational structure
    c. the functional maintenance organizational structure
    d. all of the maintenance organizational structures

    Answer: c   **Difficulty**: Med   **Reference**: p. 623

88. Effective management of systems maintenance requires:

    a. managing maintenance personnel
    b. measuring maintenance effectiveness
    c. controlling maintenance requests
    d. doing all of the above

    Answer: d   **Difficulty**: Med   **Reference**: p. 623

89. Which of the following is a true statement?

    a. Many systems professionals do not want to perform maintenance because they feel that it is more exciting to build something new rather than change an existing system.
    b. Organizations have historically provided greater rewards and job opportunities to those performing new development.
    c. It is now common to rotate individuals in and out of maintenance activities.
    d. All of the above are true statements.

    Answer: d   **Difficulty**: Med   **Reference**: p. 624

90. To measure maintenance effectiveness, you should measure:

    a. the number of failures
    b. the time between each failure
    c. the type of failure
    d. all of the above

    Answer: d   **Difficulty**: Med   **Reference**: p. 624

91. A measurement of error occurrences that can be tracked over time to indicate the quality of a system best defines:

    a. consistency ratio
    b. mean time between failures
    c. error tracking
    d. regression analysis

    Answer: b   **Difficulty**: Med   **Reference**: p. 624

92. Which of the following is a more revealing method of measurement?

    a. number of failures
    b. time between each failure
    c. type of failure
    d. none of the above

    Answer: c   **Difficulty**: Med   **Reference**: p. 625

93. The process of assuring that only authorized changes are made to a system defines:

    a. configuration management
    b. consistency management
    c. quality management
    d. business process reengineering

    Answer: a   **Difficulty**: Med   **Reference**: p. 627

94. Software modules that have been tested, documented, and approved to be included in the most recently created version of a system are called:

    a. pretested modules
    b. baseline modules
    c. quality assurance modules
    d. none of the above

    Answer: b   **Difficulty**: Med   **Reference**: p. 627

95. The person responsible for controlling the checking out and checking in of baseline modules for a system that is being developed or maintained is the:

    a. code agent
    b. systems operator
    c. system librarian
    d. catalog agent

    Answer: c   **Difficulty**: Med   **Reference**: p. 627

96. Guidelines that list the instructions to construct an executable system from the baseline source code are called:

    a. build routines
    b. base routines
    c. construction routines
    d. reference routines

    Answer: a   **Difficulty**: Med   **Reference**: p. 627

97. Which of the following is a true statement regarding the role of CASE in maintenance?

    a. A primary objective of using CASE for systems development and maintenance is to change radically the way in which code and documentation are modified and updated.
    b. When using an integrated CASE environment, analysts maintain design documents and source code.
    c. Although CASE is very beneficial during the first part of the SDLC, it is not as advantageous during maintenance.
    d. all of the above

    Answer: a   **Difficulty**: Med   **Reference**: p. 628

98. Which of the following configuration management tools stores only the most recent version of a module, with previous versions being reconstructed when needed by applying changes in reverse order?

    a. source code control
    b. version control
    c. integrity control
    d. revision control

    Answer: d   **Difficulty**: Med   **Reference**: p. 628

99. Which of the following configuration management tools addresses interrelated files?

    a. source code control
    b. version control
    c. integrity control
    d. revision control

    Answer: a   **Difficulty**: Med   **Reference**: p. 628

100. When performing Website maintenance, issues and procedures include each of the following except:

    a. checking for broken links
    b. HTML validation
    c. re-registration
    d. stability

    Answer: d   **Difficulty**: Hard   **Reference**: p. 629

Fill In the Blanks

101. ***Obtaining maintenance requests***, ***transforming requests into changes***, ***designing changes***, and ***implementing changes*** are the four major maintenance activities.

    Difficulty: Hard   **Reference**: p. 616

102. ***Obtaining maintenance requests*** equates to the SDLC phase of project identification and selection.

    Difficulty: Med   **Reference**: p. 619

103. Project initiation and planning and analysis are analogous to the maintenance process of ***transforming requests into a specific system change***.

     Difficulty: Med   **Reference**: p. 619

104. The SDLC design phase equates to the maintenance process of ***designing changes***.

     Difficulty: Easy   **Reference**: p. 619

105. The SDLC implementation phase equates to the maintenance process of ***implementing changes***.

     Difficulty: Easy   **Reference**: p. 619

106. ***Maintenance*** refers to changes made to a system to fix or enhance its functionality.

     Difficulty: Easy   **Reference**: p. 620

107. ***Adaptive maintenance*** refers to changes made to a system to evolve its functionality to changing business needs or technologies.

     Difficulty: Med   **Reference**: p. 620

108. ***Preventive maintenance*** refers to changes made to a system to avoid possible future problems.

     Difficulty: Med   **Reference**: p. 620

109. ***Perfective maintenance*** refers to changes made to a system to add new features or to improve performance.

     Difficulty: Hard   **Reference**: p. 620

110. ***Corrective maintenance*** refers to changes made to a system to repair flaws in its design, coding, or implementation.

     Difficulty: Med   **Reference**: p. 620

111. ***Maintainability*** is the ease with which software can be understood, corrected, adapted, and enhanced.

     Difficulty: Med   **Reference**: p. 621

112. The formal transfer of systems between groups improving the system and documentation quality is an advantage associated with the ***separate*** maintenance organizational structure.

     Difficulty: Hard   **Reference**: p. 623

113. The maintenance group knowing or having access to all assumptions and decisions behind the system's original design is an advantage associated with the ***combined*** maintenance organizational structure.

     Difficulty: Hard   **Reference**: p. 623

114. Personnel having a vested interest in effectively maintaining the system and having a better understanding of functional requirements is an advantage associated with the ***functional*** maintenance organizational structure.

    Difficulty: Hard   **Reference**: p. 623

115. Documentation and testing thoroughness may suffer due to a lack of a formal transfer of responsibility is a disadvantage associated with the ***combined*** maintenance organizational structure.

    Difficulty: Hard   **Reference**: p. 623

116. ***Number of failures***, ***time between each failure***, and ***type of failure*** are three factors for measuring maintenance effectiveness.

    Difficulty: Hard   **Reference**: p. 624

117. ***Mean time between failures*** is a measurement of error occurrences that can be tracked over time to indicate the quality of a system.

    Difficulty: Med   **Reference**: p. 624

118. ***Configuration management*** is the process of assuring that only authorized changes are made to a system.

    Difficulty: Med   **Reference**: p. 627

119. ***Baseline modules*** are software modules that have been tested, documented, and approved to be included in the most recently created version of a system.

    Difficulty: Hard   **Reference**: p. 627

120. A ***system librarian*** is the person responsible for controlling the checking out and checking in of baseline modules when a system is being developed or maintained.

    Difficulty: Med   **Reference**: p. 627

121. ***Build routines*** are guidelines that list the instructions to construct an executable system from the baseline source code.

    Difficulty: Hard   **Reference**: p. 627

122. ***Reverse engineering*** and ***reengineering tools*** are two special-purpose tools that are primarily used to maintain older systems that have incomplete documentation or that were developed prior to CASE use.

    Difficulty: Hard   **Reference**: p. 628

123. ***Configuration management tools*** are special software systems that manage system configuration and version control activities.

    Difficulty: Med   **Reference**: p. 627

124. ***Revision control*** and ***source code control*** are two general kinds of configuration management tools.

    Difficulty: Hard   **Reference**: p. 628

125. When maintaining Websites, *future editions*, *re-registration*, *HTML validation*, *checking for broken links*, and *24x7x365* are issues and procedures to consider.

Difficulty: Hard   **Reference**: p. 629

Matching Questions

Match each of the following terms with its corresponding definition.

a. adaptive maintenance
b. baseline modules
c. build routines
d. configuration management
e. corrective maintenance
f. maintainability
g. maintenance
h. mean time between failures
i. perfective maintenance
j. preventive maintenance
k. system librarian

126. A measurement of error occurrences that can be tracked over time to indicate the quality of a system.

Answer: h   **Reference**: p. 624

127. Changes made to a system to evolve its functionality to changing business needs or technologies.

Answer: a   **Reference**: p. 620

128. A person responsible for controlling the checking out and checking in of baseline modules for a system that is being developed or maintained.

Answer: k   **Reference**: p. 627

129. The ease with which software can be understood, corrected, adapted, and enhanced.

Answer: f   **Reference**: p. 621

130. Changes made to a system to add new features or to improve performance.

Answer: i   **Reference**: p. 620

131. The process of assuring that only authorized changes are made to a system.

Answer: d   **Reference**: p. 627

132. Changes made to a system to fix or enhance its functionality.

Answer: g   **Reference**: p. 620

133. Software modules that have been tested, documented, and approved to be included in the most recently created version of a system.

Answer: b   **Reference:** p. 627

134. Changes made to a system to repair flaws in its design, coding, or implementation.

Answer: e   **Reference:** p. 620

135. Guidelines that list the instructions to construct an executable system from the baseline source code.

Answer: c   **Reference:** p. 627

136. Changes made to a system to avoid possible future problems.

Answer: j   **Reference:** p. 620

Match each of the following terms with its corresponding definition.

    a.   baseline modules
    b.   build routines
    c.   configuration management
    d.   maintainability
    e.   maintenance
    f.   mean time between failures

137. The process of assuring that only authorized changes are made to a system.

Answer: c   **Reference:** p. 627

138. The ease with which software can be understood, corrected, adapted, and enhanced.

Answer: d   **Reference:** p. 621

139. Guidelines that list the instructions to construct an executable system from the baseline source code.

Answer: b   **Reference:** p. 627

140. Changes made to a system to fix or enhance its functionality.

Answer: e   **Reference:** p. 620

141. Software modules that have been tested, documented, and approved to be included in the most recently created version of a system.

Answer: a   **Reference:** p. 627

142. A measurement of error occurrences that can be tracked over time to indicate the quality of a system.

Answer: f   **Reference:** p. 624

Match each of the following maintenance organizational structures to corresponding descriptions.
(Answers may occur more than once.)

     a.   combined
     b.   functional
     c.   separate

143.   An advantage is that the formal transfer of systems between groups improves the system and documentation quality.

               Answer: c   **Reference:** p. 623

144.   A disadvantage is that the personnel may have limited job mobility and lack access to adequate human and technical resources.

               Answer: b   **Reference:** p. 623

145.   A disadvantage is that all things cannot be documented, so the maintenance group may not know critical information about the system.

               Answer: c   **Reference:** p. 623

146.   An advantage is that the maintenance group knows or has access to all assumptions and decisions behind the system's original design.

               Answer: a   **Reference:** p. 623

147.   A disadvantage is that the documentation and testing thoroughness may suffer due to a lack of a formal transfer of responsibility.

               Answer: a   **Reference:** p. 623

148.   An advantage is that the personnel have a vested interest in effectively maintaining the system and have a better understanding of functional requirements.

               Answer: b   **Reference:** p. 623

Match each of the following types of maintenance to its corresponding "home" example.

    a. corrective
    b. adaptive
    c. perfective
    d. preventive

149. Adding storm windows to improve the cooling performance of an air conditioner.

                    Answer: b   **Reference**: p. 620

150. Adding a new room on your house.

                    Answer: c   **Reference**: p. 620

151. Painting the exterior to protect your home from severe weather conditions.

                    Answer: d   **Reference**: p. 620

152. Repairs made to things that never worked according to the design specifications of your new home.

                    Answer: a   **Reference**: p. 620

Match each of the following maintenance organizational structures to its advantage.

    a. functional
    b. separate
    c. combined

153. An advantage is that the maintenance group knows or has access to all assumptions and decisions behind the system's original design.

                    Answer: c   **Reference**: p. 623

154. An advantage is that the personnel have a vested interest in effectively maintaining the system and have a better understanding of functional requirements.

                    Answer: a   **Reference**: p. 623

155. An advantage is that the formal transfer of systems between groups improves the system and documentation quality.

                    Answer: b   **Reference**: p. 623

Essay Questions

156. *Identify several types of maintenance.*

Four types of maintenance were identified in the text. The types are corrective maintenance, adaptive maintenance, perfective maintenance, and preventive maintenance. Corrective maintenance refers to changes made to a system to repair flaws in its design, coding, or implementation. Adaptive maintenance refers to changes made to a system to evolve its functionality to changing business needs or technologies. Changes made to a system to add new features or to improve performance are perfective maintenance changes. Changes made to a system to avoid possible future problems are preventive maintenance changes.

157. *To measure maintenance effectiveness, what three factors must be measured?*

The three factors are number of failures, time between failures, and type of failure.

158. *What is maintainability? Identify several factors that influence the maintainability of a system.*

Maintainability is the ease with which software can be understood, corrected, adapted, and enhanced. The cost elements of maintenance include defects, customers, documentation, personnel, tools, and software structure. The defect element refers to the number of unknown defects in a system when it is installed. Typically, the more latent defects, the higher the maintenance costs. The customer element refers to the number of different customers that a maintenance group must support. Generally, the more customers, the greater the maintenance costs. The documentation element refers to the quality of technical system documentation including test cases. Without quality documentation, maintenance efforts increase exponentially. The personnel element refers to the number and quality of personnel dedicated to the support and maintenance of a system. Maintenance programmers should be able to understand and change the software that they did not originally create. The tool element refers to software development tools, debuggers, hardware, and other resources. Such tools help reduce maintenance costs. Software structure refers to the structure and maintainability of the software. If programs are well-structured, they are easier to understand, modify, and fix.

159. *What is the role of CASE in maintenance?*

CASE can be used during maintenance to radically change the way code and documentation are updated and modified. An integrated CASE environment enables analysts to maintain design documents and to utilize code generators to create a new version of the system automatically. In addition to the general CASE tools, design recovery tools can be used to create high-level design documents of a program by reading and analyzing its source code.

160. *Briefly outline the advantages of the different maintenance organizational structures.*

The text presented three different maintenance organizational structures: separate, combined, and functional. The separate approach's advantage is that the formal transfer of systems between groups improves the system and documentation quality. The combined structure's advantage is that the maintenance group knows or has access to all assumptions and decisions behind the system's original design. The functional approach's advantage is that the personnel have a vested interest in effectively maintaining the system and a better understanding of the functional requirements.

161. *Briefly outline the disadvantages of the different maintenance organizational structures.*

The separate approach's disadvantage is that all things cannot be documented, so the maintenance group may not know critical information about the system. The combined approach's disadvantage is that documentation and testing thoroughness may suffer due to a lack of a formal transfer of responsibility. The functional approach's disadvantage is that the personnel may have limited job mobility and lack access to adequate human and technical resources.

162. *Identify two methods for maintaining a Website 24x7x365?*

The two approaches mentioned in the textbook are locking out use of the pages while the changes are made and including a time and date stamp of the most recent change.

163. *What is MTBF?*

Mean time between failures is a measurement of error occurrences that can be tracked over time to indicate the quality of a system.

164. *Discuss configuration management. Who is the system librarian?*

Configuration management is the process of assuring that only authorized changes are made to a system. When system maintenance is required, maintenance personnel check out the baseline modules from a system librarian. The system librarian controls the checking out and checking in of baseline modules for a system when a system is being developed or maintained.

165. *Identify the four major activities that occur within maintenance.*

Obtaining maintenance requests, transforming requests into changes, designing changes, and implementing changes are the four major activities.

166. *What are the deliverables for the maintenance phase?*

The maintenance phase produces a new version of the software and new versions of the design documents developed or modified during the maintenance phase.

Chapter 19
Rapid Application Development

True-False Questions

1. There are many different approaches to RAD.

   Answer: True   **Difficulty**: Easy   **Reference**: p. 642

2. Jeffrey Hoffer, a leading information systems specialist, invented rapid application development.

   Answer: False   **Difficulty**: Med   **Reference**: p. 642

3. Rapid application development is a technique for developing systems quickly.

   Answer: True   **Difficulty**: Easy   **Reference**: p. 643

4. Business process reengineering is an approach to developing information systems that promises better and cheaper systems and more rapid deployment.

   Answer: False   **Difficulty**: Med   **Reference**: p. 643

5. Rapid application development is an approach to developing information systems that promises better and cheaper systems and more rapid deployment.

   Answer: True   **Difficulty**: Med   **Reference**: p. 643

6. RAD grew out of the convergence of two trends: user need and the development of enterprise-wide information systems.

   Answer: False   **Difficulty**: Med   **Reference**: p. 643

7. The increased speed and turbulence of doing business in the late 1980s and early 1990s led to the growth of rapid application development.

   Answer: True   **Difficulty**: Med   **Reference**: p. 643

8. The ready availability of high-powered computer-based tools to support systems development and easy maintenance lead to the growth of rapid application development.

   Answer: True   **Difficulty**: Med   **Reference**: p. 643

9. The ability to use RAD for the development of enterprise-wide systems lead to its immediate adoption.

   Answer: False   **Difficulty**: Med   **Reference**: p. 643

10. RAD is not an appropriate approach for the development of Web-based applications.

    Answer: False   **Difficulty**: Med   **Reference**: p. 643

11. RAD is a more modern, single methodology used to develop information systems.

     Answer: False   **Difficulty**: Med   **Reference**: p. 643

12. Some RAD approaches are special life cycles, while others focus more on specific software tools and visual development environments that enable the process of rapidly developing and deploying applications.

     Answer: True   **Difficulty**: Hard   **Reference**: p. 643

13. The goal of RAD is to analyze a business problem rapidly, to design a viable system solution through intense cooperation between users and developers, and to get the finished application into the hands of the users quickly, saving time, money, and other resources in the process.

     Answer: True   **Difficulty**: Hard   **Reference**: p. 643

14. RAD phases are similar to the traditional SDLC phases but are combined to produce a more streamlined development technique.

     Answer: True   **Difficulty**: Med   **Reference**: p. 643

15. The planning and design phases in RAD are shortened by focusing work on system functional and user interface requirements at the expense of detailed business analysis and concern for system performance issues.

     Answer: True   **Difficulty**: Med   **Reference**: p. 643

16. Usually RAD looks at the system being developed in isolation from other systems.

     Answer: True   **Difficulty**: Med   **Reference**: p. 643

17. The bulk of the work in a RAD approach takes place in the planning and design phases.

     Answer: False   **Difficulty**: Med   **Reference**: p. 644

18. Iteration in the RAD life cycle is limited to the planning phase.

     Answer: False   **Difficulty**: Med   **Reference**: p. 644

19. Once RAD's design phase has begun, returning to the planning phase is rarely done.

     Answer: True   **Difficulty**: Med   **Reference**: p. 644

20. The RAD approach encourages iteration between the cutover and development phases.

     Answer: False   **Difficulty**: Med   **Reference**: p. 644

21. The emphasis in RAD is generally less on the sequence and structure of processes in the life cycle and more on doing different tasks in parallel with each other and on using prototyping extensively.

     Answer: True   **Difficulty**: Hard   **Reference**: p. 644

22. The high level of user commitment and involvement throughout RAD implies that the system that emerges should be more readily accepted by the user community than a system developed using a more traditional approach.

    Answer: True   **Difficulty**: Med   **Reference**: p. 644

23. RAD puts heavy emphasis on the use of computer-based tools to support as much of the development process as possible.

    Answer: True   **Difficulty**: Med   **Reference**: p. 644

24. RAD relies on extensive user involvement, Joint Application Design sessions, prototyping, and integrated CASE tools.

    Answer: True   **Difficulty**: Med   **Reference**: p. 645

25. One of the primary reasons for the speed associated with RAD development is the lack of end user involvement during the design and implementation phases.

    Answer: False   **Difficulty**: Med   **Reference**: p. 645

26. When using the RAD approach, throwaway prototypes are heavily used.

    Answer: False   **Difficulty**: Med   **Reference**: p. 645

27. Integrated CASE tools are one component of RAD.

    Answer: True   **Difficulty**: Med   **Reference**: p. 645

28. When using the RAD approach, the reuse of templates, components, or previous systems described in the CASE repository is strongly encouraged.

    Answer: True   **Difficulty**: Med   **Reference**: p. 645

29. Time, tools, management, and methodology are Martin's four pillars of RAD.

    Answer: False   **Difficulty**: Med   **Reference**: p. 645

30. Martin's tools pillar spells out the proper tasks to be done in the proper order.

    Answer: False   **Difficulty**: Hard   **Reference**: p. 645

31. Management is one of James Martin's RAD pillars.

    Answer: True   **Difficulty**: Med   **Reference**: p. 645

32. Martin's methodology pillar references spelling out the proper tasks to be done in the proper order.

    Answer: True   **Difficulty**: Med   **Reference**: p. 645

33. Development is one of James Martin's RAD pillars.

    Answer: False   **Difficulty**: Med   **Reference**: p. 645

34. RAD facilitators are a small group of well-trained and dedicated professionals who demonstrate the viability of RAD through pilot projects.

    Answer: False   **Difficulty**: Hard   **Reference**: p. 646

35. Visual development environments are recognized within the systems development industry as "silver bullets" for Rapid Application Development.

    Answer: False   **Difficulty**: Med   **Reference**: p. 646

36. Avoiding classic mistakes and applying development fundamentals are two of McConnell's necessary pillars for a successful RAD approach.

    Answer: True   **Difficulty**: Med   **Reference**: p. 646

37. According to McConnell, weak personnel, adding people late to a project, and unrealistic expectations are three process-related classic development mistakes.

    Answer: False   **Difficulty**: Med   **Reference**: p. 647

38. According to McConnell, the silver-bullet syndrome occurs when an application has more requirements than it needs.

    Answer: False   **Difficulty**: Med   **Reference**: p. 647

39. According to McConnell, feature creep and requirements gold-plating are process-related classic development mistakes.

    Answer: False   **Difficulty**: Hard   **Reference**: p. 647

40. Martin's RAD life cycle phases include requirements planning, user design, construction, and cutover.

    Answer: True   **Difficulty**: Med   **Reference**: p. 648

41. During the requirements planning phase of Martin's RAD life cycle, high-level managers, executives, and knowledgeable end users determine system requirements.

    Answer: True   **Difficulty**: Med   **Reference**: p. 648

42. During the user design phase of Martin's RAD life cycle, users and analysts create prototypes that capture system requirements that become the basis for the physical design of the system being developed.

    Answer: True   **Difficulty**: Med   **Reference**: p. 649

43. During the construction phase of Martin's RAD life cycle, information systems specialists generate code using the CASE tools' code generator.

    Answer: True   **Difficulty**: Med   **Reference**: p. 649

44. RAD's user design phase determines whether modules that can be reused are already in existence.

    Answer: False   **Difficulty**: Med   **Reference**: p. 652

45. RAD encourages systems administration.

Answer: False   **Difficulty**: Med   **Reference**: p. 652

46. RAD can save time, money, and human effort.

Answer: True   **Difficulty**: Easy   **Reference**: p. 653

47. A tighter fit between user requirements and system specification is an advantage of RAD.

Answer: True   **Difficulty**: Med   **Reference**: p. 653

48. A strong user stake and ownership of the system is an advantage of RAD.

Answer: True   **Difficulty**: Med   **Reference**: p. 653

49. An advantage of using the RAD approach is that there tends to be a greater alignment of the system with the business.

Answer: False   **Difficulty**: Med   **Reference**: p. 653

50. Difficulties with module reuse for future systems are a disadvantage of RAD.

Answer: True   **Difficulty**: Med   **Reference**: p. 653

Multiple Choice Questions

51. Which of the following individuals is credited with inventing Rapid Application Development?

    a. Jeffrey Hoffer
    b. James Martin
    c. Joey George
    d. Joseph Valacich

Answer: b   **Difficulty**: Med   **Reference**: p. 642

52. To conduct a project with RAD requires applying skills and concepts such as:

    a. interviewing
    b. designing screens and reports
    c. using automated tools for systems development
    d. all of the above

Answer: d   **Difficulty**: Easy   **Reference**: p. 642

53. A systems development methodology created to radically decrease the time needed to design and implement information systems is:

    a. RAD
    b. UML
    c. DFD
    d. CAD

    Answer: a   **Difficulty**: Med   **Reference**: p. 643

54. The approach to developing information systems which promises better and cheaper systems and more rapid deployment by having systems developers and end users work together jointly in real-time to develop systems is:

    a. RAD
    b. UML
    c. DFD
    d. CAD

    Answer: a   **Difficulty**: Med   **Reference**: p. 643

55. Which of the following is a trend responsible for the growth of RAD?

    a. downsizing
    b. the increased speed and turbulence of doing business in the late 1980s and early 1990s
    c. enterprise-wide information systems
    d. upsizing

    Answer: b   **Difficulty**: Med   **Reference**: p. 643

56. Which of the following is a reason for RAD adoption?

    a. increasing disenchantment with traditional systems development methods
    b. the long development times associated with traditional systems development methods
    c. the ready availability of increasingly powerful software tools created to support RAD
    d. all of the above

    Answer: d   **Difficulty**: Easy   **Reference**: p. 643

57. Which of the following is not a true statement?

    a. RAD is a single methodology for developing information systems.
    b. Some RAD methodologies are special life cycles.
    c. The goal of RAD is to rapidly analyze a business problem, design a viable system solution through intense cooperation between users and developers, and to quickly get the finished application in the hands of users.
    d. Usually, RAD looks at the system being developed in isolation from other systems.

    Answer: a   **Difficulty**: Med   **Reference**: p. 643

58. Which of the following is not a true statement?

    a. The iteration in the RAD life cycle is limited to the design and development phases.
    b. The bulk of the work in a RAD approach takes place in the design and development phases.
    c. The emphasis in RAD is placed on the sequence and structure of processes in the life cycle.
    d. The high level of user commitment and involvement throughout RAD implies that the system which emerges should be more readily accepted by the user community than would be a system developed using traditional systems development techniques.

    Answer: c   **Difficulty**: Med   **Reference**: p. 644

59. RAD deliverables include:

    a. a systems development plan
    b. logical and physical designs for the application
    c. the application's construction and implementation
    d. all of the above

    Answer: d   **Difficulty**: Easy   **Reference**: p. 644

60. Which of the following sets RAD apart from the more traditional systems development approaches?

    a. its focus on planning and system integration
    b. its use of well-trained and dedicated professionals
    c. its emphasis on speed and the use of computer-based tools
    d. the lack of end user involvement

    Answer: c   **Difficulty**: Med   **Reference**: p. 644

61. Which of the following is a true statement?

    a. RAD depends on extensive user involvement.
    b. A primary difference between RAD and JAD is that in RAD, the prototype becomes the basis for the new system.
    c. RAD may employ visual development environments instead of CASE tools with code generators.
    d. all of the above

    Answer: d   **Difficulty**: Med   **Reference**: pp. 644-645

62. Which of the following is a component of RAD?

    a. prototypes
    b. integrated CASE tools
    c. JAD sessions
    d. all of the above

    Answer: d   **Difficulty**: Easy   **Reference**: p. 645

63. Which of the following is not a component of RAD?

a. prototypes
b. integrated CASE tools
c. activity diagrams
d. JAD sessions

Answer: c   **Difficulty**: Med   **Reference**: p. 645

64. Which of the following is not one of Martin's necessary pillars for the RAD approach?

a. methodology
b. development
c. people
d. tools

Answer: b   **Difficulty**: Med   **Reference**: p. 645

65. Which of the following is one of Martin's necessary pillars for the RAD approach?

a. methodology
b. planning
c. design
d. implementation

Answer: a   **Difficulty**: Med   **Reference**: p. 645

66. According to Martin, which of the following RAD pillars spells out the proper tasks to be done in the proper order?

a. design
b. methodology
c. planning
d. management

Answer: b   **Difficulty**: Med   **Reference**: p. 645

67. A small group of well-trained and dedicated professionals created to demonstrate the viability of RAD through pilot projects best describes:

a. RAD cell
b. RAD scribes
c. RAD designers
d. RAD facilitators

Answer: a   **Difficulty**: Med   **Reference**: p. 646

68. Underlying Steve McConnell's rapid development approach is:

a. the sound if somewhat conservative management practices of careful planning
b. the efficient use of time
c. the humane use of human resources
d. all of the above

Answer: d   **Difficulty**: Med   **Reference**: p. 646

69. Which of the following is not one of McConnell's necessary pillars for the RAD approach?

    a. avoiding classic mistakes
    b. adding people as necessary to the project
    c. applying development fundamentals
    d. applying schedule-oriented practices

    Answer: b   **Difficulty**: Med   **Reference**: p. 646

70. Which of the following is one of McConnell's necessary pillars for the RAD approach?

    a. avoiding classic mistakes
    b. managing risks
    c. applying development fundamentals
    d. all of the above

    Answer: d   **Difficulty**: Med   **Reference**: p. 646

71. Which of the following occurs when developers believe a new and usually untried technology is all that is needed to cure the ills of any development project?

    a. silver-bullet syndrome
    b. requirements-gold plating
    c. quick curing
    d. problem patching

    Answer: a   **Difficulty**: Med   **Reference**: p. 646

72. Which of the following is one of McConnell's classic development mistakes?

    a. unrealistic expectations
    b. insufficient planning
    c. overestimated savings from new tools or methods
    d. all of the above

    Answer: d   **Difficulty**: Med   **Reference**: p. 647

73. Which of the following is one of McConnell's process-related classic development mistakes?

    a. weak personnel
    b. feature creep
    c. insufficient planning
    d. silver-bullet syndrome

    Answer: c   **Difficulty**: Med   **Reference**: p. 647

74. Which of the following is one of McConnell's people-related classic development mistakes?

    a. weak personnel
    b. feature creep
    c. insufficient planning
    d. silver-bullet syndrome

    Answer: a   **Difficulty**: Med   **Reference**: p. 647

75. Which of the following is one of McConnell's product-related classic development mistakes?

    a. weak personnel
    b. feature creep
    c. insufficient planning
    d. silver-bullet syndrome

    Answer: b   **Difficulty**: Med   **Reference**: p. 647

76. Which of the following is one of McConnell's technology-related classic development mistakes?

    a. weak personnel
    b. feature creep
    c. insufficient planning
    d. silver-bullet syndrome

    Answer: d   **Difficulty**: Med   **Reference**: p. 647

77. Which of the following is one of McConnell's product-related classic development mistakes?

    a. feature creep
    b. requirements gold-plating
    c. silver-bullet syndrome
    d. both a and b

    Answer: d   **Difficulty**: Med   **Reference**: p. 647

78. Which of the following refers to the tendency of systems requirements to change over the lifetime of the development project?

    a. requirements-gold plating
    b. feature creep
    c. cascading
    d. silver-bullet syndrome

    Answer: b   **Difficulty**: Med   **Reference**: p. 647

79. Which of the following means an application may have more requirements than it needs, even before the development project begins?

    a. feature loading
    b. requirements-gold plating
    c. feature creep
    d. none of the above

    Answer: b   **Difficulty**: Med   **Reference**: p. 647

80. McConnell's development fundamentals pillar includes such practices as:

    a. proper project estimating, scheduling, planning, and tracking
    b. measuring software quality and productivity
    c. managing system requirements
    d. all of the above

    Answer: d   **Difficulty**: Med   **Reference**: p. 647

81. Once the first three pillars of McConnell's RAD approach are built, you have reached:

    a. the design phase
    b. efficient development
    c. the cutover phase
    d. project close-down

    Answer: b   **Difficulty**: Hard   **Reference**: p. 647

82. Which of McConnell's RAD pillars is designed to improve development speed, reduce schedule risk, and make progress visible?

    a. avoiding classic mistakes
    b. applying development fundamentals
    c. applying schedule-oriented practices
    d. managing risks

    Answer: c   **Difficulty**: Med   **Reference**: p. 647

83. Development environments that support RAD include:

    a. Powersoft's PowerBuilder
    b. Inprise/Borland's Delphi
    c. Microsoft's Visual Basic
    d. all of the above

    Answer: d   **Difficulty**: Easy   **Reference**: p. 648

84. Martin's RAD life cycle includes each of the following phases except:

    a. requirements planning
    b. cutover
    c. selection
    d. construction

    Answer: c   **Difficulty**: Med   **Reference**: p. 648

85. During which of Martin's RAD life cycle phases will high-level managers, executives, and knowledgeable end users determine system requirements?

    a. requirements planning
    b. user design
    c. cutover
    d. construction

    Answer: a   **Difficulty**: Easy   **Reference**: p. 648

86. During which of Martin's RAD life cycle phases will end users and information systems professionals participate in JAD workshops, where those involved use integrated CASE tools to support the rapid prototyping of system design?

    a. requirements planning
    b. user design
    c. cutover
    d. construction

    Answer: b   **Difficulty**: Med   **Reference**: p. 649

87. During which of Martin's RAD life cycle phases will the same information system professionals who created the design now generate code using the CASE tools' code generator?

    a. requirements planning
    b. user design
    c. cutover
    d. construction

    Answer: d   **Difficulty**: Med   **Reference**: p. 649

88. The primary advantage of RAD is the:

    a. ability to develop information systems in as little as one-quarter the usual time
    b. ability to use smaller development teams
    c. significant cost savings
    d. ability to rapidly change a system's design

    Answer: a   **Difficulty**: Med   **Reference**: p. 651

89. Which of the following is not one of the software engineering concepts that is overlooked by the RAD process?

    a. time
    b. consistency
    c. programming standards
    d. scalability

    Answer: a   **Difficulty**: Hard   **Reference**: p. 652

90. Disadvantages of RAD include:

    a. difficulties with module reuse for future systems
    b. lack of scalability designed into the system
    c. high costs of commitment on the part of the user
    d. all of the above

    Answer: d   **Difficulty**: Med   **Reference**: p. 653

Fill In the Blanks

91. ***Rapid application development*** is a systems development methodology created to decrease the time needed to design and implement information systems radically.

   Difficulty: Med   **Reference**: p. 643

92. James Martin's four pillars of RAD are ***tools***, ***people***, ***methodology***, and ***management***.

   Difficulty: Hard   **Reference**: p. 645

93. Martin's ***methodology*** pillar spells out the proper tasks to be done and the proper order of these tasks.

   Difficulty: Med   **Reference**: p. 645

94. ***Avoiding classic mistakes***, ***applying development fundamentals***, ***managing risks***, and ***applying schedule-oriented practices*** are McConnell's four RAD pillars.

   Difficulty: Hard   **Reference**: p. 646

95. A ***RAD cell*** is a small group of well-trained and dedicated professionals that demonstrate the viability of RAD through pilot projects.

   Difficulty: Hard   **Reference**: p. 646

96. ***Conservative management practices of careful planning***, ***efficient use of time***, and the ***humane use of human resources*** underlie Steve McConnell's RAD approach.

   Difficulty: Hard   **Reference**: p. 646

97. McConnell's ***weak personnel*** classic development mistake refers to employees that are not as well trained in the skills necessary to a particular project.

   Difficulty: Med   **Reference**: p. 646

98. McConnell's ***silver-bullet syndrome*** classic development mistake occurs when developers believe a new and usually untried technology is all that is needed to cure the ills of any development project.

   Difficulty: Hard   **Reference**: p. 646

99. McConnell's ***feature creep*** classic development mistake refers to the tendency of system requirements to change over the lifetime of the development project.

   Difficulty: Med   **Reference**: p. 647

100. McConnell's ***requirements gold-plating*** classic development mistake refers to an application that may have more requirements than it needs, even before the development project begins.

   Difficulty: Med   **Reference**: p. 647

101. ***Weak personnel***, ***adding people to a project late***, and ***unrealistic expectations*** are McConnell's people-related classic development mistakes.

   Difficulty: Hard   **Reference**: p. 647

102. *__Insufficient planning__*, *__overly optimistic schedules__*, and *__planning to catch up later__* are McConnell's process-related classic development mistakes.

           Difficulty: Hard   **Reference**: p. 647

103. *__Feature creep__* and *__requirements gold-plating__* are McConnell's product-related classic development mistakes.

           Difficulty: Hard   **Reference**: p. 647

104. *__Silver-bullet syndrome__* and *__overestimated savings from new tools or methods__* are McConnell's technology-related classic development mistakes.

           Difficulty: Hard   **Reference**: p. 647

105. McConnell's *__development fundamentals__* pillar stresses such practices as proper project estimating, scheduling, planning, and tracking; measuring software quality and productivity; managing system requirements; engaging in good design techniques; and assuring quality.

           Difficulty: Med   **Reference**: p. 647

106. Once you have successfully built McConnell's first three pillars, you have reached *__efficient development__*.

           Difficulty: Hard   **Reference**: p. 647

107. McConnell's fourth pillar, *__schedule-oriented practices__*, is designed to improve development speed, reduce schedule risk, and make progress visible.

           Difficulty: Med   **Reference**: p. 647

108. *__Requirements planning__*, *__user design__*, *__construction__* and *__cutover__* are the basic phases of Martin's RAD life cycle.

           Difficulty: Hard   **Reference**: p. 648

109. During the *__requirements planning__* phase of Martin's RAD life cycle, high-level managers, executives, and knowledgeable end users determine system requirements.

           Difficulty: Med   **Reference**: p. 648

110. During the *__user design__* phase of Martin's RAD life cycle, end users and analysts work closely and quickly to create prototypes that capture system requirements that become the basis for the physical design of the system being developed.

           Difficulty: Med   **Reference**: p. 649

111. During the *__construction__* phase of Martin's RAD life cycle, information systems professionals generate code using the CASE tools' code generator.

           Difficulty: Med   **Reference**: p. 649

112. During the *__cutover__* phase of Martin's RAD life cycle, the new system is delivered to the end users.

           Difficulty: Med   **Reference**: p. 649

113.   Java *__applets__* are embedded in HTML code on Web pages and are downloaded to the customer client machine and executed by the client Web browser.

Difficulty: Med   **Reference**: p. 651

114.   *__Servlets__* are programming modules, written in Java, that reside on the server and expand the functions of the Web server.

Difficulty: Med   **Reference**: p. 651

115.   According to Bourne, the RAD process overlooks such software engineering concepts as *__consistency__*, *__programming standards__*, *__module reuse__*, *__scalability__*, and *__systems administration__*.

Difficulty: Hard   **Reference**: p. 652

Matching Questions

Match each of the following Martin RAD life cycle phases with its corresponding description.

   a.   requirements planning
   b.   user design
   c.   construction
   d.   cutover

116.   During this phase, the new system is delivered to its end users.

Answer: d   **Reference**: p. 649

117.   During this phase, the same information systems professionals who created the design now generate code using the CASE tools' code generator.

Answer: c   **Reference**: p. 649

118.   During this phase, end users and information systems professionals participate in JAD workshops, where those involved use integrated CASE tools to support the rapid prototyping of system design.

Answer: b   **Reference**: p. 649

119.   During this phase, high-level managers, executives, and knowledgeable end users determine system requirements, but the determination is done in the context of a discussion of business problems and business areas.

Answer: a   **Reference**: p. 648

For each of the following, answer "a" if it is an advantage of RAD or answer "b" if it is a disadvantage of RAD.

120. Can save time, money, and human effort

                                      Answer: a   **Reference**: p. 653

121. Lack of scalability

                                        Answer: b   **Reference**: p. 653

122. Module reuse for future systems

                                        Answer: b   **Reference**: p. 653

123. Tighter fit between user requirements and system specifications

                                        Answer: a   **Reference**: p. 653

124. High costs of commitment on the part of key user

                                        Answer: b   **Reference**: p. 653

125. System optimized for users involved in RAD process

                                        Answer: a   **Reference**: p. 653

126. Concentrates on essential system elements from user viewpoint

                                        Answer: a   **Reference**: p. 653

127. Ability to rapidly change system design as demanded by users

                                        Answer: a   **Reference**: p. 653

128. Lack of attention to later systems administration built into the system

                                        Answer: b   **Reference**: p. 653

129. Possible violation of programming standards related to inconsistent naming conventions and insufficient documentation

                                        Answer: b   **Reference**: p. 653

Match each of McConnell's classic development mistake categories with its corresponding mistakes.
(Answers may occur more than once.)

        a.   people-related
        b.   process-related
        c.   product-related
        d.   technology-related

130.   Requirements gold-plating

           Answer: c   **Reference**: p. 647

131.   Unrealistic expectations

           Answer: a   **Reference**: p. 647

132.   Adding people to a project late

           Answer: a   **Reference**: p. 647

133.   Planning to catch up later

           Answer: b   **Reference**: p. 647

134.   Feature creep

           Answer: c   **Reference**: p. 647

135.   Overly optimistic schedules

           Answer: b   **Reference**: p. 647

136.   Weak personnel

           Answer: a   **Reference**: p. 647

137.   Silver-bullet syndrome

           Answer: d   **Reference**: p. 647

138.   Overestimated savings from new tools or methods

           Answer: d   **Reference**: p. 647

139.   Insufficient planning

           Answer: b   **Reference**: p. 647

Match each of the following RAD systems development life cycle phases with its corresponding standard SDLC phase. (Answers may occur more than once.)

    a. planning
    b. design
    c. development
    d. cutover

140.   Implementation

               Answer: d   **Reference:** p. 644

141.   Project Initiation and Planning

               Answer: a   **Reference:** p. 644

142.   Project Identification and Selection

               Answer: a   **Reference:** p. 644

143.   Design

               Answer: b, c   **Reference:** p. 644

144.   Analysis

               Answer: b   **Reference:** p. 644

145.   Maintenance

               Answer: d   **Reference:** p. 644

Match each of the following terms with its corresponding definition.

      a. code generators
      b. JAD
      c. prototyping
      d. RAD

146.   Systems development methodology created to radically decrease the time needed to design and implement information systems.

                    Answer: d   **Reference:** p. 643

147.   An iterative process of systems development in which requirements are converted to a working system which is continually revised through close work between an analyst and users.

                    Answer: c   **Reference:** p. 645

148.   A structured process in which users, managers, and analysts work together for several days in a series of intensive meetings to specify or review system requirements.

                    Answer: b   **Reference:** p. 645

149.   CASE tools that enable the automatic generation of program and database definition code directly from the design documents, diagrams, forms, and reports stored in the repository.

                    Answer: a   **Reference:** p. 645

Essay Questions

150.   *What is RAD?*

RAD is a systems development methodology created to decrease the time needed to design and implement information systems radically.

151.   *What are Martin's four necessary pillars for the RAD approach?*

James Martin's four necessary pillars for the RAD approach are tools, people, methodology, and management.

152.   *Briefly discuss the phases of Martin's RAD life cycle.*

Martin's RAD life cycle includes four phases: requirements planning, user design, development, and cutover. During requirements planning, high-level managers, executives, and knowledgeable end users determine system requirements. During user design, end users and information systems professionals participate in JAD workshops, where those involved use integrated CASE tools to support the rapid prototyping of system design. During construction, the same information systems professionals who created the design now generate code using the CASE tools' code generator. During cutover, the new system is delivered to the end users.

153. *Identify three advantages of RAD.*

RAD advantages include: (1) saving time, money, and human effort, (2) the ability to rapidly change the system design as demanded by users, and (3) a strong user stake and ownership of the system. Table 19-2 provides additional advantages.

154. *Identify three disadvantages of RAD.*

RAD disadvantages include: (1) more speed and lower cost may lead to lower overall system quality, (2) may have inconsistent internal designs within and across systems, and (3) difficulties with module reuse for future systems. Table 19-2 provides additional disadvantages.

155. *What is a RAD cell?*

A RAD cell is a small group of well-trained and dedicated professionals who demonstrate the viability of RAD through pilot projects.

156. *Identify two trends that encourage the use of RAD.*

The two trends mentioned in the textbook are the increased speed and turbulence of doing business in the late 1980s and early 1990s and the availability of high-powered computer-based tools.

157. *Identify the deliverables and outcomes of RAD.*

RAD deliverables include a systems development plan, a description of user and business process requirements for the application, logical and physical designs for the application, and the application's construction and implementation, with a plan for its continued maintenance and support.

158. *Discuss the sliver-bullet syndrome, requirements gold-plating, and feature creep.*

The silver-bullet syndrome, requirements gold-plating, and feature creep are three of the ten classic development mistakes identified in the text. The silver-bullet syndrome occurs when developers believe a new and usually untried technology is all that is needed to cure the ills of any development project. Requirements gold-plating means an application may have more requirements than it needs, even before the development project begins. Feature creep refers to the tendency of system requirements to change over the lifetime of the development project.

159. *Identify three RAD components.*

Prototyping, JAD-like sessions, and integrated CASE tools are three essential RAD components.

Chapter 20
Object-Oriented Analysis and Design

True-False Questions

1. The object-oriented systems development life cycle consists of progressively developing an object representation through the phases of analysis, design, and implementation.

   Answer: True   **Difficulty**: Med   **Reference**: p. 657

2. Use cases show the static structure of data and the operations that act on data.

   Answer: False   **Difficulty**: Med   **Reference**: p. 657

3. Class diagrams represent the functional requirements or the "what" of the system.

   Answer: False   **Difficulty**: Med   **Reference**: p. 657

4. State diagrams represent dynamic models of interactions between objects.

   Answer: False   **Difficulty**: Hard   **Reference**: p. 657

5. Sequence diagrams represent dynamic models of how objects change their states in response to events.

   Answer: False   **Difficulty**: Hard   **Reference**: p. 657

6. Diagrams and repository descriptions are the deliverables associated with the object-oriented modeling approach.

   Answer: True   **Difficulty**: Med   **Reference**: p. 659

7. The Unified Modeling Language is a notation that allows the modeler to specify, visualize, and construct the artifacts of software systems, as well as business models.

   Answer: True   **Difficulty**: Med   **Reference**: p. 660

8. A use case model is developed during the analysis phase of the object-oriented systems development life cycle.

   Answer: True   **Difficulty**: Med   **Reference**: p. 660

9. Referencing use case modeling, a source is an external entity that interacts with the system.

   Answer: False   **Difficulty**: Med   **Reference**: p. 661

10. A use case is a complete sequence of related actions initiated by an actor; it represents a specific way to use the system.

    Answer: True   **Difficulty**: Med   **Reference**: p. 661

11.   On a use case diagram, an actor is shown using a stickman symbol with its name below.

   Answer: True   **Difficulty**: Easy   **Reference**: p. 661

12.   An actor always initiates a use case.

   Answer: True   **Difficulty**: Med   **Reference**: p. 661

13.   A use case is used to represent an individual action that is part of an overall function.

   Answer: False   **Difficulty**: Hard   **Reference**: p. 662

14.   A use case participates in relationships with actors, not other use cases.

   Answer: False   **Difficulty**: Med   **Reference**: p. 662

15.   On a use case diagram, an extend relationship extends a use case by adding new actions or behaviors.

   Answer: True   **Difficulty**: Easy   **Reference**: p. 662

16.   On a use case diagram, a linking relationship arises when one use case references another use case.

   Answer: False   **Difficulty**: Med   **Reference**: p. 663

17.   An object is an entity that has a well-defined role in the application domain, and has state, behavior, and identity.

   Answer: True   **Difficulty**: Easy   **Reference**: p. 666

18.   An object class is a set of objects that share a common structure and a common behavior.

   Answer: True   **Difficulty**: Med   **Reference**: p. 666

19.   In UML, a class is represented by a rounded rectangle with two compartments separated by horizontal lines.

   Answer: False   **Difficulty**: Med   **Reference**: p. 666

20.   An object diagram shows the static structure of an object-oriented model: the object classes, their internal structure, and the relationships in which they participate.

   Answer: False   **Difficulty**: Hard   **Reference**: p. 667

21.   A component diagram is a graph of instances that are compatible with a given class diagram.

   Answer: False   **Difficulty**: Med   **Reference**: p. 667

22.   A static object diagram is an instance of a class diagram.

   Answer: True   **Difficulty**: Med   **Reference**: p. 667

23.   Operations provide an external interface to a class.

   Answer: True   **Difficulty**: Med   **Reference**: p. 668

24. The technique of hiding the internal implementation details of an object from its external view is called incorporation.

Answer: False   **Difficulty**: Med   **Reference**: p. 668

25. An association is a relationship between instances of object classes.

Answer: True   **Difficulty**: Easy   **Reference**: p. 668

26. On a class diagram, an association is signified by a double-ended arrow that connects the participating object classes.

Answer: False   **Difficulty**: Med   **Reference**: p. 668

27. Participation level is an indication of how many objects participate in a given relationship.

Answer: False   **Difficulty**: Med   **Reference**: p. 669

28. On a class diagram, an exclamation point represents a multiplicity with an infinite upper bound.

Answer: False   **Difficulty**: Med   **Reference**: p. 669

29. On a class diagram, a multiplicity specification of 0..1 indicates optional one.

Answer: True   **Difficulty**: Med   **Reference**: p. 670

30. On a class diagram, a multiplicity of a single 1 implies optional one.

Answer: False   **Difficulty**: Med   **Reference**: p. 670

31. On a class diagram, a solid triangle next to an association name shows the direction in which the association is read.

Answer: True   **Difficulty**: Med   **Reference**: p. 670

32. On a class diagram, a ternary relationship is represented by a rounded rectangle.

Answer: False   **Difficulty**: Med   **Reference**: p. 670

33. Abstracting the common features among multiple classes, as well as the relationships they participate in, is called generalization.

Answer: True   **Difficulty**: Med   **Reference**: p. 674

34. When classes are generalized, the classes that are generalized are called superclasses.

Answer: False   **Difficulty**: Hard   **Reference**: p. 674

35. On a class diagram, placing a discriminator next to the generalization path specifies the basis of a generalization.

Answer: True   **Difficulty**: Hard   **Reference**: p. 675

36. A subclass inherits all the features from its superclass.

    Answer: True   **Difficulty**: Easy   **Reference**: p. 676

37. Inheritance is one of the major advantages of using the object-oriented model.

    Answer: True   **Difficulty**: Med   **Reference**: p. 676

38. A concrete class is a class that has no direct instances, but whose descendants may have direct instances.

    Answer: False   **Difficulty**: Med   **Reference**: p. 676

39. On a class diagram, the complete semantic constraint means that all subclasses have been specified.

    Answer: True   **Difficulty**: Hard   **Reference**: p. 676

40. On a class diagram, the overlapping semantic constraint means that a descendant may not be descended from more than one of the subclasses.

    Answer: False   **Difficulty**: Hard   **Reference**: p. 676

41. An aggregation expresses a *Part-of* relationship between a component object and an aggregate object.

    Answer: True   **Difficulty**: Med   **Reference**: p. 680

42. On a state diagram, an event is something that takes place at a certain point in time.

    Answer: True   **Difficulty**: Med   **Reference**: p. 684

43. An event occurs when a person purchases a car.

    Answer: True   **Difficulty**: Easy   **Reference**: p. 684

44. On a state diagram, a state is considered to be instantaneous.

    Answer: False   **Difficulty**: Med   **Reference**: p. 684

45. On a state diagram, a guard condition is shown within square brackets.

    Answer: True   **Difficulty**: Med   **Reference**: p. 684

46. A sequence diagram depicts the interactions among objects during a certain period of time.

    Answer: True   **Difficulty**: Med   **Reference**: p. 689

47. A simple message is a message in which the sender does not have to wait for the recipient to handle the message.

    Answer: False   **Difficulty**: Med   **Reference**: p. 690

48. On a sequence diagram, a synchronous message is shown as a half arrowhead.

    Answer: False   **Difficulty**: Med   **Reference**: p. 690

49. A package is a set of cohesive, tightly coupled classes representing a subsystem.

Answer: True   **Difficulty**: Med   **Reference**: p. 698

50. Component and deployment diagrams are generated during the requirements analysis phase.

Answer: False   **Difficulty**: Med   **Reference**: p. 699

Multiple Choice Questions

51. The object-oriented development life cycle consists of:

   a. analysis, design, and implementation phases
   b. identification, planning, design, and implementation phases
   c. selection, analysis, design, and implementation phases
   d. identification, design, and implementation phases

Answer: a   **Difficulty**: Med   **Reference**: p. 657

52. Which of the following represent dynamic models of how objects change their states in response to events?

   a. use cases
   b. class diagrams
   c. state diagrams
   d. sequence diagrams

Answer: c   **Difficulty**: Med   **Reference**: p. 657

53. Which of the following represent dynamic models of interactions between objects?

   a. use cases
   b. class diagrams
   c. state diagrams
   d. sequence diagrams

Answer: d   **Difficulty**: Med   **Reference**: p. 657

54. Which of the following show the static structure of data and the operations that act on the data?

   a. use cases
   b. class diagrams
   c. state diagrams
   d. sequence diagrams

Answer: b   **Difficulty**: Med   **Reference**: p. 657

55. You define how the application-oriented analysis model will be realized in the implementation environment during the:

    a. analysis phase of the object-oriented systems development life cycle
    b. design phase of the object-oriented systems development life cycle
    c. implementation phase of the object-oriented systems development life cycle
    d. selection phase of the object-oriented systems development life cycle

    Answer: b   **Difficulty**: Med   **Reference**: p. 658

56. In which object-oriented systems development life cycle phase is the design implemented using a programming language and/or database management system?

    a. analysis
    b. design
    c. implementation
    d. selection

    Answer: c   **Difficulty**: Med   **Reference**: p. 659

57. Benefits of the object-oriented modeling approach include:

    a. the ability to tackle more challenging problem domains
    b. improved communication among users, analysts, designers, and programmers
    c. reusability of analysis, design, and programming results
    d. all of the above

    Answer: d   **Difficulty**: Med   **Reference**: p. 659

58. Which of the following is a true statement?

    a. The UML notation is useful for graphically depicting object-oriented analysis and design models.
    b. The UML notation allows you to specify the requirements of a system and capture design decisions.
    c. The UML notation promotes communication among key persons involved in the development effort.
    d. All of the above are true statements.

    Answer: d   **Difficulty**: Med   **Reference**: p. 660

59. A notation that allows the modeler to specify, visualize, and construct the artifacts of software systems, as well as business models, best defines:

    a. Unified Modeling Language
    b. structured English
    c. pseudocode
    d. logic modeling

    Answer: a   **Difficulty**: Med   **Reference**: p. 660

60. Generally speaking, a use case model is developed during:

   a. analysis
   b. design
   c. implementation
   d. selection

   Answer: a   **Difficulty**: Med   **Reference**: p. 660

61. Referencing use case modeling, an external entity that interacts with the system best defines:

   a. player
   b. actor
   c. source
   d. target

   Answer: b   **Difficulty**: Med   **Reference**: p. 661

62. A complete sequence of related actions initiated by an actor to accomplish a specific goal best describes:

   a. class
   b. transaction
   c. use case
   d. message

   Answer: c   **Difficulty**: Med   **Reference**: p. 661

63. A diagram that depicts the use cases and actors for a system is called a:

   a. deployment diagram
   b. component diagram
   c. sequence diagram
   d. use case diagram

   Answer: d   **Difficulty**: Easy   **Reference**: p. 661

64. On a use case diagram, an actor can represent:

   a. a hardware device
   b. another system
   c. a human
   d. all of the above

   Answer: d   **Difficulty**: Med   **Reference**: p. 661

65. On a use case diagram, use cases are shown as:

   a. squares with their names written inside
   b. rounded rectangles with their names written inside
   c. stickmen symbols with their names written below the symbol
   d. ellipses with their names underneath

   Answer: d   **Difficulty**: Med   **Reference**: p. 661

66. A type of use case relationship that adds new behavior or actions is a(n):

    a. generalized relationship
    b. extend relationship
    c. recursive relationship
    d. abstract relationship

    Answer: b   **Difficulty**: Hard   **Reference**: p. 662

67. On a use case diagram, the type of relationship that arises when one use case references another use case is called a(n):

    a. extend relationship
    b. working relationship
    c. include relationship
    d. definitive relationship

    Answer: c   **Difficulty**: Hard   **Reference**: p. 663

68. An entity that has a well-defined role in the application domain and has state, behavior, and identity defines:

    a. object
    b. attribute
    c. actor
    d. class

    Answer: a   **Difficulty**: Med   **Reference**: p. 666

69. An object can be:

    a. a tangible entity
    b. a concept or event
    c. an artifact of the design process
    d. all of the above

    Answer: d   **Difficulty**: Easy   **Reference**: p. 666

70. Which of the following encompasses an object's properties and the values those properties have?

    a. behavior
    b. class
    c. state
    d. encapsulation

    Answer: c   **Difficulty**: Med   **Reference**: p. 666

71. Which of the following represents how an object acts and reacts?

    a. behavior
    b. class
    c. state
    d. encapsulation

    Answer: a   **Difficulty**: Med   **Reference**: p. 666

72. Which of the following is not a true statement?

    a. An object's behavior depends on its state and the operation being performed.
    b. An object's state is determined by its attribute values and links to other objects.
    c. An operation is simply an action that one object performs upon another in order to get a response.
    d. Object class refers to an entity that has a well-defined role in the application domain, and has state, behavior, and identity.

    Answer: d   **Difficulty**: Hard   **Reference**: p. 666

73. A manner that represents how an object acts and reacts best describes:

    a. event
    b. property
    c. attribute
    d. behavior

    Answer: d   **Difficulty**: Med   **Reference**: p. 666

74. A set of objects that share a common structure and a common behavior best defines:

    a. entity
    b. object class
    c. object collection
    d. multiplicity

    Answer: b   **Difficulty**: Med   **Reference**: p. 666

75. In UML, a class is represented by:

    a. a rectangle with three compartments separated by horizontal lines
    b. a circle in which the activity name is recorded
    c. a double-lined ellipse in which the activity name is recorded
    d. a diamond in which the activity name is recorded

    Answer: a   **Difficulty**: Med   **Reference**: p. 666

76. Showing the static structure of an object-oriented model: the object classes, their internal structure, and the relationships in which they participate is the purpose of a:

    a. class diagram
    b. sequence diagram
    c. use case diagram
    d. collaboration diagram

    Answer: a   **Difficulty**: Med   **Reference**: p. 666

77. A graph of instances that are compatible with a given class diagram is a(n):

    a. object diagram
    b. sequence diagram
    c. use case diagram
    d. collaboration diagram

    Answer: a   **Difficulty**: Med   **Reference**: p. 667

78. A function or a service that is provided by all the instances of a class best defines:

    a. encapsulation
    b. task set
    c. operation
    d. multiplicity

    Answer: c   **Difficulty**: Med   **Reference**: p. 668

79. Which of the following provides an external interface to a class?

    a. constructor
    b. operation
    c. view
    d. association

    Answer: b   **Difficulty**: Hard   **Reference**: p. 668

80. The technique of hiding the internal implementation details of an object from its external view is called:

    a. disassociation
    b. encryption
    c. encapsulation
    d. generalization

    Answer: c   **Difficulty**: Med   **Reference**: p. 668

81. The end of an association where it connects to a class best describes:

    a. encapsulation
    b. scope
    c. association role
    d. composition

    Answer: c   **Difficulty**: Med   **Reference**: p. 668

82. A relationship among instances of object classes best defines:

    a. encapsulation
    b. scope
    c. association
    d. composition

    Answer: c   **Difficulty**: Med   **Reference**: p. 668

83. The degree of an association relationship can be:

    a. unary
    b. binary
    c. ternary
    d. all of the above

    Answer: d   **Difficulty**: Easy   **Reference**: p. 668

84. When indicating the multiplicity for a role, an infinite upper bound is denoted by a:

   a. dash
   b. diamond
   c. hollow point arrow
   d. star

   Answer: d   **Difficulty**: Med   **Reference**: p. 669

85. Which of the following indicates a minimum of 0 and a maximum of 1?

   a. 1..0
   b. 0..1
   c. 1 – 0
   d. 1:M

   Answer: b   **Difficulty**: Med   **Reference**: p. 670

86. Which of the following indicates how many objects participate in a given relationship?

   a. association role
   b. object count
   c. multiplicity
   d. association class

   Answer: c   **Difficulty**: Med   **Reference**: p. 669

87. Abstracting the common features among multiple classes, as well as the relationships they participate in, into a more general class is known as:

   a. aggregation
   b. overlapping
   c. multiplicity
   d. generalization

   Answer: d   **Difficulty**: Med   **Reference**: p. 674

88. A class that has no direct instances, but whose descendants may have direct instances best defines:

   a. concrete class
   b. abstract class
   c. super class
   d. incomplete class

   Answer: b   **Difficulty**: Med   **Reference**: p. 676

89. A class that can have direct instances best defines:

   a. abstract class
   b. complete class
   c. concrete class
   d. direct class

   Answer: c   **Difficulty**: Med   **Reference**: p. 676

90. The semantic constraint specifying that no instance can be an instance of more than one subclass at the same time is:

 a. complete
 b. disjoint
 c. overlapping
 d. incomplete

 Answer: b   **Difficulty**: Hard   **Reference**: p. 676

91. Which of the following is a stronger form of an association relationship?

 a. composition
 b. aggregation
 c. multiplicity
 d. consolidation

 Answer: b   **Difficulty**: Hard   **Reference**: p. 680

92. Changes in the attributes of an object or in the links an object has with other objects best defines:

 a. event
 b. operation
 c. state transition
 d. method

 Answer: c   **Difficulty**: Med   **Reference**: p. 684

93. Something that takes place at a certain point in time best defines:

 a. event
 b. operation
 c. state transition
 d. method

 Answer: a   **Difficulty**: Med   **Reference**: p. 684

94. A model of the states of an object and the events that cause the object to change from one state to another best describes a(n):

 a. entity relationship diagram
 b. collaboration diagram
 c. sequence diagram
 d. state diagram

 Answer: d   **Difficulty**: Med   **Reference**: p. 684

95. Types of interaction diagrams include:

 a. state diagrams and sequence diagrams
 b. sequence diagrams and collaboration diagrams
 c. data flow diagrams and entity-relationship diagrams
 d. component diagrams and deployment diagrams

 Answer: b   **Difficulty**: Hard   **Reference**: p. 688

96. Which of the following depicts the interactions among objects during a certain period of time?

    a. class diagrams
    b. data flow diagrams
    c. sequence diagrams
    d. collaboration diagrams

    Answer: c   **Difficulty**: Med   **Reference**: p. 689

97. Which of the following shows the time period during which an object performs an operation, either directly or through a call to some subordinate operation?

    a. asynchronous message
    b. activation
    c. critical path
    d. simple message

    Answer: b   **Difficulty**: Med   **Reference**: p. 690

98. A type of message in which the caller has to wait for the receiving object to finish executing the called operation before it can resume execution itself is a(n):

    a. synchronous message
    b. simple message
    c. asynchronous message
    d. half-duplex message

    Answer: a   **Difficulty**: Med   **Reference**: p. 690

99. Which of the following shows the conditional logic for the sequence of system activities needed to accomplish a business process?

    a. component diagram
    b. activity diagram
    c. deployment diagram
    d. use case diagram

    Answer: b   **Difficulty**: Med   **Reference**: p. 696

100. Which of the following shows the software components or modules and their dependencies?

    a. component diagram
    b. state diagram
    c. deployment diagram
    d. use case diagram

    Answer: a   **Difficulty**: Med   **Reference**: p. 699

Fill In the Blanks

101. On a use case diagram, an ***actor*** is an external entity that interacts with the system.

                        Difficulty: Med   **Reference**: p. 661

102. On a use case diagram, a ***use case*** is a complete sequence of related actions initiated by an actor; it represents a specific way to use the system.

                        Difficulty: Med   **Reference**: p. 661

103. A ***use case diagram*** is a diagram that depicts the use cases and actors for a system.

                        Difficulty: Easy   **Reference**: p. 661

104. An ***object*** is an entity that has a well-defined role in the application domain, and has state, behavior, and identity.

                        Difficulty: Med   **Reference**: p. 666

105. ***State*** encompasses an object's properties and the values those properties have.

                        Difficulty: Med   **Reference**: p. 666

106. A ***behavior*** is a manner that represents how an object acts and reacts.

                        Difficulty: Med   **Reference**: p. 666

107. An ***object class*** is a set of objects that share a common structure and a common behavior.

                        Difficulty: Med   **Reference**: p. 666

108. A ***class diagram*** is a diagram that shows the static structure of an object-oriented model: the object classes, their internal structure, and the relationships in which they participate.

                        Difficulty: Med   **Reference**: p. 666

109. An ***object diagram*** is a graph of instances that are compatible with a given class diagram.

                        Difficulty: Med   **Reference**: p. 667

110. An ***operation*** is a function or service that is provided by all the instances of a class.

                        Difficulty: Med   **Reference**: p. 668

111. ***Encapsulation*** is the technique of hiding the internal implementation details of an object from its external view.

                        Difficulty: Med   **Reference**: p. 668

112. An ***association*** is a relationship among instances of object classes.

                        Difficulty: Easy   **Reference**: p. 668

113.   On a class diagram, an ***association role*** is the end of an association where it connects to a class.

   Difficulty: Hard   **Reference**: p. 668

114.   ***Multiplicity*** is an indication of how many objects participate in a given relationship.

   Difficulty: Hard   **Reference**: p. 669

115.   An ***abstract class*** is a class that has no direct instances, but whose descendants may have direct instances.

   Difficulty: Med   **Reference**: p. 676

116.   A ***concrete class*** is a class that can have direct instances.

   Difficulty: Med   **Reference**: p. 676

117.   ***Aggregation*** is a *part-of* relationship between a component object and an aggregate object.

   Difficulty: Med   **Reference**: p. 680

118.   ***State transition*** refers to the changes in the attributes of an object or in the links an object has with other objects.

   Difficulty: Med   **Reference**: p. 684

119.   An ***event*** is something that takes place at a certain point in time.

   Difficulty: Med   **Reference**: p. 684

120.   A ***sequence diagram*** depicts the interactions among objects during a certain period of time.

   Difficulty: Med   **Reference**: p. 689

121.   ***Activation*** is the time period during which an object performs an operation.

   Difficulty: Med   **Reference**: p. 690

122.   A ***synchronous message*** is a type of message in which the caller has to wait for the receiving object to finish executing the called operation before it can resume execution itself.

   Difficulty: Hard   **Reference**: p. 690

123.   A ***simple message*** is a message that transfers control from the sender to the recipient without describing the details of the communication.

   Difficulty: Med   **Reference**: p. 690

124.   A ***package*** is a set of cohesive, tightly coupled classes representing a subsystem.

   Difficulty: Med   **Reference**: p. 698

125.   A ***component diagram*** is a diagram that shows the software components or modules and their dependencies.

Difficulty: Med   **Reference**: p. 699

Matching Questions

Match each of the following terms with its corresponding definition.

    a.   class diagram
    b.   component diagram
    c.   object diagram
    d.   sequence diagram
    e.   state diagram
    f.   use case diagram

126.   A diagram that depicts the use cases and actors for a system.

Answer: f   **Reference**: p. 661

127.   Shows the static structure of an object-oriented model: the object classes, their internal structure, and the relationships in which they participate.

Answer: a   **Reference**: p. 666

128.   A graph of instances that are compatible with a given class diagram.

Answer: c   **Reference**: p. 667

129.   A model that depicts the various state transitions or changes an object can experience during its lifetime, along with the events that cause those transitions.

Answer: e   **Reference**: p. 684

130.   Depicts the interactions among objects during a certain period of time.

Answer: d   **Reference**: p. 689

131.   Shows the software components or modules and their dependencies.

Answer: b   **Reference**: p. 699

Match each of the following terms with its corresponding definition.

a. composition
b. multiple classification
c. package
d. query operation
e. scope operation
f. update operation

132. A set of cohesive, tightly coupled classes representing a subsystem.

Answer: c   **Reference**: p. 698

133. An operation that alters the state of an object.

Answer: f   **Reference**: p. 668

134. A part object that belongs to only one whole object, and that lives and dies with the whole.

Answer: a   **Reference**: p. 682

135. An operation that applies to a class rather than an object instance.

Answer: e   **Reference**: p. 668

136. An object is an instance of more than one class.

Answer: b   **Reference**: p. 680

137. An operation that accesses the state of an object but does not alter the state.

Answer: d   **Reference**: p. 668

Match each of the following terms with its corresponding definition.

    a.   actor
    b.   behavior
    c.   state
    d.   object
    e.   object class
    f.   class diagram
    g.   use case
    h.   use case diagram

138.   A diagram that depicts the use cases and actors for a system.

                 Answer: h   **Reference:** p. 661

139.   An entity that has a well-defined role in the application domain, and has state, behavior, and identity.

                 Answer: d   **Reference:** p. 666

140.   Shows the static structure of an object-oriented model: the object classes, their internal structure, and the relationships in which they participate.

                 Answer: f   **Reference:** p. 666

141.   A complete sequence of related actions initiated by an actor; it represents a specific way of using the system.

                 Answer: g   **Reference:** p. 661

142.   Encompasses an object's properties and the values those properties have.

                 Answer: c   **Reference:** p. 666

143.   A set of objects that share a common structure and a common behavior.

                 Answer: e   **Reference:** p. 666

144.   Represents how an object acts and reacts.

                 Answer: b   **Reference:** p. 666

145.   An external entity that interacts with the system.

                 Answer: a   **Reference:** p. 661

Match each of the following terms with its corresponding definition.

      a.   aggregation
      b.   association
      c.   behavior
      d.   encapsulation
      e.   event
      f.   operation

146.   A manner that represents how an object acts and reacts.

                         Answer: c   **Reference:** p. 666

147.   A function or service that is provided by all the instances of a class.

                         Answer: f   **Reference:** p. 668

148.   The technique of hiding the internal implementation details of an object from its external view.

                         Answer: d   **Reference:** p. 668

149.   A relationship between object classes.

                         Answer: b   **Reference:** p. 668

150.   A *part-of* relationship between a component object and an aggregate object.

                         Answer: a   **Reference:** p. 680

151.   Something that takes place at a certain point in time.

                         Answer: e   **Reference:** p. 684

Match each of the following terms with its corresponding description.

     a.   activation
     b.   encapsulation
     c.   multiplicity
     d.   operation
     e.   state

152.   A condition that encompasses an object's properties and the values those properties have.

           Answer: e   **Reference:** p. 666

153.   A function or service that is provided by all the instances of a class.

           Answer: d   **Reference:** p. 668

154.   The technique of hiding the internal implementation details of an object from its external view.

           Answer: b   **Reference:** p. 668

155.   An indication of how many objects participate in a given relationship.

           Answer: c   **Reference:** p. 669

156.   The time period during which an object performs an operation.

           Answer: a   **Reference:** p. 690

Essay Questions

157.   *What is the Unified Modeling Language?*

According to the 1997 UML Documentation Set cited in the textbook, UML is "a language for specifying, visualizing, and constructing the artifacts of software systems, as well as for business modeling."

158.   *Identify seven benefits of the object-oriented modeling approach.*

Seven benefits are: (1) the ability to tackle more challenging problem domains; (2) improved communication among users, analysts, designers, and programmers; (3) increased consistency among analysis, design, and programming activities; (4) explicit representation of commonality among system components; (5) robustness of systems; (6) reusability of analysis, design, and programming results; (7) increased consistency among the models developed during object-oriented analysis, design, and programming.

159.   *Define use case diagram, class diagram, state diagram, and sequence diagram.*

A use case diagram represents the functional requirements of a system. A class diagram shows the static structure of data and operations that act on the data. A state diagram represents dynamic models of how objects change their states in response to events. A sequence diagram represents dynamic models of interactions between objects.

160. *What is a use case diagram? What are its components?*

A use case diagram depicts the use cases and actors for a system. The primary components are actors and use cases. An actor is an external entity that interacts with the system. A use case is a complete sequence of related actions initiated by an actor.

161. *Distinguish object, state, and behavior.*

An object is an entity that has a well-defined role in the application domain. A state is a condition that encompasses an object's properties, and behavior represents how an object acts and reacts.

162. *What is an abstract class? What is a concrete class?*

An abstract class is a class that has no direct instances, but whose descendants may have direct instances. In contrast, a concrete class is a class that can have direct instances.

163. *What is polymorphism?*

Polymorphism occurs when the same operation may apply to two or more classes in different ways.

164. *What is an operation? Briefly describe three types of operations.*

An operation is a function or a service that is provided by all the instances of a class. Constructor, query, and update are the three types of operations. A constructor operation creates a new instance of a class. A query operation accesses the state of an object but does not alter its state. An update operation alters the state of an object.

165. *What is a class-scope attribute? Provide an example. How does a class-scope attribute differ from a default value?*

A class-scope attribute is an attribute of a class which specifies a value common to the entire class, rather than a specific value for an instance. A class-scope attribute forces all instances to share the same value. A monthly $20 service fee assessed to all checking accounts is one example. A default value is an initial value assigned to an attribute; this value can be changed, so instances may have different values for this attribute.

166. *What is inheritance for extension? Inheritance for restriction?*

Inheritance for extension means that a subclass augments the features inherited from its ancestors. Inheritance for restriction means that the subclass constrains some of the ancestor attributes or operations.